Introduction to Automatic Control Systems

Introduction to Automatic Control Systems

Robert N. Clark

Associate Professor of

Electrical Engineering

University of Washington

John Wiley and Sons, Inc.

New York   London

Library of Congress Catalog Card Number: 62-15172
Printed in the United States of America

To my wife

Mary Quiatt Clark

Preface

Since 1940 the application of automatic control technology to industrial and military engineering problems has produced remarkable achievements in manufacturing and weapon system development. It is clear that control system technology will continue to have increasingly wider application and that more and more professional engineers will need to learn the fundamentals of automatic control system theory.

Linear servomechanism theory, which is the subject of this book, has come to be regarded as fundamental to the study of automatic control system engineering. The organization of this text, including both the arrangement of the material and the relative emphasis given to each subject area, is one which I have found to be most effective in giving the student a comprehensive grasp of servomechanism theory within a reasonable length of time.

I began to develop this approach to teaching servomechanism theory in 1953 when I taught an out-of-hours course in control theory to practicing engineers at the Minneapolis-Honeywell Regulator Company, and I have further developed it, since 1957, in a senior course in electrical engineering at the University of Washington.

Linear servomechanism theory involves several concepts and principles which are essentially unfamiliar to most beginners. These include transformation mathematics (Laplace transformation) the transfer function, feedback, stability analysis, graphical techniques such as the root locus method, real frequency response, and the associated techniques of Nyquist, Bode, and Nichols. In this book only one of these new ideas is presented to the student at a time, each new presentation forming a logical extension of his existing background. Each new idea is applied to a simple system where it can be illustrated without being obscured by computational difficulties. The ideas are then applied to progressively more complex problems so that in the end the student finds himself able to perform the analysis (and simple design) of an nth order, multiloop, feedback system and to express its dynamic behavior in either time domain or real frequency domain language.

In the first four chapters the pole-zero methods for the dynamic analysis of linear systems are developed. These are illustrated in terms of the transient response of simple nonfeedback electrical, mechanical, and hydraulic mechanisms. In Chapter 5 the notion of feedback is introduced, and its value in engineering systems is illustrated qualitatively. In Chapter 6 the basic tools which were developed earlier are applied to the quantitative study of feedback control systems, using the root locus method as an avenue to the transient response of those systems. In Chapter 7 some basic design principles are illustrated by examples, using servomechanism systems. The real frequency response method of dynamic analysis is introduced for the first time in Chapter 8, where the special definitions and techniques associated with this method are illustrated by their application to nonfeedback examples. In Chapter 9 the real frequency response method is applied to the analysis and design of feedback systems, and Nyquist's stability criterion is developed. Finally, in Chapter 10 some advanced topics are introduced to demonstrate the limitations of linear servomechanism theory and to suggest avenues of further study to both the systems engineer and the components engineer.

Control system analysis is approached from the engineering point of view. Emphasis is placed on the quantitative dynamic analysis of linear systems, and the theorems of transformation mathematics are put to work toward this end; however, no attempt is made to prove those theorems. The book does not treat the constructional features of control system hardware in detail, but rather deals with the salient physical characteristics of the components and shows how each of these is related to the dynamic performance of the entire system. Approximation techniques for simplifying high order systems are developed in some detail, and normalized transient response curves for second and third order systems are plotted accurately for reference use. Laplace transformation tables and a list of physical constants, units, and conversion factors are included in the appendices.

This book is intended as an *introduction* to automatic control system theory, not as an exhaustive treatment of that subject. It will prepare the serious student to read with understanding the present day technical literature on linear control systems and to do analysis and routine design work on servomechanism systems. It will also provide a background for further study in the advanced areas described in Chapter 10.

The book may be used by anyone who has a background in elementary mechanics, electric circuit analysis, and mathematics through integral calculus. A first course in differential equations would also be useful as background but is not essential, as an introduction to that subject is given in Chapter 2. An advanced junior or a senior in most engineering colleges has ordinarily acquired the necessary background to begin the study of control system engineering. The experienced engineer whose mathematical background is weak from lack of exercise may spend more time on the first three chapters than would a student who has had more recent experience with mathematics.

The problems should be considered to be an integral part of the text; not only do they provide strategic exercise of the principles of analysis covered in the text, but some of them require the student to derive new relationships not explicitly covered in the text. I have tried to hold the labor of numerical computation to a minimum and have supplied answers to the problems which will facilitate the use of the book for self-study. The material in this book is covered in about thirty-five hours of lecture plus twenty hours of directed problem sessions at the University of Washington.

I am indebted to many of my former associates at the Minneapolis-Honeywell Regulator Company for their indirect contributions to this volume. In particular, O. H. Schuck, F. W. Ainsworth, J. A. Miller, J. H. Tamura, C. B. Thompson, D. L. Markusen, R. E. Michel, J. J. Rudolf, W. D. Owens, G. Swanlund, W. Ito, and B. H. Ciscel have all provided me with wise counsel at various times during the early years of the development of this material. I am also indebted to the senior faculty of the Electrical Engineering Department, University of Washington, for encouraging me to develop this material through classroom use to its present form. By far the largest contribution was made by my wife Mary, who edited and typed the original manuscript, spent many hours proofreading, and gave me the domestic support and encouragement which was essential to the completion of the book.

ROBERT N. CLARK

Seattle, Washington
March, 1962

Contents

1 Introduction

The first step in the dynamic analysis of a physical system is usually a description in mathematical form of the physical properties of the system. This form is often called the *mathematical model* of the system. Frequently it is necessary to ignore certain physical properties of the system in order to keep the mathematical model simple enough to be useful. Hopefully, the advantage gained by the mathematical simplicity more than offsets the errors introduced by ignoring some of the physical facts. Most mathematical models of physical systems are integrodifferential equations, difference equations, or sets of these equations. When these equations are linear the system is said to be linear, and when they are not linear the system is said to be nonlinear. As we see shortly, it will always be necessary to ignore some facts concerning the physical system in order to make the mathematical model linear.

Only linear systems are treated in this book, except for the short discussion in Chapter 10 intended as a descriptive introduction to some forms of nonlinear analysis. This book is limited to linear systems because linear integrodifferential equations are understood so much more thoroughly than are nonlinear integrodifferential equations. This is particularly true if the linear equations are ordinary (have no partial derivatives) and have constant coefficients, since the general solution to this type of equation is relatively easy to obtain. Most of the book is restricted to systems whose mathematical models are ordinary, linear, integrodifferential equations having constant coefficients.

The most significant difference between linear and nonlinear equations, from the engineering point of view, is that linear equations obey the law of superposition, while nonlinear equations do not. The law

1

Fig. 1.1.   Cantilever beam.

of superposition is simply this: If a linear system exhibits a response $x_1(t)$ to a stimulus $y_1(t)$ and a response $x_2(t)$ to a stimulus $y_2(t)$, it will exhibit a response $[x_1(t) + x_2(t)]$ to a stimulus $[y_1(t) + y_2(t)]$.   The significance of the property of superposition is this: The general form of the response of a linear system may be determined by a stimulus of any magnitude.   If the magnitude of the stimulus is changed, only the magnitude and not the form of the response will change.   Hence, if a linear system is stable for a small stimulus it will also be stable for a large one, whereas a nonlinear system might be stable for a small stimulus but become unstable for a large stimulus!   This suggests that some extremely interesting dynamic phenomena which cannot be found in linear systems may be associated with nonlinear systems. Unfortunately, since we are restricted here to a study of linear systems we will not see any of these phenomena.

Consider the cantilever beam shown in Fig. 1.1.   This is a simple physical system in which the end load P may be regarded as a stimulus and the deflection x as the response.   If the dynamics of the problem are neglected for the moment, the static relationship between the stimulus and the response would be that shown in the deflection curve in Fig. 1.2.   The deflection is very nearly proportional to the load up to the point where the material yields, but if the load is increased much beyond the yield point the beam will fracture.

If the total load on the beam is always restricted to less than P_3, the static deflection characteristic of the beam can be described by a mathematical model which is linear, namely

$$P = kx \qquad (1.1)$$

where k is called the *spring constant* of the beam and is determined from the slope of the deflection curve in its linear range.

$$k = \frac{P_1}{x_1} = \frac{P_2}{x_2} = \frac{P_3}{x_3} \qquad (1.2)$$

Because Eq. 1.1 is linear it will follow the law of superposition. Equation 1.1 dictates that if P_1 produces deflection x_1 and P_2 gives x_2, then $(P_1 + P_2)$ must result in a deflection $(x_1 + x_2)$. There is nothing in Eq. 1.1 to warn us that if $(P_1 + P_2)$ happens to exceed P_3, even though P_1 and P_2 are each less than P_3, the system might fail entirely. Clearly, the physical system does not follow the law of superposition, even though the mathematical model does. We must expect, therefore, that analytical results obtained from solving linear equations will not always jibe with experimental measurements made upon physical systems. In this example we could expect good correlation between analysis and experiment only if we did not force the physical system beyond its linear range.

All physical systems have limitations similar to the yield and break property of the cantilever beam. The torque of an electric motor at stall may be approximately proportional to the applied voltage if that applied voltage is less than the rated voltage of the motor. But if the voltage is increased beyond the point at which the motor iron is saturated, the torque will reach a fixed limit. Similarly, the voltage across a resistor is approximately proportional to the current through the resistor only when the temperature of the resistive material is constant. If the power rating is exceeded, the volt-ampere characteristic will become nonlinear, and the resistor may even fail by burning out. It may be seen that all physical systems are nonlinear when their physical characteristics are viewed in the large.

Because all physical systems are nonlinear we must justify our use of

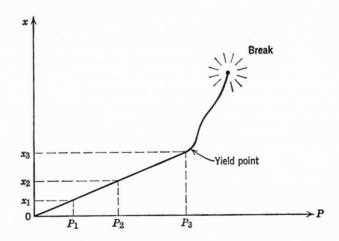

Fig. 1.2. Deflection-load curve for cantilever beam.

linear mathematical models in their analysis. Three reasonable justifications for the study of linear systems are presented below.

1. Many physical systems are approximately linear, provided the stimulus magnitude does not exceed a certain level, as in the cantilever beam example where $P < P_3$. Here a linear analysis will give results which are very close to those realized in the physical system. We must know the *linear range* of our physical system.

2. Much nonlinear analysis is based upon linear analysis, or is a logical extension of linear analysis. The piece-wise linear method of approximating nonlinear physical characteristics is one example, and the *describing function* method of stability analysis for control systems (see Chapter 10) is another. To understand these techniques we must know linear analysis, which, in a sense, is the first step toward nonlinear system analysis.

3. Linear analysis is quick and easy to apply. It is sometimes better to have a quick answer to a dynamics problem, even though that answer may be rather greatly in error, than to have no answer at all (or one which requires an excessive time to obtain). However, we must have a considerable amount of insight into the problem before we can invoke this justification for a linear analysis, because it is often true, also, that a quick but inaccurate answer is *worse* than no answer at all.

Some important systems are nonlinear even for small variations in the exciting force. Many household temperature controllers or thermostats are of this type. The control action is a switching function in which the power is either completely on or completely off, and there is no in-between or proportional state. Relay actuated motors are also an example of this type of system. Since a dynamic analysis of a system of this kind usually begins with the nonlinear differential equation, it is not treated here, although it is an important class of control system. In fact, it has been proven that for a large class of control systems the relay (or bang-bang) stimulus is the most effective way to drive the controlled mechanism.

One major disadvantage in approaching a study of control system engineering through linear analysis is that the engineer who is so introduced to control system theory tends to think in terms of linear systems, and when he begins to design a system (and not simply to analyze it) he may try to force the physical characteristics of his system to be as linear as possible in order to be able to predict their dynamic behavior from his linear analysis. This tendency on the part of a designer may lead to the design of a physical system which is more complex, more expensive, less reliable, and less effective than a system which is designed from the nonlinear point of view. This is such a serious consequence of a training in linear analysis, in fact, that many educators and practicing engineers feel that a course in nonlinear mechanics should be taken by all those who study linear system analysis.

1.2 AUTOMATIC CONTROL SYSTEM THEORY

An automatic control system is a physical system; consequently, all the remarks in Section 1.1 about physical systems and their mathematical models apply to automatic control systems. Any *theory* of automatic control must therefore pertain to or be based upon sets of integrodifferential or difference equations and their solutions. In this book we are concerned only with linear control systems having constant parameters. The theory developed here consists simply of special ways of working with linear differential equations. This collection of techniques is called *servomechanism theory* because it was developed in the early 1940s to help engineers understand the dynamic behavior of servomechanism systems. Other theories and analytical techniques, such as those of nonlinear mechanics, are applicable to some control systems, but they are not discussed in this book.

Servomechanism theory is based upon the *transfer function* concept. A transfer function for a physical system is a mathematical model of the system which is derived from the integrodifferential equations of the system through a transformation process (the Laplace transformation), converting the equations into algebraic equations and making their manipulation very simple. The exact details of this process are presented in Chapter 2.

The transfer function of a system is used in one of two ways in the dynamic analysis of control systems. One of these methods is a technique for finding the solution of the system equations when the input is a transient signal. This, the simplest method for finding the dynamic response of a system, is developed in Chapters 2, 3, and 4. The second method, which is actually a special case of the first, is based upon the real frequency response of the system. It is introduced in Chapter 8. This method, although the older of the two, is more abstract, since it deals with the frequency response of systems and not directly with their time response. Therefore, the engineer must interpret the frequency response in terms of what it means to a real system operating in real time.

The distinguishing physical feature of most automatic control systems is its feedback connection.   It is demonstrated in Chapter 5 that, for several practical reasons, feedback is desirable in most control systems.   Along with its desirable features, however, feedback introduces a problem in system stability.   It is the study of the stablity problem—the techniques which are used to analyze this problem—which constitutes the bulk of servomechanism theory.   Two general approaches are used in the stability analysis here.   The first, in Chapters 6 and 7, is based directly upon the transfer function and is called the *root locus method*.   The second and more abstract method, based upon the frequency response of the system, is developed in Chapters 8 and 9.

In summary, servomechanism theory is simply an array of special techniques for solving linear integrodifferential equations and for gaining useful information about the system without actually solving the equations.   The information which is usually sought concerns the influence of the individual system parameters upon the dynamic performance of the whole system, with particular attention given to the stability problem.

2 The Laplace Transformation

2.1 OPERATIONAL MATHEMATICS

An analytical statement of an engineering problem is usually presented in the form of one or more mathematical expressions, such as a set of integrodifferential equations. Often these expressions are difficult to manipulate; it is then desirable to transform them into a form which makes their solution easier. A simple example of such a transformation process is the logarithm, which is used to solve multiplication problems, as in the following example:

$$AB = x \qquad \qquad \text{(Problem)}$$

$$\log (AB) = \log x \qquad \text{(Transformation)}$$

$$\log A + \log B = \log (AB) = \log x \qquad \text{(Operation)}$$

$$x = \log^{-1} (\log A + \log B) \qquad \text{(Inverse transformation, answer)} \qquad (2.1)$$

Transformation of the original problem into the logarithmic domain changes the mathematical operation required for the solution of the problem from multiplication to addition, a simpler process, and the answer may be obtained by an inverse transformation process. Since the transformation and inverse transformation may be accomplished with the use of tables of logarithms, the only analytical work performed is the addition of $\log A$ to $\log B$. A well-known application of the logarithmic transformation process outlined in Eq. 2.1 occurs in the slide rule, which is used to obtain products and quotients by adding or subtracting lengths proportional to the logarithms of numbers marked on the scales of the instrument.

Many types of boundary value problems occurring in electric and magnetic fields or in fluid flow spaces are amenable to a transformation process which simplifies the analysis required for the solution of the

7

problem. A conformal transformation is often used to simplify the geometrical boundaries associated with the problem—for example, to change a square corner into a plane, or an elliptical surface into a circular one. Any form of mathematical transformation used in the manner indicated in these examples falls within the realm of operational mathematics.

Analytical work in automatic control systems involves one or more integrodifferential equations which must be solved simultaneously in order to determine the dynamic behavior of the system. A form of operational mathematics known as the Laplace transformation is used to transform these equations into algebraic equations which are readily solved by algebraic techniques. A brief review of simple linear integrodifferential equations is given first in this chapter, followed by a definition of the Laplace transformation and some of its important properties. The Laplace transform is then applied to the solution of linear integrodifferential equations. In Chapter 3 the *transfer function*, which is of fundamental importance in the study of automatic control systems, is defined directly from the transformed differential equation. In the following material the term *differential equation* is often used instead of *integrodifferential equation*.

2.2 ORDINARY LINEAR DIFFERENTIAL EQUATIONS

A physical mechanism or system composed of elements which may be considered to be lumped and constant-valued will have a dynamic behavior which may be described by an ordinary linear differential equation with constant coefficients. So many mechanisms and electric circuits used in servomechanisms have approximately lumped and constant elements that this class of differential equation is the only type of equation to be treated in any detail in this book.

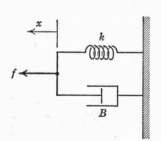

Fig. 2.1. Spring and dashpot.

As the first example of a mechanism with lumped and constant valued parameters, consider the spring and dashpot combination in Fig. 2.1. An applied force f is used to move the spring and dashpot, the displacement of the left-hand side of the spring being measured by x. If the neutral position of the spring is defined at $x = 0$, the force required to deflect the spring will be

$$f = kx + B\frac{dx}{dt} \quad \text{lb} \qquad (2.2)$$

where k is the spring constant measured in pounds per foot, B is the dashpot coefficient (assumed linear) measured in pounds per foot per second, and dx/dt is the velocity of the point at which the force f is applied (feet per second). In this example the mass of the system is considered to be negligible, so that there is no $M\,(d^2x/dt^2)$ term in Eq. 2.2, and the applied force f will be the sum of the forces required by the deflection of the spring and the velocity of the dashpot. Equation 2.2 is an ordinary linear differential equation with constant coefficients, since the spring and dashpot coefficients k and B are assumed to be constant and lumped—that is, they transmit force only between two points. If the transmitted force were distributed over an area, the system might be said to have *distributed parameters*, and its behavior would be described by a partial differential equation rather than an ordinary differential equation. The solution to Eq. 2.2 may be found by any one of several methods, and it will appear in the following form:

$$x(t) = x_t(t) + x_s(t) \tag{2.3}$$

where $x_t(t)$ is the solution of Eq. 2.2 for $f = 0$ and is called the *complementary function* by mathematicians and the *transient response* by engineers. $x_s(t)$ is any particular solution to Eq. 2.2 (with $f = f(t)$ the specific force used in the problem) and is called the *particular integral* or *steady-state response*. One arbitrary constant will appear in Eq. 2.3, since the differential equation is of the first order, and this constant may be determined by the initial value of $x(t)$—that is, $x(t)$ for $t = 0$. As an example, assume that a sinusoidal driving force is applied to this system and that the initial displacement of the spring is x_0.

$$f(t) = A \sin \omega t$$

$$x(0) = x_0 \tag{2.4}$$

ω is the frequency of the applied force in radians per second, and A is the maximum instantaneous magnitude of the force in pounds. Under these conditions the solution to Eq. 2.2 is

$$x(t) = \left(\frac{A\omega B}{B^2\omega^2 + k^2} + x_0\right)\epsilon^{-(k/B)t}$$

$$\underset{\substack{\text{Complementary function}\\ \text{(Transient)}}}{}$$

$$+ \frac{A}{B^2\omega^2 + k^2}\,(k \sin \omega t - \omega B \cos \omega t) \tag{2.5}$$

$$\underset{\substack{\text{Particular integral}\\ \text{(Steady state)}}}{}$$

This may be verified as a solution by substitution into the original differential Eq. 2.2. Notice that the transient part of the solution dies out as time goes by, and, in fact, if the initial displacement x_0 happens to be equal to $-A\omega B/(B^2\omega^2 + k^2)$, the transient term will be zero. The steady-state part of the solution oscillates continuously. Notice also that the *force-free* solution may be obtained from Eq. 2.5 by setting A equal to zero, in which event the entire solution is simply a transient whose magnitude is proportional to the initial displacement.

A second simple example will illustrate the dynamic similarity between mechanical and electrical systems. A differential equation for the R-L circuit in Fig. 2.2 may be written from Kirchhoff's voltage law, which states that the sum of all voltage drops around a closed circuit must equal zero. This equation is

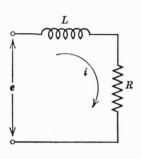

Fig. 2.2.   R-L circuit.

$$e = iR + L\frac{di}{dt} \text{ volts} \qquad (2.6)$$

where e is the applied voltage measured in volts, i is the current through the resistor and inductor in amperes, R is the resistance of the circuit measured in ohms and assumed to be constant, and L is the inductance in henrys, also assumed to be a constant. Notice that Eq. 2.6 is of exactly the same form as Eq. 2.2, with voltage, current, resistance, and inductance playing roles analogous to force, displacement, spring constant, and dashpot coefficient, respectively. If a sinusoidal voltage is applied to the R-L circuit and an initial current I_0 exists—that is, if

$$e(t) = E \sin \omega t$$

$$i(0) = I_0 \qquad (2.7)$$

the resulting current $i(t)$ is found by solving Eq. 2.6.

$$i(t) = \left(\frac{E\omega L}{L^2\omega^2 + R^2} + I_0\right)\epsilon^{-(R/L)t}$$
$$\text{(Transient)}$$

$$+ \frac{E}{L^2\omega^2 + R^2}(R \sin \omega t - \omega L \cos \omega t) \qquad (2.8)$$
$$\text{(Steady state)}$$

An analysis of this circuit by the methods of steady-state a-c circuit theory will yield the second term on the right-hand side of Eq. 2.8. The observations made above in connection with the spring-dashpot system apply equally to the *R-L* circuit. This is borne out by the exact similarity of the two solutions, Eqs. 2.5 and 2.8.

The classical methods of solving linear differential equations often involve a form of guesswork in which a solution is assumed and tested by substitution into the original equation. For the solution of low order equations the classical methods are as simple as the operational method using the Laplace transform. However, for the solution of high order equations or sets of equations, operational methods are much less tedious to apply and are therefore used extensively in control engineering.

2.3 THE LAPLACE TRANSFORMATION

The Laplace transformation is a mathematical operation which, when applied to a function of time, transforms that function into one which is not a function of time. All functions of time which are of concern in this discussion are considered to be equal to zero up to a given instant of time, usually $t = 0$, and are defined by the function only for positive values of time. If $f(t)$ is such a function, its Laplace transformation is written as $\mathcal{L}\{f(t)\}$ and is defined to be

$$\mathcal{L}\{f(t)\} = \lim_{\substack{a \to 0 \\ b \to \infty}} \int_a^b f(t)\epsilon^{-st}\, dt = F(s) \tag{2.9}$$

provided this limit exists. All functions used in this book are transformable, so Eq. 2.9 may be written without the limit notation.*

$$\mathcal{L}\{f(t)\} = \int_0^\infty f(t)\epsilon^{-st}\, dt = F(s) \tag{2.10}$$

This equation shows the Laplace transformation to be simply an integral operation on $f(t)$ which transforms $f(t)$ into $F(s)$, where s is called the *Laplace variable*. Notice that $F(s)$ does not contain t but is a function of s only. Several examples are given below to show the application of Eq. 2.10 to some commonly used functions of time.

Example 1. Unit step function. A unit step function $u(t - \tau)$ is defined by the sketch in Fig. 2.3. If τ is taken to be zero, the step will occur at the origin of the time axis, and its Laplace transformation will be, from Eq. 2.10,

$$\mathcal{L}\{u(t)\} = \int_0^\infty u(t)\epsilon^{-st}\, dt = \int_0^\infty 1\epsilon^{-st}\, dt = -\frac{1}{s}\epsilon^{-st}\bigg]_0^\infty = \frac{1}{s} \tag{2.11}$$

* See Appendix 1 for the restrictions on $f(t)$ which make it transformable by Eq. 2.10.

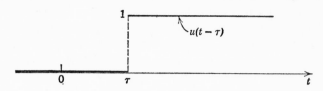

Fig. 2.3. Unit step function occurring at $t = \tau$.

Notice here that the time function $u(t)$ is transformed into a function of the variable s; t does not appear in the new function. The Laplace transformation of $Au(t)$, where A is a constant, is written as

$$\mathcal{L}\{A\} = \frac{A}{s} \tag{2.12}$$

Example 2. Exponential function. Let $f(t) = \epsilon^{-at}$. Apply Eq. 2.10 to determine its Laplace transformation.

$$\mathcal{L}\{\epsilon^{-at}\} = \int_0^\infty \epsilon^{-at}\epsilon^{-st}\,dt = \frac{1}{s+a} \tag{2.13}$$

Notice again that the function of time has been transformed into a function of s.

Example 3. Sinusoidal function. Let $f(t) = \sin \omega t$. Apply Eq. 2.10 to determine its Laplace transformation.

$$\mathcal{L}\{\sin \omega t\} = \int_0^\infty \epsilon^{-st} \sin \omega t\,dt = \frac{\omega}{s^2 + \omega^2} \tag{2.14}$$

If the reader follows through the integration involved in these three examples he will increase his familiarity with the definition of the Laplace transform.

Many other functions used in servomechanism analysis have been transformed and tabulated in the fashion of integral tables. Such a table appears in Appendix 1. This table contains most of the transform pairs required for the analysis performed in this book, and more extensive tables appear elsewhere in the literature. The reader will find it advantageous at this point to become familiar with the table in Appendix 1 by deriving as many of the transform pairs as he can. This is done simply by applying Eq. 2.10 to each $f(t)$. A familiarity with the concept of transformation will permit the reader to use the table of transforms with confidence in the same way he uses a table of integrals or a table of logarithms.

It is shown in Chapters 3 and 4 that except for Pair 1 and Pair 2 all of the transform pairs listed in Appendix 1 can be derived from Pair 8, through the use of a partial fraction expansion of $F(s)$.

The inverse transformation of $F(s)$ is written as

$$\mathcal{L}^{-1}\{F(s)\} = f(t) \tag{2.15}$$

where $F(s)$ is the Laplace transformation of $f(t)$. A formal definition of the inverse Laplace transformation is

$$f(t) = \frac{1}{2\pi j} \int_{c-j\infty}^{c+j\infty} F(s)\epsilon^{st} \, ds \tag{2.16}$$

where c is a constant which must exceed a certain value determined by $F(s)$. An understanding of this definition and the significance of the constant c must be based upon a study of the functional theory of complex variables. Such a complete understanding of this definition is not essential to the work in this book, since we can regard the inverse transformation simply as the operation of moving from $F(s)$ to $f(t)$ in the table in the same way as we regard the transformation as the operation of moving from $f(t)$ to $F(s)$.

2.4 SOME PROPERTIES OF THE LAPLACE TRANSFORMATION

Certain properties of the Laplace transformation process make it especially suitable for use in servomechanism analysis. Some of its more important properties are discussed here; however, a complete and mathematically rigorous treatise on the Laplace transformation is beyond the scope and purpose of this text.

Linearity. An important relationship between functions and their Laplace transforms is the linearity relationship

$$\mathcal{L}\{C_1 f_1(t) + C_2 f_2(t) + \cdots\} = C_1 F_1(s) + C_2 F_2(s) + \cdots \tag{2.17}$$

where C_1 and C_2 are constants. This relationship can easily be derived from the definition, Eq. 2.10.

Differentiation. In applying the Laplace transform in the solution of differential equations it is necessary to take the Laplace transform of a derivative term. This is accomplished as follows:

$$\mathcal{L}\left\{\frac{df}{dt}\right\} = sF(s) - f(0^+) \tag{2.18}$$

$f(0^+)$ is the value of $f(t)$ at the instant $t = 0^+$—that is, it is the initial value of $f(t)$ taken just *after* $t = 0$, rather than just *before* $t = 0$. The distinction between $f(0^+)$ and $f(0^-)$ is an important one when a discontinuity appears in $f(t)$ at $t = 0$. The Laplace transform of the nth derivative of a function is

$$\mathcal{L}\left\{\frac{d^n f}{dt^n}\right\} = s^n F(s) - s^{n-1} f(0^+) - s^{n-2} f'(0^+) - \cdots$$

$$- f^{(n-1)}(0^+) \quad (2.19)$$

where $f'(0^+)$ is the first derivative of $f(t)$ evaluated at $t = 0^+$. If all the initial conditions on $f(t)$ and its derivatives happen to be zero, Eq. 2.19 becomes

$$\mathcal{L}\left\{\frac{d^n f}{dt^n}\right\} = s^n F(s) \quad (2.20)$$

which shows that the derivative operation on $f(t)$ corresponds to multiplication of $F(s)$ by s. The reader should check these relationships by applying them to some functions. For example, let $f(t) = \sin \omega t$ and find $\mathcal{L}\{d^2 f/dt^2\}$ first by applying Eq. 2.10, and then by applying Eq. 2.19.

$$\frac{d^2 f}{dt^2} = -\omega^2 \sin \omega t$$

$$(2.21)$$

$$\mathcal{L}\{-\omega^2 \sin \omega t\} = -\frac{\omega^3}{s^2 + \omega^2} \quad \text{by Eq. 2.10}$$

$$\mathcal{L}\left\{\frac{d^2 f}{dt^2}\right\} = s^2\left(\frac{\omega}{s^2 + \omega^2}\right) - s(0) - (\omega)$$

$$(2.22)$$

$$= \frac{s^2 \omega}{s^2 + \omega^2} - \omega = -\frac{\omega^3}{s^2 + \omega^2} \quad \text{by Eq. 2.19}$$

Both these operations give the same answer, showing that Eq. 2.19 holds, at least for this function.

Integration. It is often desirable to take the Laplace transform of an integral function. From Eq. 2.10 this is found to be

$$\mathcal{L}\{\textstyle\int f(t)\, dt\} = \frac{F(s)}{s} + \frac{f^{(-1)}(0^+)}{s} \quad (2.23)$$

where $f^{(-1)}(0^+)$ is $\int f(t)\, dt$ evaluated at $t = 0^+$. If the initial value of the integral is zero, Eq. 2.23 reduces to

$$\mathcal{L}\{\textstyle\int f(t)\, dt\} = \frac{F(s)}{s} \quad (2.24)$$

which shows that the operation of integration on $f(t)$ corresponds to dividing $F(s)$ by s.   The reader should check Eq. 2.23 by working an example in the same manner as that for Eqs. 2.21 and 2.22.

Delay Function.   Sometimes it is desirable to take the transform of a time function which has suffered a pure delay in passing through a network or some other device.   This means that the function at the output of the device is exactly the same as that at the input, but it occurs at a different point along the time axis.   The unit step function shown in Fig. 2.3 could be considered to be a delayed function, the delay time from the origin being τ seconds.   If $f(t)$ is a given function of time, the delayed function is $f(t - \tau)$, and its Laplace transform is

$$\mathcal{L}\{f(t - \tau)\} = \epsilon^{-\tau s}F(s) \tag{2.25}$$

The reader may derive this expression by applying the definition, Eq. 2.10, to $f(t - \tau)$.   From Eq. 2.25 the Laplace transform of the unit step shown in Fig. 2.3 is seen to be

$$\mathcal{L}\{u(t - \tau)\} = \frac{\epsilon^{-\tau s}}{s} \tag{2.26}$$

Exponential Multiplier.   Another interesting property which may be demonstrated easily by applying the definition in Eq. 2.10 is the transformation of a time function multiplied by an exponential.

$$\mathcal{L}\{\epsilon^{-\beta t}f(t)\} = F(s + \beta) \tag{2.27}$$

Pairs 11 and 12 in the Laplace transform table (Appendix 1) are of this type.

Impulse and Doublet Impulse.   A unit impulse is defined as

$$u_1(t) = \lim_{b \to 0} \frac{u(t) - u(t - b)}{b} \tag{2.28}$$

where $u(t)$ is the unit step function.   This is sketched in Fig. 2.4.   As b approaches zero, the height of the unit impulse increases in such a way that the area under the impulse curve is always unity.   The Laplace transform of the unit impulse function is defined as

$$\mathcal{L}\{u_1(t)\} = 1 \tag{2.29}$$

which may be derived by applying the definition of the Laplace transform to Eq. 2.28 and making use of the transform for a delay function (Eq. 2.25).

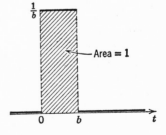

Fig. 2.4.   Unit impulse.

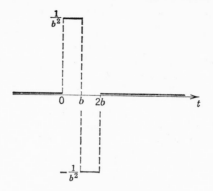

Fig. 2.5. Unit doublet impulse.

One important property of the unit impulse is that its time integral is the unit step function.

A unit doublet is sketched in Fig. 2.5, and it is defined as

$$u_2(t) = \lim_{b \to 0} \frac{u(t) - 2u(t - b) + u(t - 2b)}{b^2} \qquad (2.30)$$

which has a Laplace transform

$$\mathcal{L}\{u_2(t)\} = s \qquad (2.31)$$

The time integral of the unit doublet is the unit impulse. Higher order impulses may be defined by continuing the process indicated by Eqs. 2.28 and 2.30 and maintaining the property that the time integral of the nth order impulse is equal to the $(n - 1)$th order impulse. The impulse functions are used whenever the inverse Laplace transform of an improper rational fraction in s is encountered. As an example, calculate the inverse Laplace transform of $(s + a)/(s + \beta)$.

$$\mathcal{L}^{-1}\left\{\frac{s + a}{s + \beta}\right\} = \mathcal{L}^{-1}\left\{1 + \frac{a - \beta}{s + \beta}\right\} = u_1(t) + (a - \beta)\epsilon^{-\beta t} \quad (2.32)$$

Whenever the numerator of $F(s)$ is of equal or higher order than the denominator, an impulse will appear in $f(t)$.

Time Scale Change. It is sometimes convenient in analysis to speed up or slow down a function of time by changing the time scale. This is sometimes called normalizing a time function so that the result can be applied directly to a large class of systems having similar properties. If t/α is substituted for t in the defining equation of the Laplace transform, the result will be

$$\mathcal{L}\left\{f\left(\frac{t}{\alpha}\right)\right\} = \alpha F(\alpha s) \qquad (2.33)$$

provided α is a positive constant. Suppose that the function

$$f(t) = \epsilon^{-2t}$$

is to be slowed down by a factor of 10. The transformed function will be

$$\mathcal{L}\{\epsilon^{-2t}\} = \frac{1}{s+2} \tag{2.34}$$

whereas the transformed version of the slowed function will be

$$\mathcal{L}\{\epsilon^{-0.2t}\} = \frac{10}{10s+2} = \frac{1}{s+0.2} \tag{2.35}$$

These two functions are plotted in Fig. 2.6 to show the time scale change, the original function being ten times as fast as the slowed function. Notice that a slowed function is not the same thing as a delayed function.

Initial Value Theorem. This useful theorem makes it possible for us to calculate the initial value of a time function from the Laplace transform of the function. This calculation may always be accomplished by taking the inverse Laplace transform to get the time function and then letting t approach zero. However, the mechanics of taking the inverse Laplace transform are often tedious, and, if the initial value of the time function is the only piece of information desired, the initial value theorem saves the effort of taking the inverse transform. The initial value theorem is stated as

$$\lim_{t \to 0^+} f(t) = f(0^+) = \lim_{s \to \infty} sF(s) \tag{2.36}$$

provided the limit on $sF(s)$ exists. Notice that in the limiting process t approaches zero from positive values of t, so the initial value of $f(t)$ as defined here is $f(0^+)$, not $f(0^-)$.

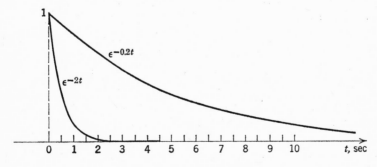

Fig. 2.6. Illustrating time scale change.

As an example of the application of the initial value theorem, find $f(0^+)$ if the Laplace transform of the time function is $\dfrac{as + 1}{s(\tau s + 1)}$.

$$f(0^+) = \lim_{s \to \infty} s \frac{as + 1}{s(\tau s + 1)} = \frac{a}{\tau} \tag{2.37}$$

The reader may check this result by taking the inverse transform and letting t approach 0.

As a second example, find $f(0^+)$ if $F(s)$ is $(s + a)/(s + \beta)$. Application of the initial value theorem yields

$$f(0^+) = \lim_{s \to \infty} \frac{s(s + a)}{s + \beta} = \infty \tag{2.38}$$

The limit does not exist, indicating that the initial value theorem does not apply to this particular function, which happens to be an impulse plus a decaying exponential, as shown in Eq. 2.32.

Final Value Theorem. Another theorem which is used in a manner similar to the initial value theorem is one which allows the final value of $f(t)$ to be calculated rapidly from $F(s)$. The theorem is stated as

$$\lim_{t \to \infty} f(t) = f(\infty) = \lim_{s \to 0} sF(s) \tag{2.39}$$

subject to certain limitations on $F(s)$. It is important to be aware of the limitations on $F(s)$, since a wrong value for $f(\infty)$ will result if the theorem is applied to a function which is outside those limitations. Stated mathematically, the limitation is that $sF(s)$ must be analytic in the right-half s plane and on the imaginary axis of that plane. The meaning of this limitation is brought out in Chapters 3 and 4, but for the present it may be considered to imply that $f(t)$ must settle down to a final value if the final value theorem is to be applied. An example in which the final value theorem does not apply is the function $(1 - \epsilon^{\beta t})$ in which β is a positive constant. Here $f(\infty)$ is infinite, but the final value theorem gives

$$\lim_{s \to 0} sF(s) = \lim_{s \to 0} s \frac{-\beta}{s(s - \beta)} = 1 \tag{2.40}$$

which is clearly wrong. If the denominator of $sF(s)$ includes a factor of the form $(as^2 + bs + c)$, where a, b, and c are not all of like algebraic sign, or if b is zero, the final value theorem will not apply. Such a function is said to be unstable—that is, $f(t)$ does not settle down to a final value as t approaches infinity. After some practice the reader will find no difficulty in identifying unstable time functions from their transforms.

Inverse Laplace Transform. In many analysis problems the major portion of the work required is in finding the inverse Laplace transform of a function of s. Many times the function appears in a form which is not listed in the transform tables available to the engineer. In this case it is always possible to expand the function in partial fractions.* Each term will then be a simple function which can be found in the tables, and the inverse transform process will be completed by application of the linearity principle outlined in Eq. 2.17.

As an example, assume that the inverse transformation of the function $4s/(s + 1)^2(s + 3)$ is required. This form cannot be found in the table appearing in Appendix 1, although it could be found in a more extensive table. However, this function may be expanded easily in partial fractions to

$$\frac{4s}{(s + 1)^2(s + 3)} = \frac{3}{s + 1} - \frac{2}{(s + 1)^2} - \frac{3}{s + 3} \qquad (2.41)$$

so that the inverse transform may be taken term by term

$$\mathcal{L}^{-1}\left\{\frac{4s}{(s + 1)^2(s + 3)}\right\} = 3\epsilon^{-t} - 2t\epsilon^{-t} - 3\epsilon^{-3t} \qquad (2.42)$$

using pairs 6 and 7 in the table. Familiarity with the partial fraction expansion process is highly desirable, as it is used extensively in the problems of this sort in control system analysis. Partial fraction expansion is treated in detail in Chapter 3, Section 3.7.

2.5 SOLUTION OF DIFFERENTIAL EQUATIONS BY THE LAPLACE TRANSFORM METHOD

After the physical relationships in a linear system are described by means of one or more integrodifferential equations, the analysis of the dynamic behavior of the system may be completed by solving the equations and incorporating the initial conditions into the solution. Three examples which follow illustrate the procedure to be followed when the Laplace transform is used to solve linear differential equations with constant coefficients. The Laplace procedure is straightforward and follows this outline:

1. Take the Laplace transform of each term in the differential equation. This eliminates t and all the time derivatives, leaving an algebraic equation in s.

2. Rearrange the algebraic equation so that the dependent variable is on one side and all other terms are on the other side.

---

* In linear systems with constant and lumped parameters the functions of s which arise are always the ratio of two algebraic polynomials in s, a fact which greatly simplifies the analysis.

3. Take the inverse Laplace transform of the rearranged equation; this yields the solution directly.

Example 1. Assume that the spring and dashpot system in Fig. 2.1 is to be forced sinusoidally as described by Eqs. 2.2 and 2.4, and that the initial displacement is x_0. The differential equation to be solved is thus

$$A \sin \omega t = kx + B\frac{dx}{dt} \quad \text{and} \quad x(0^+) = x_0 \quad (2.43)$$

The solution is $x(t)$, the motion of the point of applied force. To find $x(t)$, follow the Laplace transform procedure outlined above. First, take the Laplace transform of each term in Eq. 2.43.

$$\frac{A\omega}{s^2 + \omega^2} = kX(s) + BsX(s) - Bx_0 \quad (2.44)$$

Notice that t and dx/dt have been eliminated by the transformation so that Eq. 2.44 is an algebraic equation in s. $X(s)$ is the Laplace transform of $x(t)$, the function which is as yet undetermined. Next, rearrange Eq. 2.44 so that $X(s)$ appears alone on one side.

$$X(s) = \frac{x_0}{s + \dfrac{k}{B}} + \frac{A\omega/B}{\left(s + \dfrac{k}{B}\right)(s^2 + \omega^2)} \quad (2.45)$$

Finally, take the inverse Laplace transform of Eq. 2.45 term by term to arrive at the solution. This step may be accomplished directly from the table of transforms, pairs 6 and 29.

$$x(t) = x_0\epsilon^{-(k/B)t} + \frac{AB\omega}{k^2 + B^2\omega^2}\epsilon^{-(k/B)t} + \frac{A}{(k^2 + B^2\omega^2)^{1/2}} \sin(\omega t - \psi) \quad (2.46)$$

where

$$\psi = \tan^{-1}\left(\frac{\omega B}{k}\right)$$

This is equivalent to the solution obtained in Eq. 2.5. Notice that the initial condition x_0 was inserted into the solution when the equation was transformed from the time domain to the s domain, so that no undetermined coefficients resulted in the expression for $x(t)$, as is the case when a classical method of solution is used.

Example 2. Assume that the switch S is closed at $t = 0$ in the R-C circuit in Fig. 2.7, and that there is a charge Q_0 on the capacitor just before the switch is closed. The equation which describes the current flow in the circuit is derived by applying Kirchhoff's voltage law to the circuit.

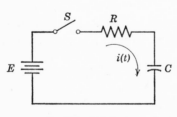

$$E = iR + \frac{1}{C}\int_{-\infty}^{t} i\,dt \quad (2.47)$$

where

$$\int_{-\infty}^{0} i\,dt = Q_0 = i^{(-1)}(0)$$

Fig. 2.7.   R-C circuit.

This integral equation could be differentiated once to make it a differential equation. However, it is not necessary to do this in order to solve the equation by means of the Laplace transform. Following the same procedure as in Example 1, transform Eq. 2.47 term by term.

$$\frac{E}{s} = RI(s) + \frac{1}{C}\left[\frac{I(s)}{s} + \frac{Q_0}{s}\right] \tag{2.48}$$

$I(s)$ is the Laplace transform of $i(t)$. The equation rearranged is

$$I(s) = \frac{(EC - Q_0)/RC}{s + 1/RC} \tag{2.49}$$

The solution $i(t)$ is obtained directly from the inverse transformation of Eq. 2.49.

$$i(t) = \left(\frac{EC - Q_0}{RC}\right)\epsilon^{-t/RC} \tag{2.50}$$

Notice that the role played by the initial change Q_0 is made very clear in the direct solution of the equation by this method. Equation 2.50 indicates that if the capacitor is charged initially to E volts there will be zero current flow when the switch is closed.

Example 3. Solve the following differential equation subject to the initial conditions which are stated:

$$\frac{d^3x}{dt^3} + \frac{dx}{dt} = \epsilon^{2t} \tag{2.51}$$

$$x(0^+) = 2 \qquad x'(0^+) = x''(0^+) = 0$$

Equation 2.51 transformed is

$$[s^3X(s) - s^2x(0^+) - sx'(0^+) - x''(0^+)] + sX(s) - x(0^+) = \frac{1}{s - 2} \tag{2.52}$$

which, after substitution of the initial values for x, x', and x'', becomes

$$s^3X(s) - 2s^2 + sX(s) - 2 = \frac{1}{s - 2} \tag{2.53}$$

This is then rearranged to give $X(s)$.

$$X(s) = \frac{2s^3 - 4s^2 + 2s - 3}{s(s^2 + 1)(s - 2)} \tag{2.54}$$

This form is not available in the table of transforms and must be expanded in partial fractions as follows:

$$X(s) = \frac{0.1}{s - 2} + \frac{1.5}{s} + \frac{0.4s}{s^2 + 1} - \frac{0.2}{s^2 + 1} \tag{2.55}$$

The solution is obtained by taking the inverse transform term by term.

$$x(t) = 0.1\epsilon^{2t} + 1.5 + 0.4\cos t - 0.2\sin t \tag{2.56}$$

This can be verified by substituting into the original equation and checking the initial conditions.

2.6 SUMMARY

The Laplace transform method of solving differential equations is a straightforward procedure by which the total solution of the equation may be found in an orderly fashion.   It is unnecessary to solve for a transient term separately from the steady-state term, or to manipulate arbitrary constants to fit boundary conditions as is sometimes the case when a classical method is used.   The solution of high order differential equations is accomplished by algebraic operations and the use of transform tables, thereby eliminating the need for more complex mathematical operations and leaving less opportunity for error in the calculations.   The Laplace method is particularly advantageous in control systems work, where usually a set of simultaneous equations must be solved.

In a situation where all initial conditions are zero, the transformation of a differential equation simply amounts to replacing d/dt with s, d^2/dt^2 with s^2, etc., and $\int dt$ with $1/s$, $\int\int dt\, dt$ with $1/s^2$, etc.   In this case the Laplace method is the same as the *Heaviside operational calculus* method, in which p, m or D, rather than s, is used as the operational symbol.   In most of the analysis of servomechanism systems the initial conditions are zero, and the Laplace method turns out the same result as the Heaviside method, but in other problems in engineering the Laplace method is applicable where the Heaviside method is not.

It should be remembered, however, that the Laplace transform method of solving integrodifferential equations is limited to linear integrodifferential equations and is more suitable to linear equations with constant coefficients than to linear equations with time varying coefficients.   The use of the Laplace transform method of analysis in this book will therefore limit the reader's attention to physical systems which are linear and which have constant parameters.

REFERENCES

1. Gardner and Barnes, *Transients in Linear Systems*, Wiley, 1942.
2. Cheng, *Analysis of Linear Systems*, Addison-Wesley, 1959.
3. Churchill, *Modern Operational Mathematics in Engineering*, McGraw-Hill, 1944.
4. Kaplan, *Ordinary Differential Equations*, Addison-Wesley, 1958.
5. LePage, *Complex Variables and Laplace Transform for Engineers*, McGraw-Hill, 1960.
6. Nixon, *Handbook of Laplace Transformation*, Prentice-Hall, 1960.

3 Dynamic Response of Physical Systems

3.1 INTRODUCTION

The action of an external agent upon a system is called the input to the system and is denoted as x_1 in Fig. 3.1. The system responds

Fig. 3.1. Input-output relationship in a physical system.

x_1 → Physical system x_0

Input (cause) (stimulus)   Output (effect) (response)

in some fashion to the input stimulus, and the response is called the output, denoted as x_0 in the diagram. In a dynamic study of the system, x_1 and x_0 are time varying quantities. Given an input $x_1(t)$ and a complete description of the physical system, it is possible to compute the output $x_0(t)$ by the methods developed in this chapter.

Most input signals occurring in practical systems vary in a random manner with respect to time, as does the signal indicated in Fig. 3.2. It is therefore desirable for the control systems engineer to be able to

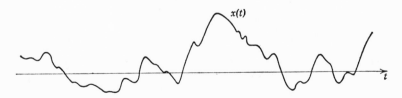

Fig. 3.2. Randomly varying signal.

analyze the dynamic behavior of a system subjected to such randomly varying input signals. However, the analysis of randomly varying signals requires the application of probability theory and some concepts of mathematical statistics. Since this mathematical background is beyond that included in most undergraduate engineering curricula, the statistical analysis of control system response is usually deferred to the graduate level. No statistical analysis is presented in this book; only input signals which may be represented by relatively simple and predictable functions such as the step function, the ramp function, the sinusoid, or a power series in time are treated.

The system designer is nevertheless confronted with the practical problem of determining the behavior of his system with random inputs, and at some point he must develop the ability to handle the problem of random response. Deferring the study of random signals in order to concentrate on response to simple analytical signals like the step input is justified, however, for the following reasons: (1) The response of a linear system to a simple analytical input signal is easily determined, and changes in the response which result from changes in the physical parameters of the system made by the designer may be detected easily. This expedites the design process. (2) Performance specifications of a system are sometimes adequately expressed in terms of the response to simple signals, so that the designer has no need to undertake a more refined analysis. (3) A more refined statistical analysis depends upon a knowledge of the system response to the simpler input signals. Therefore, the study of the response of physical systems to step, sinusoidal, and other simple inputs is in every way a logical place to begin a general study. Later, after the student acquires a mathematical background in probability and statistics, the study may be extended to include more practical types of signals.

3.2 THE TRANSFER FUNCTION

A control system is usually composed of several separate units arranged in chain-like fashion so that the output of one unit is the input to the next unit in the chain. An example of such an arrangement in a servomechanism system is shown in Fig. 3.3. The amplifier

Fig. 3.3. Portion of a servomechanism.

output current i excites the field winding of the generator in response to the input voltage e_i. The generator in turn responds to a change in i with a change in its output voltage e_m, which is the input variable to the motor. Finally, the motor velocity ω exhibits a response to the voltage e_m.

In making a dynamic study of this system it is necessary to calculate the response of the motor $\omega(t)$ to an input $e_i(t)$ to the amplifier. If this problem were to be approached by means of the classical differential equation technique, each of the three components in the system would be described by one or more differential equations, forming a set of three or more equations. This set of equations, with $e_i(t)$ as a forcing function, would be solved simultaneously for the answer, $\omega(t)$.

In problems having more than two equations in the set an operational procedure such as the Laplace transformation is usually employed to simplify the solution. Actually, the simplification is brought about before the set of simultaneous equations are written by employing what is known as a transfer function for each of the units in the system. The transfer function approach permits the dynamic response of several cascaded units to be calculated in a single step, since, as it will soon be seen, the transfer functions of the individual units may be combined to form a single system transfer function simply by multiplying them together.

As a first example of the derivation of a transfer function, consider the spring and dashpot system shown in Fig. 3.4a. A time varying force $f(t)$ is applied to the left side of the system and this causes the spring to deflect, its displacement from neutral position being denoted as $x(t)$. A block diagram of this system is drawn in Fig. 3.4b to indicate the cause and effect relationship described above. Here the applied force $f(t)$ is considered to be the input (or cause) to the system, while the deflection of the spring $x(t)$ is considered to be the output

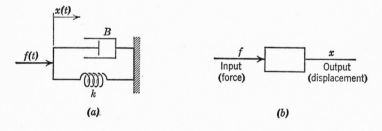

(a).   (b)

Fig. 3.4. Spring and dashpot system.

quantity (or effect).* The dynamic behavior of this system is described by the differential equation

$$f(t) = kx(t) + B\frac{dx}{dt} \tag{3.1}$$

where k is the spring constant and B is the dashpot coefficient of viscous friction. The mass of the system is taken to be zero. It is assumed that $f(t)$ is Laplace transformable, and in this book only simple analytical expressions, such as the step, the ramp, or the sine functions, are used. To derive the transfer function for this system transform the differential equation, 3.1.

$$F(s) = kX(s) + B(sX(s) - x(0^+)) \tag{3.2}$$

where $F(s) = \mathcal{L}\{f(t)\}$

$X(s) = \mathcal{L}\{x(t)\}$

$x(0^+) = x(t)\Big|_{t=0^+}$ (the *initial condition* of $x(t)$)

An important restriction upon the derivation of the transfer function is that the initial condition $x(0^+)$ must be zero. Assuming this to be true, we see that Eq. 3.2 becomes

$$F(s) = X(s)(k + Bs) \tag{3.3}$$

Notice that $X(s)$ appears as an algebraic factor on the right-hand side of Eq. 3.3. This is possible because in transformation the original differential equation, 3.1, becomes an algebraic equation in the variable s; hence it may be factored in the form of Eq. 3.3. One further algebraic rearrangement results in the ratio

$$\frac{X(s)}{F(s)} = \frac{1}{k + Bs} \tag{3.4}$$

It is this ratio which is defined as the transfer function. That is,

$$\text{transfer function} = \frac{\mathcal{L}\{x(t)\}}{\mathcal{L}\{f(t)\}} = \frac{X(s)}{F(s)} \tag{3.5}$$

The transfer function is the ratio of the Laplace transform of the output quantity to the Laplace transform of the input, with the restriction

* Notice that several physical quantities in addition to $x(t)$ could be considered to be the output. Other choices might be the velocity of the plunger dx/dt, or the tension in the spring, or the compressive force in the dashpot shaft, etc. In setting up a problem of this type it is important to state explicitly which quantity is to be called the output and which the input.

that the initial conditions appearing in the transformed differential equation (or equations) are all zero. Thus the transfer function is an algebraic function of the variable s, and it is often represented by the symbol $G(s)$. In this problem, then

$$\text{Transfer function} = G(s) = \frac{1}{k + Bs} = \frac{1/k}{1 + (B/k)s} = \frac{1/B}{s + k/B} \quad (3.6)$$

In most problems it is desirable to use one of the two forms at the right in Eq. 3.6—that is, the transfer function is usually arranged so that the constant term in the denominator is unity, or so that the coefficient of the s term is unity.

Figure 3.5 shows the way in which the transfer function is incorporated into a block diagram of the system. The input to the block

Fig. 3.5. Transfer function incorporated into block diagram.

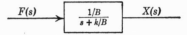

$$F(s) \rightarrow \boxed{\frac{1/B}{s + k/B}} \rightarrow X(s)$$

is $F(s)$, the Laplace transform of the actual input $f(t)$, and the output is $X(s)$, the Laplace transform of the actual output $x(t)$. From the defining equation for the transfer function, Eq. 3.4, the following algebraic relationship is apparent.

$$X(s) = F(s)\left(\frac{1/B}{s + k/B}\right) \quad (3.7)$$

Thus the output $X(s)$ may be calculated simply by multiplying the input $F(s)$ by the transfer function.

A simple example illustrates the usefulness of the transfer function. Say that the spring-dashpot system is subjected to a constant force of C pounds applied in step-like fashion at time $t = 0$. That is,

$$f(t) = Cu(t)$$

where $u(t)$ is the unit step function at $t = 0$. The dynamic response $x(t)$ may be calculated quickly as follows.

First, find $F(s)$. From the expression for $f(t)$ given above $F(s)$ is easily found to be

$$F(s) = \mathcal{L}\{f(t)\} = \frac{C}{s} \quad (3.8)$$

Next, calculate the output $X(s)$ as indicated in Eq. 3.7.

$$X(s) = \frac{C}{s}\left(\frac{1/B}{s + k/B}\right) \quad (3.9)$$

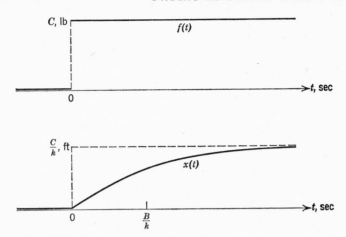

Fig. 3.6.   Dynamic response of spring-dashpot system to step-input force.

Now find the inverse Laplace transform of Eq. 3.9.   This appears in the table of transforms in Appendix 1, pair Number 21.

$$\mathcal{L}^{-1}\{X(s)\} = x(t) = \frac{C}{k}\,(1 - \epsilon^{-(k/B)t}) \tag{3.10}$$

This is a simple rising exponential response having a time constant B/k and a final value C/k, as illustrated in Fig. 3.6.

Equations 3.7 and 3.9, along with Fig. 3.5, show clearly the simple algebraic relationship among $F(s)$, the input function, $G(s)$, the system transfer function, and $X(s)$, the output function. $X(s)$ is simply the product of $F(s)$ and $G(s)$.   This convenient relationship has led some to describe the transfer function as a *dynamic gain factor*, since the dynamic response is obtained by algebraic manipulations in the s domain in much the same way as the steady-state output voltage of an amplifier is calculated by multiplying the magnitude of the input voltage by the *gain* of the amplifier.

A second example illustrates two interesting points.   Consider the simple R-L circuit shown in Fig. 3.7, where the battery with voltage E is considered to be the driving or input agent, and the current i will be called the output.   If the current is zero and the switch S is closed at time $t = 0$, the following differential equation will describe the dynamic behavior of $i(t)$:

$$E = Ri(t) + L\frac{di}{dt} \tag{3.11}$$

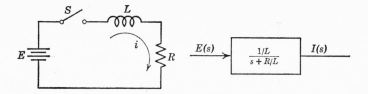

Fig. 3.7.   R-L circuit and its transfer function.

Equation 3.11 may be transformed and rearranged to find the transfer function between input and output.

$$\frac{I(s)}{E(s)} = \frac{1/L}{s + R/L} \tag{3.12}$$

Now $E(s)$ is the Laplace transform of the input voltage, and this voltage is a step of E volts occurring at $t = 0$. Therefore $E(s) = E/s$, and Eq. 3.12 may be written as

$$I(s) = \frac{E}{s}\left(\frac{1/L}{s + R/L}\right) \tag{3.13}$$

Notice that this expression is of the same form as that of Eq. 3.9, which was derived for the spring-dashpot system. The voltage E enters Eq. 3.13 in the same way in which the force C enters Eq. 3.9. L and B appear in similar roles, as do R and k, and $I(s)$ and $X(s)$. Whenever this similarity exists between two physical systems, one is said to be the *dual* of the other, and the *principle of duality* is said to apply to the two systems. Obviously the dynamic behavior of $i(t)$ in the electrical circuit will be analogous to that of $x(t)$ in the mechanical system, so that the electrical circuit is called the analogue of the mechanical system or vice versa.

Often the voltage developed across the resistor of the circuit shown in Fig. 3.7 is called the output of the circuit. A transfer function relating this voltage to the driving voltage may be developed easily from the one already obtained. The relationship between $i(t)$ and the voltage across the resistor is simply

$$e_R(t) = i(t)R \tag{3.14}$$

which may be transformed into

$$E_R(s) = I(s)R \tag{3.15}$$

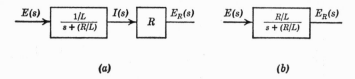

(a)   (b)

Fig. 3.8.   Obtaining the composite transfer function $E_R(s)/E(s)$.

Equation 3.15 is rearranged to form a transfer function between $E_R(s)$ and $I(s)$.

$$\frac{E_R(s)}{I(s)} = R \qquad (3.16)$$

This transfer function, which is simply a constant, may be placed in a block diagram with the first transfer function to form the two block system shown in Fig. 3.8a.   Now, because of the algebraic nature of the transfer function it is possible to combine these two transfer functions simply by multiplying them together.

$$\left[\frac{I(s)}{E(s)}\right] \times \left[\frac{E_R(s)}{I(s)}\right] = \frac{E_R(s)}{E(s)} \qquad (3.17)$$

This operation eliminates the intermediate variable $I(s)$.   Figure 3.8b shows the final result.   Any number of transfer functions which occur in cascade may be so combined to form a single transfer function relating the input of the first block in the chain to the output of the last block in the chain.   This property of the transfer function contributes greatly to its usefulness as an analytical tool in control system engineering, since most control systems are composed of several components arranged in the chain-like fashion illustrated in Fig. 3.8a.

3.3 TRANSFER FUNCTIONS AND TRANSIENT RESPONSES FOR VARIOUS COMPONENTS

The beginner encounters more difficulty in deriving the transfer function for a system from the basic physical parameters than in applying the transfer function in useful analysis.   Consequently, some practice in deriving transfer functions for several common types of control system components is given in this section.   The procedure usually followed in deriving a transfer function was illustrated in Section 3.2 and is outlined as follows.

(a) Decide which physical quantity is to be considered the input variable and which the output variable.

(b) See to it that the system is linear, since a transfer function can be derived only for linear systems. Often some nonlinear characteristic of the system, such as dry friction in a moving shaft or iron saturation in an inductance coil, will have to be ignored. We should, of course, carefully note all of the linerizing assumptions made during the analysis so that we will be able to go over our results and see precisely where the assumptions have proved to be justified and where they have not.

(c) Decide which linear properties of the system, if any, may also be ignored in order to keep the calculations as simple as possible. For example, the mass of the spring-dashpot system in Fig. 3.4a was assumed to be negligible, and the distributed capacitance always present in an inductance coil was ignored in the circuit in Fig. 3.7. Only those quantities which do not appreciably affect the dynamic response *for the purpose at hand* may be ignored. It is conceivable that the mass of the spring-dashpot system could reasonably be ignored in one situation but not in another.

(d) Using the assumptions made in (b) and (c) above, write the differential equation (or equations) describing the dynamic behavior of the system.

(e) Transform and arrange the equation (or equations) algebraically to form the transfer function. All initial conditions appearing in the transformed equations must be considered to be zero. If more than one equation is used to describe the system behavior it may be necessary to eliminate an intermediate variable (such as the current $I(s)$ in Fig. 3.8) in order to arrive at the desired transfer function.

From the description of the five steps listed above it may be concluded that the transfer function approach to the dynamic analysis of physical systems has certain limitations as to its usefulness. One of these is that the initial conditions must be zero. A first order differential equation has one initial condition, a second order equation has two, etc. This restriction is actually a minor one, since for most control system purposes it is just as convenient to assume that the initial conditions are zero as it would be to assume them to be nonzero. In cases where nonzero initial conditions must be incorporated into the analysis the dynamic response may be calculated by application of the principle of superposition. The response to the input signal is calculated as demonstrated in Section 3.2, and a separate calculation is made for the response due to the initial conditions. The two responses are then added to give the response which would result if the input is applied at the time the initial conditions exist.

A more serious limitation of the transfer function method of analysis is that it is applicable only to linear systems. This limitation has two aspects. First, the engineer should constantly be aware of the possible inaccuracies which may be introduced by ignoring nonlinear phenomena, or by *linearizing* a characteristic which is not truly linear. It is difficult to make an exact assessment of the inaccuracies introduced by assuming complete linearity, as this would require a comparison between the linear solution and the nonlinear solution. Generally, if the nonlinear solution could be obtained readily there would be no point in simplifying the problem to the linear case! However, this much can be said: the inaccuracy introduced by ignoring nonlinearities will depend upon the range of magnitudes of the variables which are of interest in the problem at hand. For example, if a rotating shaft has a dry friction torque of about one inch-ounce in its bearings, and if the problem at hand involves calculating the dynamic response for applied torques in the range of several foot-pounds, then neglect of the dry friction will introduce only small errors. If the applied torques are to be in the range of several inch-ounces, however, then large errors will exist in the analysis.

The second aspect of this limitation is less obvious. The transfer function method is a useful analytical tool used by design engineers to help them arrive at the proper dimensions for control system hardware. The designer has a tendency to force his hardware to be as nearly linear as possible in order to fit it in well with his analysis and design data. In some cases it is really necessary to use linear hardware, but in many cases a linear unit is built and used where a nonlinear device could have performed the same control function more effectively and at a savings in cost, size, weight, and complexity. The only disadvantage in using a nonlinear element may be that it is more difficult to analyze!

With these limitations in mind one can proceed to use the transfer function judiciously, exploiting its usefulness in the analysis of systems which may be assumed to be linear for the purpose at hand, and avoiding the temptation to force linearity in the analysis when it is inappropriate.

Electric networks

Electric networks are often used in a control system to filter or modify a signal in order to obtain satisfactory performance of the system. Four such networks are described here, and their transfer

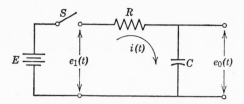

Fig. 3.9. Simple lag network.

functions and transient responses are calculated. A wide variety of networks are used in control systems; these four particular examples are treated here because they typify the most commonly used networks in servomechanism systems.

Example 1. Simple lag network. The network shown in Fig. 3.9 is called a simple lag network because of its frequency response characteristics. (These are discussed in Chapter 8.) Here the voltage e_1 is to be considered the input signal, whereas the voltage e_0 will be called the output signal. Two equations may be written to describe the dynamic behavior of this circuit. They are

$$e_1(t) = Ri(t) + \frac{1}{C} \int_{-\infty}^{t} i \, dt \tag{3.18}$$

$$e_0(t) = \frac{1}{C} \int_{-\infty}^{t} i \, dt \tag{3.19}$$

The desired transfer function is obtained by transforming these two equations by the Laplace method.

$$E_1(s) = I(s) \left(R + \frac{1}{Cs} \right) \tag{3.20}$$

$$E_0(s) = I(s) \left(\frac{1}{Cs} \right) \tag{3.21}$$

The charge on the capacitor at $t = 0$ is assumed to be zero. Now, the transfer function can be formed simply by dividing Eq. 3.21 by Eq. 3.20, thereby eliminating the intermediate variable $I(s)$.

$$\frac{E_0(s)}{E_1(s)} = \frac{1/RC}{s + 1/RC} \tag{3.22}$$

This is the transfer function relating the specified output quantity $E_0(s)$ to the quantity $E_1(s)$, which was specified as the input variable*.

The transient response of all physical systems treated in this book are taken to be the response of the system to a step input with the step applied

* Actually, $e_1(t)$ is the input and $e_0(t)$ the output, but often $E_1(s)$, the transformed version of the input, is called the input, and $E_0(s)$ the output.

at time $t = 0$. The transient response of the simple lag network is the response which would result if the battery E were switched across the input terminals at time $t = 0$. If this is done the transform of $e_1(t)$ is

$$E_1(s) = \frac{E}{s} \tag{3.23}$$

When this information is applied in Eq. 3.22 the solution is

$$E_0(s) = \frac{E}{s} \times \frac{1/RC}{s + 1/RC} \tag{3.24}$$

It is necessary only to find the inverse Laplace transform of Eq. 3.24 to have the transient response in the time domain.

$$e_0(t) = E(1 - \epsilon^{-t/RC}) \tag{3.25}$$

This is sketched in Fig. 3.10, where it is seen to be identical in form to the

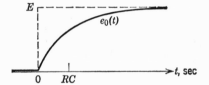

Fig. 3.10. Transient response of simple lag network.

response of the spring-dashpot system appearing in Fig. 3.6. This R-C network is a dual of both the R-L network in Fig. 3.7 and the spring-dashpot system. Notice that the time constant of this network is the product RC; with R expressed in ohms and C in farads, the time constant is in seconds.

Example 2. Lag network. A second type of lag network, which exhibits a slightly different type of dynamic response from that of the simple lag network is shown in Fig. 3.11a. If $e_1(t)$ and $e_0(t)$ are taken to be the input and output quantities, respectively, the transfer function is derived in exactly the same manner as that for the simple lag network. In this instance the two defining equations are

$$e_1(t) = R_1 i(t) + R_2 i(t) + \frac{1}{C} \int_{-\infty}^{t} i\, dt \tag{3.26}$$

$$e_0(t) = R_2 i(t) + \frac{1}{C} \int_{-\infty}^{t} i\, dt \tag{3.27}$$

which, when transformed and divided (Eq. 3.26 into Eq. 3.27), yield the transfer function

$$\frac{E_0(s)}{E_1(s)} = \frac{\dfrac{R_2}{R_1 + R_2}\left(s + \dfrac{1}{R_2 C}\right)}{s + \dfrac{1}{(R_1 + R_2)C}} \tag{3.28}$$

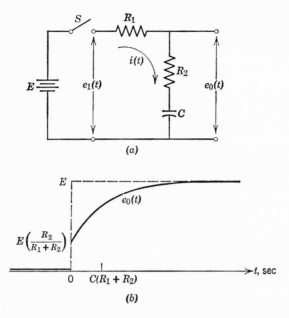

Fig. 3.11.   Lag network and its transient response.

Notice that this transfer function differs from that of the simple lag network in that it has a term $(s + 1/R_2C)$ in the numerator and a constant multiplier $R_2/(R_1 + R_2)$. The significance of these differences are developed fully in Chapter 4. For the present it is sufficient to compute the transient response of the lag network and to compare it with the simple exponential response observed for the simple lag network. Assuming the battery E to be switched at $t = 0$, we find the output to be

$$E_0(s) = \frac{E}{s} \times \frac{\dfrac{R_2}{R_1 + R_2}\left(s + \dfrac{1}{R_2C}\right)}{s + \dfrac{1}{(R_1 + R_2)C}} \tag{3.29}$$

The inverse Laplace transform of $E_0(s)$ is

$$e_0(t) = E\left[1 - \left(\frac{R_1}{R_1 + R_2}\right)\epsilon^{-t/(R_1+R_2)C}\right] \tag{3.30}$$

Equation 3.30 has the same general form as Eq. 3.25, the only differences being in the constant which multiplies the exponential term, and in the value of the time constant, which in Eq. 3.30 is $(R_1 + R_2)C$. Equation 3.30 is plotted in Fig. 3.11b. Notice that the output voltage is discontinuous at time $t = 0$, jumping from zero to $ER_2/(R_1 + R_2)$ as the switch is closed. From the initial starting point the rise is exponential with the time constant $(R_1 + R_2)C$.

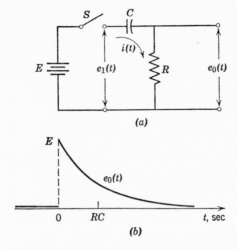

Fig. 3.12. Simple lead network and its transient response.

Example 3. Simple lead network. The network shown in Fig. 3.12a is called a lead network because of its frequency response properties (see Chapter 8). A transfer function relating e_0 and e_1 may be derived in the usual manner from these two equations which describe the dynamic behavior of the system:

$$e_1(t) = \frac{1}{C} \int_{-\infty}^{t} i \, dt + Ri(t) \tag{3.31}$$

$$e_0(t) = Ri(t) \tag{3.32}$$

These equations are transformed, assuming that the initial charge on the capacitor is zero. The quotient gives the transfer function.

$$\frac{E_0(s)}{E_1(s)} = \frac{s}{s + 1/RC} \tag{3.33}$$

If the switch is closed at $t = 0$ the transient response is given by

$$E_0(s) = \frac{E\cancel{s}}{\cancel{s}(s + 1/RC)} \tag{3.34}$$

which, when inversely transformed, becomes

$$e_0(t) = E\epsilon^{-t/RC} \tag{3.35}$$

This is plotted in Fig. 3.12b.

Example 4. Lead network. As the last example of simple electrical networks, consider the circuit in Fig. 3.13*a*. The describing equations for this circuit are:

$$i = i_1 + i_2 \tag{3.36}$$

$$e_1 = i_1 R_1 + i R_2 \tag{3.37}$$

$$i_1 R_1 = \frac{1}{C} \int_{-\infty}^{t} i_2 \, dt \tag{3.38}$$

$$e_0 = i R_2 \tag{3.39}$$

These equations are transformed and rearranged in the proper manner to obtain the transfer function

$$\frac{E_0(s)}{E_1(s)} = \frac{s + \dfrac{1}{R_1 C}}{s + \dfrac{R_1 + R_2}{R_1 R_2 C}} \tag{3.40}$$

The transient response may be computed as

$$e_0(t) = E\left[\frac{R_2}{R_1 + R_2} + \left(1 - \frac{R_2}{R_1 + R_2}\right) \epsilon^{-\frac{R_1 + R_2}{R_1 R_2 C} t} \right] \tag{3.41}$$

which is plotted in Fig. 3.13*b*.

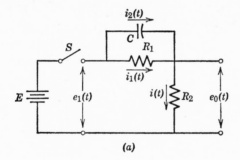

(a)

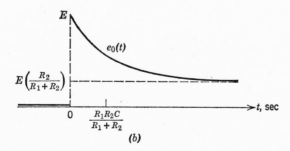

(b)

Fig. 3.13. Lead network and its transient response.

In each of these four examples the characteristic time constant which appears in the transient response is the reciprocal of the constant term in the denominator of the transfer function, provided the transfer function is arranged so that the coefficient of the s term in the denominator is unity. Furthermore, each of the four expressions for $e_0(t)$ has the same general form, but the difference in the responses arises from the different values taken on by the coefficients in $e_0(t)$. These coefficients depend upon the constant terms in both the numerator and denominator of the transfer function, and, in addition, upon the magnitude of the exciting voltage E.

When deriving the transfer function for an electrical network it is not actually necessary to write out the equations expressing Kirchhoff's laws, as illustrated in the above four examples. One may employ the *complex impedance* concept as a short cut in arriving at the transfer function. The *complex impedance* of a two terminal electric element is defined as the ratio of the Laplace transform of the voltage across the terminals to the Laplace transform of the current through the element, as indicated in Fig. 3.14. In other words, the complex

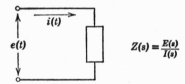

$$Z(s) = \frac{E(s)}{I(s)}$$

Fig. 3.14. Complex impedance of two terminal elements.

impedance is a transfer function relating voltage to current. If the two terminal element is a resistance of R ohms, its complex impedance is

$$Z_R(s) = R \qquad (3.42)$$

The complex impedance of a capacitance of C farads is

$$Z_C(s) = 1/Cs \qquad (3.43)$$

and that of an inductance of L henries is

$$Z_L(s) = sL \qquad (3.44)$$

It is assumed that the initial energy stored in the L and C elements is zero.

Complex impedances connected in series or in parallel are combined in exactly the same way as are ordinary impedances. Thus, a transfer function for a given circuit may be written by inspection, as shown in

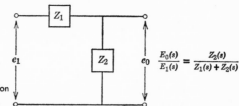

Fig. 3.15. Deriving transfer function using the complex impedance concept.

Fig. 3.15.   If the diagram of Fig. 3.15 is applied to the lead network in Fig. 3.13, the impedances Z_1 and Z_2 are defined as

$$Z_1(s) = \frac{Z_C(s)Z_{R_1}(s)}{Z_C(s) + Z_{R_1}(s)} = \frac{R_1/sC}{1/sC + R_1} \qquad (3.45)$$

$$Z_2(s) = R_2 \qquad (3.46)$$

Impedances defined in this manner are called complex impedances because they are functions of the variable s, and s is, in general, a complex variable.   The implications of this terminology become apparent gradually as the material in Chapters 4 and 8 is studied and applied in the dynamic analysis of linear systems.   It is seen in Chapter 8 that the impedance of an R, L, or C element, as it is defined in classical a-c circuit theory, is a special case of the complex impedance.   The special a-c case is defined by restricting the complex variable s to pure imaginary values, $s = j\omega$.

Most networks used in control systems for signal shaping or filtering are R-C networks.   Inductance elements are seldom used; since the time constants of networks used for this purpose are often in the range of 0.01 to 1 sec, and the desired impedance levels in the range of hundreds or thousands of ohms, inductance elements used in such networks would have to be larger, heavier, and more expensive than capacitive elements.   For example, a simple lag network designed to have a time constant of 0.1 second and an impedance level of 10,000 ohms could be realized by either of the networks shown in Fig. 3.16.

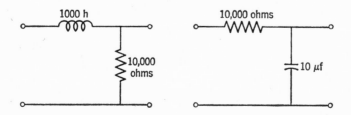

Fig. 3.16.   Lag networks having $\tau = 0.1$ second at an impedance level of 10,000 ohms.

An inductance of 1000 henries is ordinarily much less practical than a capacitance of 10 μf.

Integrators

A device whose output signal is proportional to the time integral of its input signal is called an integrator. If $x_1(t)$ is the input and $x_0(t)$ the output, as in Fig. 3.17, then the defining equation of the integrator is

$$x_0(t) = \int_0^t x_1(t)\, dt \tag{3.47}$$

The transfer function is derived in the usual manner.

$$\frac{X_0(s)}{X_1(s)} = \frac{1}{s} \tag{3.48}$$

It is easily verified that the dynamic response of the integrator to a square pulse is the truncated ramp function shown in Fig. 3.17. This response illustrates an interesting property of the integrator. If the *gain* of an integrator is roughly defined as the output divided by the input, it follows that for time $t > t_1$ in Fig. 3.17 the *gain* of the integrator is infinite, since during this period the output of the device is finite while the input is zero. This so-called *infinite gain* property of the integrator is helpful in attaining accuracy in feedback control systems (see Chapters 5 and 6).

As a first example of a physical system which is an integrater, consider the ball and disc arrangement in Fig. 3.18. The disc is rotated by a prime mover at a constant angular velocity Ω rad/sec. The ball, with radius r, is mounted on a shaft which is free to rotate and to move axially. No slippage occurs between the ball and the disc as the disc turns, so that the angular velocity of the mounting shaft of the ball is

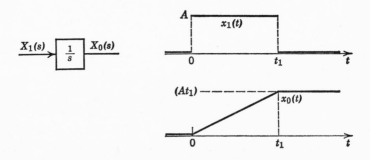

Fig. 3.17.   Integrator and its dynamic response to a rectangular pulse input.

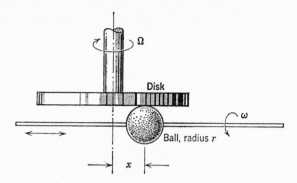

Fig. 3.18. Ball-and-disk integrator.

proportional to the distance between the point of contact and the center of the disc. That is,

$$\omega = \frac{\Omega x}{r} \text{ rad/sec} \tag{3.49}$$

Now, if the displacement x is considered to be the input to this mechanism, and the angular *position* of the shaft of the ball is considered to be the output quantity, the device becomes an integrator. The kinematic relationship between angular position θ and angular velocity ω is a single integration with respect to time:

$$\theta(t) = \int_0^t \omega \, dt \tag{3.50}$$

so

$$\theta(s) = \frac{\omega(s)}{s} \tag{3.51}$$

Equations 3.51 and 3.49 combined give the desired transfer function

$$\frac{\theta(s)}{X(s)} = \frac{\Omega/r}{s} \tag{3.52}$$

Consequently, the mechanism in Fig. 3.18 is called a ball-and-disc integrator.

A second example of an integrating device is the electronic operational amplifier shown in Fig. 3.19. If the transfer function of the amplifier is a constant* and if the current into the amplifier is negli-

---

* This is impossible to realize exactly, since all amplifiers have, in addition to a finite rise time, other dynamic properties which make the actual transfer function more complex than a simple constant. Nevertheless, for many practical purposes these dynamic properties may be neglected.

gibly small, the following equations will describe the dynamic behavior
of the system:

$$e_0 = -A e_g \tag{3.53}$$

$$-i_1 = i_2 \tag{3.54}$$

$$i_1 = \frac{e_i - e_g}{R} \tag{3.55}$$

$$e_0 - e_g = \frac{1}{C} \int_0^t i_2 \, dt \tag{3.56}$$

The gain of the amplifier is $-A$, the minus sign indicating that the
algebraic sign of e_g is opposite to that of e_0. If these four equations
are transformed and combined algebraically to eliminate i_1, i_2, and e_g,
and if A is taken to be very much larger than unity, the transfer function between e_i and e_0 is found to be

$$\frac{E_0(s)}{E_1(s)} \cong \frac{-1/RC}{s} \tag{3.57}$$

and the amplifier circuit is seen to be an integrating device.

If the amplifier output voltage becomes excessive the amplifier will
saturate, Eq. 3.53 will no longer be valid, and the system will cease to

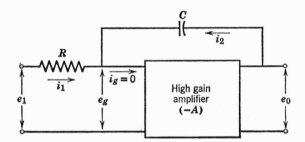

Fig. 3.19.   Integrating amplifier.

be an integrator.   Therefore, when this circuit is used as an integrator,
it is important to insure that all the necessary operating conditions
specified above are met.

Many physical systems operate as integrators.   Because of the
kinematic relationship between velocity and position, most speed control systems can be considered to be integrators if *position* is taken as
the output quantity.   For example, if the velocity of a locomotive
along a straight track is assumed to be directly proportional to the
throttle setting, the *position* of the locomotive along the track will be

proportional to the time integral of the throttle setting. Similarly, if the shaft speed of an electric motor is assumed to be proportional to the applied voltage, the angular *position* of the shaft is proportional to the time integral of the applied voltage. A positional control system for a locomotive or an electric motor (or any one of many other types of mechanisms and vehicles) therefore includes an integrator. It is seen later that the integration has advantages from the standpoint of system accuracy, but it also introduces a problem in system stability.

Differentiators

A device whose output is proportional to the time derivative of the input is called a differentiator. If $x_0(t)$ is the output and $x_1(t)$ the input, and

$$x_0(t) = \frac{d}{dt}(x_1(t)) \tag{3.58}$$

then the transfer function between x_1 and x_0 is simply

$$\frac{X_0(s)}{X_1(s)} = s \tag{3.59}$$

as illustrated in Fig. 3.20. The dynamic behavior of a differentiator is

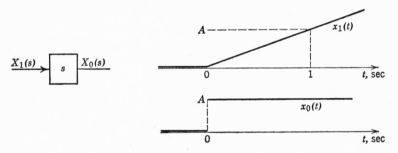

Fig. 3.20. Differentiator and its dynamic response to a ramp input.

the inverse of that of an integrator, as illustrated by the step response to a ramp input shown in Fig. 3.20.

A differentiator widely used in servomechanism systems is the tachometer. This device is simply a small electric generator whose terminal voltage is proportional to the velocity of the driven shaft. Because the velocity of the shaft is the time derivative of the shaft position, the tachometer is a differentiator when the shaft *position* is taken as the input quantity and the terminal voltage as the output quantity.

If the resistor and capacitor in the amplifier circuit shown in Fig. 3.19 are interchanged, the output voltage $e_0(t)$ will be proportional to the derivative of $e_i(t)$. This can be verified by deriving the transfer function, using the assumptions made for the amplifier as an integrator.

Differentiators are frequently used in servomechanism systems for stabilizing purposes and in analog computers to perform differentiation of time-varying voltages. One practical disadvantage inherent in the differentiator and one which presents a certain limitation on its use in such applications is that it nearly always decreases the signal-to-noise ratio of the signal which passes through it.

For example, assume that a tachometer is used to generate the derivative of its shaft position and that the shaft is driven through a gear train which introduces some undesired "jitter" or *noise* motion on the shaft. Ordinarily the amplitude of the jitter is much smaller than amplitude of the motions which are the true signal, so that the signal-to-noise ratio at the shaft may be quite large. However, the noise is usually fluctuating much more rapidly than is the true signal, hence when the derivative is taken, the noise voltage at the terminals is accentuated at the expense of the signal-to-noise ratio. A decrease in the signal-to-noise ratio by a factor of ten or more is not uncommon, so ordinarily it is not wise to employ more than two differentiators in cascade in a system, and often it is impractical to use more than one. Sometimes in a computer system a differentiator can be eliminated and the signal-to-noise ratio improved by redesigning computer circuits to make use of an integrator which will perform the necessary mathematical function in an inverse manner.

Electric motors

A servomechanism must have a power converter or *muscle* element to translate the low-powered command signals into mechanical motions which require the expenditure of more power than that available from the signal itself. Many systems employing electrical signal transmission use electric motors as the power converter. These motors range from tiny two phase induction motors rated at less than 1 watt to large d-c motors rated at several horsepower. Motors intended for use in servomechanism systems differ slightly in their internal construction from motors designed for other purposes. The internal features of servomotors are discussed here only in light of their effect upon the dynamic performance of the machines—that is, upon the transfer function for the motor. Space for detailed treatment of the electrical and mechanical properties of the motors cannot be taken here, nor is it actually essential to the purpose of this study.

Both a-c and d-c servomotors have certain similar dynamic characteristics which in many instances lead to similar transfer functions for
both types of machines. Transfer functions for both types of servomotors are derived below.

A simplified schematic diagram for a d-c motor is drawn in Fig. 3.21.
The following is a partial list of the symbols used here, along with a
consistent set of dimensional units.

e_a voltage applied to armature terminals, *volts*
i_a armature current, *amperes*
e_f voltage applied to field terminals, *volts*
i_f field current, *amperes*
Φ air-gap flux, *webers*
T torque developed at shaft by electromagnetic field, *newton-meters*
T_L load torque, *newton-meters*
J moment of inertia of rotating member, *kilogram (meter)²*
B viscous friction coefficient, *newton-meters per radian per second*
ω angular velocity of rotating member, *radians per second*

At least two different transfer functions can be used to describe this
machine. One is the transfer function relating the applied armature
voltage to the shaft velocity, the field current being held fixed. The
other relates the applied field voltage to the shaft velocity, the armature current being held fixed. Both of these are developed here; the
machine is assumed to have the following characteristics:

1. The air-gap flux is proportional to field current

$$\Phi = K_1 i_f \tag{3.60}$$

where K_1 is the constant of proportionality, *webers per ampere*.

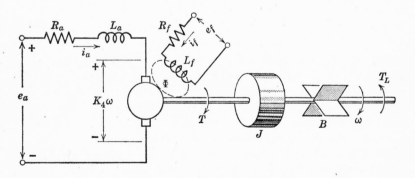

Fig. 3.21.   D-c motor.

2. The torque developed on the shaft is proportional to the product of the air-gap flux and the armature current.

$$T = K_2 \Phi i_a \tag{3.61}$$

K_2 has the dimensions *newton-meters per weber-ampere*.

3. Only viscous friction exists on the rotating member, and this is characterized by the coefficient B. There is no static or coulomb friction.

On the basis of these assumptions the transfer function relating armature voltage to shaft velocity, i_f being held constant, is derived as follows: Since i_f is fixed, the torque developed on the shaft is proportional to armature current,

$$T = K_3 i_a \tag{3.62}$$

where $K_3 = K_1 K_2 i_f$ newton-meters per ampere   (3.63)

Now i_a is related to the armature voltage in this manner:

$$e_a = R_a i_a + L_a \frac{di_a}{dt} + K_4 \omega \tag{3.64}$$

where R_a is the resistance of the armature circuit, L_a is the inductance of the armature circuit, and $K_4 \omega$ is the back emf induced in the armature circuit, the dimensions of K_4 being *volts per radian per second*. It is often permissible to neglect the inductance of the armature circuit if it is quite small.   If this is done, Eq. 3.64 will be reduced to

$$e_a = R_a i_a + K_4 \omega \tag{3.65}$$

A substitution of Eq. 3.62 into 3.65 will eliminate i_a to give

$$e_a = K_5 T + K_4 \omega \tag{3.66}$$

where $K_5 = \dfrac{R_a}{K_3}$ volts per newton-meter   (3.67)

The equation which describes the dynamic behavior of the rotating member upon application of the developed torque is

$$T = J \frac{d\omega}{dt} + B\omega + T_L \tag{3.68}$$

For this analysis T_L will be assumed to be zero, since this approximates the operating condition of many servomotors.   Equations 3.66 and 3.68 are combined to eliminate T, thus forming a single equation with

e_a and ω, the input and output quantities of the desired transfer function, as the only variables.

$$e_a = K_5 \left(J \frac{d\omega}{dt} + B\omega \right) + K_4\omega \tag{3.69}$$

It is of interest to note that K_3 is equal to K_4; this may be proved in the following way: When the motor is running in the steady state, the power delivered to the rotor circuit is $(K_4\omega)(i_a)$ watts (the power dissipated in the rotor resistance being neglected). The power delivered to the shaft is $(T)(\omega)$ newton-meters/second (or watts). Since Φ and i_a are constant, the energy stored in the magnetic field is also constant. Therefore $K_4\omega i_a = T\omega$, which, with Eq. 3.62, shows that K_3 and K_4 have the same numerical value when both are expressed in MKS units.

The transfer function is determined by taking the Laplace transform of Eq. 3.69, assuming zero initial velocity, and rearranging the terms.

$$\frac{\omega(s)}{E_a(s)} = \frac{K_T}{Js + B + K_4K_T} \tag{3.70}$$

where
$$K_T = \frac{1}{K_5} \frac{\text{newton-meters}}{\text{volt}} \tag{3.71}$$

K_T is called the torque constant of the motor.

Notice that the term K_4K_T has the same dimensions as the viscous friction coefficient. These two terms may be combined to form an *equivalent viscous friction* coefficient for the motor,

$$B + K_4K_T = f \tag{3.72}$$

and the transfer function may be written

$$\frac{\omega(s)}{E_a(s)} = \frac{K_T}{Js + f} \tag{3.73}$$

If measurements can be made to determine K_T, J, and f on a machine of this type the transfer function can be determined. A few simple speed-torque-voltage measurements on a d-c machine will yield the constants K_T and f. It is apparent from Eq. 3.66 that K_5 can be found if a locked rotor voltage-torque measurement is made. For this condition $\omega = 0$, and Eq. 3.66 becomes

$$e_a = K_5T \tag{3.74}$$

so that
$$K_T = \frac{T}{e_a} \tag{3.75}$$

When several such measurements are made using applied voltages from, say, 10 percent of rated voltage up to rated voltage, the ratio T/e_a will be approximately the same for each measurement.

The constant f may be determined from an unaccelerated or steady-state speed-torque-voltage measurement. A combination of Eqs. 3.66 and 3.68 forms a relationship between applied voltage, velocity, and load torque.

$$K_T e_a = J \frac{d\omega}{dt} + f\omega + T_L \qquad (3.76)$$

For unaccelerated motion this becomes

$$K_T e_a = f\omega + T_L \qquad (3.77)$$

Here T_L is the load torque applied by the dynamometer for measurement purposes only. When the motor is in use in a servomechanism, T_L must be zero if the transfer function in Eq. 3.73 is to be used. Once K_T is known and one set of ω, T_L, and e_a data points are determined by dynamometer measurements, f can be determined from Eq. 3.77.

$$f = \frac{K_T e_a - T_L}{\omega} \qquad (3.78)$$

It is interesting to note that the constant f is the negative reciprocal of the slope of steady-state speed-torque curve. From Eq. 3.77 it follows that

$$\frac{\partial \omega}{\partial T_L} = -\frac{1}{f} \qquad (3.79)$$

Some typical speed-torque curves are drawn in Fig. 3.22 to illustrate this relationship.

It is also apparent that the torque constant can be determined from the speed-torque curves in Fig. 3.22.

$$K_T = \frac{T_1}{E_1} = \frac{T_2}{E_2} = \frac{T_3}{E_3} \text{ etc.} \qquad (3.80)$$

This equation is based on the assumption that the speed-torque curves are mutually parallel. In a d-c machine of the type considered here these curves will be nearly parallel, and any slight deviations may be averaged out by considering only the more important portions of the speed-torque region. In many cases this is the area lying below a certain speed, usually taken to be about two-thirds of the maximum unloaded speed of the motor. Since one of the most important aspects

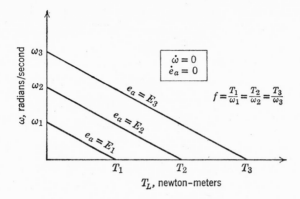

Fig. 3.22.   Steady-state speed-torque curves for d-c motor.

of the analysis of servomechanisms is the determination of system stability at the "null" condition—that is, in the region of low speed—this area is of considerable significance.

Once the torque constant and equivalent viscous friction (or damping) coefficients are determined from steady-state speed-torque measurements on the machine, the only information required to complete the transfer function is the value of the moment of inertia J of the rotor.   This may be determined in any one of four ways.

First, this value may be made available by the manufacturer.   It is necessary to add to this value if some auxiliary parts, such as gears, are attached to the rotor.

Second, the moment of inertia can be computed if the dimensions and materials of the rotor are known.

Third, J may be determined by performing a torsional pendulum experiment in which the period of oscillation of the pendulum is measured.   If the oscillations are very lightly damped, the moment of inertia is very nearly

$$J = \frac{KT^2}{4\pi^2} \tag{3.81}$$

where K is the torsional spring constant of the elastic shaft used in the experiment, and T is the period of the oscillation in seconds. J will be the moment of inertia in kilogram (meter)^2 if K is in newton-meters per radian, and J will be gram (centimeter)^2 if K is in dyne-centimeters per radian.

Fourth, the moment of inertia may be determined from the transient response of the motor to an applied voltage.   For example, if a step of

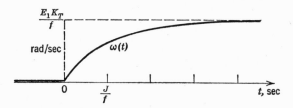

Fig. 3.23. Response of d-c motor to step input voltage.

E_1 volts is applied to the motor with an unloaded shaft, the resulting shaft velocity may easily be determined from the transfer function.

$$\omega(s) = E_a(s) \left(\frac{K_T}{Js + f} \right) \tag{3.82}$$

$$E_a(s) = \frac{E_1}{s} \tag{3.83}$$

so

$$\omega(s) = \frac{E_1}{s} \left(\frac{K_T/J}{s + f/J} \right) \tag{3.84}$$

and

$$\omega(t) = \frac{E_1 K_T}{f} (1 - \epsilon^{-(f/J)t}) \tag{3.85}$$

$\omega(t)$ is plotted in Fig. 3.23. The characteristic time constant J/f may be measured by making a dynamic record of $\omega(t)$. J will then be known, since f is known from the speed-torque measurements described above. This fourth method is quite practical compared to the second and third methods, since it does not require that the motor be disassembled, and it is possible to include in this test as many auxiliaries, such as gears, as may be desired.

When a motor is used as the power element in a servomechanism, it is usually the angular position of the shaft rather than the angular velocity which is considered to be the output quantity of the motor. The transfer function relating applied voltage to shaft position must be used. Because of the simple kinematic relationship between shaft velocity and shaft position, namely

$$\theta(t) = \int \omega(t) \, dt \tag{3.86}$$

the desired transfer function is easily derived from Eq. 3.73.

$$\frac{\theta(s)}{E_a(s)} = \frac{K_T}{s(Js + f)} = \frac{K_T/J}{s(s + f/J)} = \frac{K_T/f}{s[(J/f)s + 1]} \tag{3.87}$$

Of these three forms for the transfer function, one of the latter two is usually preferred, since Laplace transform tables are arranged so that the factors in the denominators or numerators have unity as the constant term, as in $[(J/f)s + 1]$, or unity as a coefficient for the s term, as in $(s + f/J)$. A further advantage of the latter two forms is that the number of characterizing parameters required to determine the transfer function is just two, K_T/J and f/J for the second form or K_T/f and J/f for the third form, whereas three parameters are required if the first form is used. The constant K_T/f is called the *velocity constant* of the motor, since this is the ratio of steady-state velocity to applied voltage, radians per second per volt. J/f is the time constant of the motor. From Fig. 3.23 it is easy to see how both constants can be determined from a transient speed-voltage test.

A derivation of the transfer function relating shaft velocity to field voltage when the armature current is held fixed is as follows. The field current $i_f(t)$ is related to the applied field voltage $e_f(t)$ in this manner.

$$e_f(t) = L_f \frac{di_f}{dt} + R_f i_f \qquad (3.88)$$

L_f and R_f are the inductance and resistance of the field circuit, respectively. A transfer function relating $E_f(s)$ and $I_f(s)$ may be derived. This is

$$\frac{I_f(s)}{E_f(s)} = \frac{1/L_f}{s + R_f/L_f} \qquad (3.89)$$

Next, if it is assumed that the torque developed on the shaft is proportional to the air-gap flux (armature current is constant here) and that the flux is proportional to field current (Eq. 3.60) the transfer function relating torque to field current is a constant

$$\frac{T(s)}{I_f(s)} = K_1 K_2 I_a = K_6 \frac{\text{newton-meters}}{\text{amp}} \qquad (3.90)$$

where K_1 and K_2 are defined above, and I_a is the constant armature current.

Finally, with the use of Eq. 3.68 the transfer function between developed torque and shaft velocity is obtained, assuming zero load torque.

$$\frac{\omega(s)}{T(s)} = \frac{1/J}{s + B/J} \qquad (3.91)$$

A combination of these three transfer functions gives the overall relationship between velocity and field voltage.

$$\frac{\omega(s)}{E_f(s)} = \frac{I_f(s)}{E_f(s)} \cdot \frac{T(s)}{I_f(s)} \cdot \frac{\omega(s)}{T(s)} = \frac{K_6/L_f J}{(s + R_f/L_f)(s + B/J)} \quad (3.92)$$

This transfer function shows some of the disadvantages of using field control rather than armature control. Two time constants are associated with this transfer function, L_f/R_f and J/B. The response to a step input of field voltage, say E_1 volts, is determined by taking the inverse Laplace transform of

$$\omega(s) = \frac{E_1 K_6/L_f J}{s(s + R_f/L_f)(s + B/J)} \quad (3.93)$$

which is $\quad \omega(t) = \dfrac{E_1 K_6}{R_f B} \left[1 + \left(\dfrac{B L_f}{R_f J - B L_f} \right) \epsilon^{-(R_f/L_f)t} \right.$

$$\left. - \left(\frac{R_f J}{R_f J - B L_f} \right) \epsilon^{-(B/J)t} \right] \quad (3.94)$$

Now, the time constant J/B in this instance is always greater than the time constant J/f in the armature controlled machine because B is a fraction of f (Eq. 3.72). In most machines, B is in fact a very small fraction of f—that is, most of the damping comes from the back emf term and not from the viscous drag term—so that the dynamic response of the field controlled machine is much slower than that of the armature controlled machine. Furthermore, the time constant of the field circuit L_f/R_f is comparable to, if not larger than J/f, and this also contributes to a sluggish response. In a control system the response speed of the actuator is a limiting factor in the performance of the system, a higher response speed being more desirable than a lower one. (See Chapter 7 for elaboration.) For this reason, and also because of practical difficulties associated with supplying field current from a variable source, armature control is the more widely used scheme in servomechanism systems which employ d-c motors.

Low powered electric servomechanisms ordinarily employ small, two-phase a-c induction motors as the actuating element. A schematic diagram of such a machine appears in Fig. 3.24. In order to develop torque on the shaft the voltages on the two windings must be out of phase with each other, the most efficient phase difference being 90°. If a two-phase power supply is unavailable, one of the windings may be connected to the single-phase line through a capacitor which

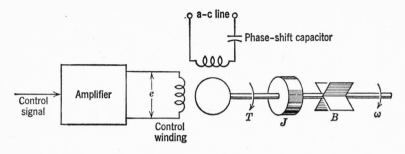

Fig. 3.24.   Two-phase a-c servomotor.

will provide the desired phase shift, as indicated in Fig. 3.24.   The
second winding, called the control winding, is excited from an amplifier
so that the voltage e may be varied in accordance with the demands of
the system.

In operation the instantaneous voltage which appears across the
terminals of the control winding is of the form

$$e(t) = E(t) \sin \beta t \qquad (3.95)$$

where β is the frequency of the a-c voltage ($\beta = 377$ for a 60 cps a-c
line) and $E(t)$ is proportional to the control signal. $E(t)$ is the modulating function of the applied voltage and is sometimes called the
envelope of the instantaneous voltage.   Unless $E(t)$ changes rapidly, as
compared to the sinusoidal fluctuations of the line voltage, the torque
developed on the shaft may be assumed to be directly proportional
to $E(t)$.   This situation is illustrated in Fig. 3.25.   The torque constant for the induction motor may be determined by locked rotor,
torque-voltage measurements on the motor.   This information may
be read directly off the speed-torque curves for the motor.

Figure 3.26 shows a set of steady state speed-torque curves representing the characteristics of a two-phase induction motor.   Each
curve has the same applied voltage, but the rotor resistance varies.
Curve 1 shows a low rotor resistance, Curve 2 shows a higher rotor
resistance, and Curve 3 a still higher rotor resistance.

The characteristic represented by Curve 1 is desirable for most
industrial type drive motors where maximum torque should be
developed somewhere near the synchronous speed.   This particular
speed-torque characteristic is undesirable for servomotors, however,
for two reasons: first, because the slope of the speed-torque curve
reverses at the maximum torque point, and second, because the torque
T_1 which is available for accelerating from standstill is less than the

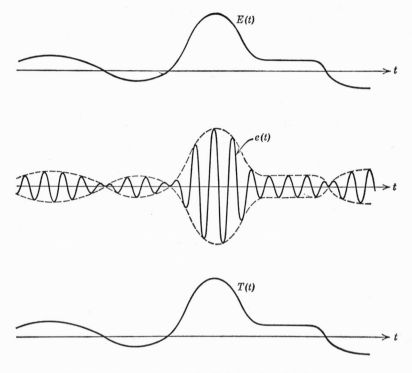

Fig. 3.25.   Torque-voltage relationship in two-phase induction motor.

maximum obtainable.   The slope of the curve determines to a large
extent the damping coefficient of the system, and the damping is
negative for speeds below ω_1 in a motor having a Curve 1 characteristic.
For these reasons motors designed for use in servomechanisms have
higher rotor resistances than do industrial drive motors.   Curve 3
represents a desirable servomotor characteristic.

A family of speed-torque curves for a two-phase induction motor
with rated voltage applied to one winding and various voltages applied
to the other winding, as indicated on each curve, is drawn in Fig. 3.27.
The torque constant for the motor is

$$K_T = \frac{T_1}{E_1} \cong \frac{T_2}{E_2} \cong \frac{T_3}{E_3} \text{ etc.} \tag{3.96}$$

where the various ratios of torque to voltage are assumed to be equal;
this is quite closely realized in most motors for voltages up to rated
voltage.   An equivalent viscous friction coefficient for this motor may

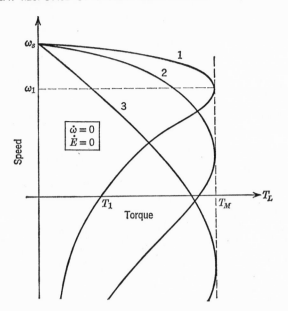

Fig. 3.26. Steady-state speed-torque curves for induction motor; various rotor resistances.

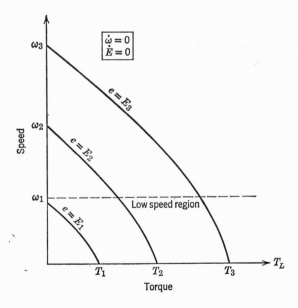

Fig. 3.27. Steady-state speed-torque curves for a-c servomotor.

be derived from the slope of the speed-torque curve in much the same way as that of Eq. 3.79 for the d-c motor.

Speed-torque curves for a-c motors are sometimes less linear than those for d-c motors. The slope of the curve may vary by a factor as large as 10 between the zero torque and zero speed points on a single curve, and also the slope at corresponding points on different curves for the same motor may differ slightly. In stability analysis the slope in the low-speed region is used, since the stability analysis is applied to operation in this region. Any variations in the slope of a single curve in this region or differences between curves in the family can usually be minimized sufficiently by judiciously averaging the difference in the slopes.

The moment of inertia of the motor may be determined by any one of the four methods described above for the d-c motor. The a-c servomotor has a transfer function similar to that for the armature controlled d-c motor.

$$\frac{\omega(s)}{E(s)} = \frac{K_T}{Js + f} = \frac{K_v}{\tau s + 1} = \frac{K_T/J}{s + f/J} \tag{3.97}$$

$E(s)$ is the Laplace transform of $E(t)$ (see Fig. 3.25), and K_v and τ are the velocity constant and time constant whose definition for the a-c machine is the same as that for the armature controlled d-c machine.

From the above discussion it is evident that the transfer functions for the armature controlled d-c motor and the a-c motor are defined by three parameters—K_T, J, and f. A fourth motor parameter is often used in servomechanism design, although it does not appear in the transfer function. This parameter is called the *torque-to-inertia ratio* and is defined as the maximum torque which can be developed by the motor at standstill divided by the moment of inertia of the rotor. This ratio is therefore the maximum acceleration which the motor can achieve. It will appear as radians per second per second if consistent units are used for torque and moment of inertia. Three such sets of consistent units are listed in Fig. 3.28. Sets 1 and 3 are used for large machines, and Set 2 is used for small machines, so that the magnitudes of the quantities will be reasonably sized numbers, the difference in the magnitudes being on the order of 10^7, as indicated in Fig. 3.28. A discussion of units, dimensions, and conversion factors is given in Appendix 2.

Another parameter sometimes used in place of the torque to inertia ratio is the torque squared to inertia ratio, defined as the maximum torque squared divided by the moment of inertia. The reason for the

Set	Torque	Moment of Inertia	Torque-to-Inertia Ratio
1	foot-pound	slug (ft)^2	rad/(sec)^2
2	dyne-centimeter	gram (cm)^2	rad/(sec)^2
3	newton-meter	kg (meter)^2	rad/(sec)^2

1 slug (ft)^2 = 13.56 × 10^6 gram (cm)^2

Fig. 3.28. Sets of consistent units for servomotor parameters.

use of this parameter is brought out in the following discussion of gear trains.

Gear trains

In most servomechanism systems the servomotor is capable of much higher speed than that either required or desired for the load which it drives.   Therefore, a speed-reducing gear train is used between the shaft of the motor and that on the load.   Such a gear train is represented schematically in Fig. 3.29.   If g_1, g_2, g_3, and g_4 represent the number of teeth on the respective gears, the **gear ratio** is defined as

$$\text{gear ratio} = n = \frac{g_2}{g_1} \times \frac{g_4}{g_3} \qquad (3.98)$$

If the gears are perfectly meshed—that is, if no backlash occurs—the displacement, velocity, and acceleration of the motor shaft will be related to those of the load shaft simply by the gear ratio.

$$\theta_L n = \theta_M$$
$$\dot{\theta}_L n = \dot{\theta}_M$$
$$\ddot{\theta}_L n = \ddot{\theta}_M \qquad (3.99)$$

The gear ratio acts as a "torque amplifier" as well as a speed reducer. In unaccelerated motion the torque transmitted from the motor shaft through the gear train to the load shaft is

$$T_L = nT_M\sigma \qquad (3.100)$$

σ is an efficiency factor which accounts for a loss in torque due to friction between meshing teeth and in the bearings.   An approximation for σ

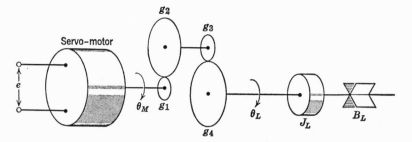

Fig. 3.29.   Servomotor coupled to load through a gear train.

which has been found suitable for well-constructed spur gear trains used in servomechanisms is

$$\sigma \cong (0.95)^m \qquad (3.101)$$

where m is the number of meshes in the gear train. In Fig. 3.29, for example, $m = 2$. For the discussion here, however, a frictionless gear train will be assumed, and σ will be considered to be unity.

In deriving a transfer function for a motor-gear train combination we must combine the moments of inertia for the motor, the gears, and the load in the proper manner. As an illustration of this method of combination, consider the system in Fig. 3.29 to have frictionless, inertialess gears with no backlash. In this instance the torque equation for the motor shaft is

$$eK_T = J_M \ddot{\theta}_M + f_M \dot{\theta}_M + T_M \qquad (3.102)$$

where T_M is the torque on the motor shaft which is transmitted through the gear train to the load. The torque T_M will be amplified through the gear train and will be felt as nT_M at the load shaft. If the load is composed only of a moment of inertia J_L and a viscous damper whose coefficient is B_L, the torque equation for the load shaft is

$$nT_M = J_L \ddot{\theta}_L + B_L \dot{\theta}_L \qquad (3.103)$$

Now, if Eqs. 3.99, 3.102, and 3.103 are combined to eliminate $\dot{\theta}_M$ and $\ddot{\theta}_M$, the torque equation relating the applied voltage to the load shaft is

$$enK_T = (J_M n^2 + J_L)\ddot{\theta}_L + (f_M n^2 + B_L)\dot{\theta}_L \qquad (3.104)$$

and the transfer function relating load shaft velocity ω_L to applied voltage is

$$\frac{\omega_L(s)}{E(s)} = \frac{nK_T}{(J_L + n^2 J_M)s + (B_L + n^2 f_M)} \qquad (3.105)$$

The torque constant is nK_T, the combined moment of inertia referred to the load shaft is $(J_L + n^2 J_M)$, and the combined viscous damping coefficient is $(B_L + n^2 f_M)$.

A transfer function derived with motor shaft velocity as the output will be

$$\frac{\omega_M(s)}{E(s)} = \frac{K_T}{(J_M + J_L/n^2)s + (f_M + B_L/n^2)} \qquad (3.106)$$

Another important quantity is the torque-to-inertia ratio of the entire system. If T_1 is the maximum torque which can be produced on the motor shaft, the torque-to-inertia ratio, referred to the motor shaft, is simply

$$\left. \frac{T}{J} \right|_{\theta_M} = \frac{T_1}{J_M + J_L/n^2} \qquad (3.107)$$

and referred to the load shaft it is

$$\left. \frac{T}{J} \right|_{\theta_L} = \frac{nT_1}{J_L + n^2 J_M} \qquad (3.108)$$

Notice that the torque-to-inertia ratio referred to the motor shaft is n times that referred to the load shaft. Because of this difference it is always necessary when quoting the torque-to-inertia ratio of a system to specify which shaft is used as the reference.

In order to avoid confusion in quoting specifications the ratio of torque squared to inertia is often used in place of the torque-to-inertia ratio. For the motor and load shafts this ratio is

$$\left. \frac{T^2}{J} \right|_{\theta_M} = \frac{T_1{}^2}{J_M + J_L/n^2} \qquad (3.109)$$

$$\left. \frac{T^2}{J} \right|_{\theta_L} = \frac{n^2 T_1{}^2}{J_L + n^2 J_M} \qquad (3.110)$$

These equations show the torque squared to inertia ratios to be the same at both ends of the gear train.

If the four gears shown in Fig. 3.29 are assumed to have finite moments of inertia, say J_1, J_2, J_3, and J_4, the transfer function for the whole system will be

$$\frac{\omega_L(s)}{E(s)} =$$

$$\frac{nK_T}{[J_L + J_4 + (J_2 + J_3)(g_4/g_3)^2 + (J_1 + J_M)n^2]s + (B_L + n^2 f_M)}$$

$$(3.111)$$

The derivation of this transfer function is left as an exercise for the reader.

3.4 FIRST ORDER SYSTEMS

A first order system is one whose transfer function has a denominator of the first order—that is, the highest power of s in the denominator is unity. Similarly, a second order system has a transfer function with two as the highest power of s in the denominator. In general, if the highest power of s in the denominator of the transfer function is n, the system is said to be an nth order system.

Consider a first order system having a transfer function of the form

$$\frac{X_0(s)}{X_1(s)} = G(s) = \frac{K}{s + \alpha} \tag{3.112}$$

The simple lag network and the a-c and d-c motors described in Section 3.3 have transfer functions of this form. If the input to the system is a unit step, the expression for the output is

$$X_0(s) = X_1(s)G(s) = \frac{K}{s(s + \alpha)} \tag{3.113}$$

The time solution can be found by computing the inverse Laplace transform of $X_0(s)$. In Section 3.3 this "computation" was accomplished simply by looking up the transform pair in the table of transforms and identifying the parameters of the $X_0(s)$ function with their counterparts in the table. In a first order system having simple input functions this is the best method to use. However, a different approach is required if $X_0(s)$ should be more complex than any of the functions listed in an available table, as is frequently the case when the system is of high order or when $X_1(s)$ is of high order, or both. One much used approach is that of making a partial fraction expansion of $X_0(s)$, so that it appears as a sum of simple functions, each one of which may be found in a table. In fact, by memorizing a few simple transform pairs one can eliminate the need for a table, since the individual terms in any sum will be very simple.

A partial fraction expansion of Eq. 3.113 is

$$X_0(s) = \frac{K}{s(s + \alpha)} = \frac{K_1}{s} + \frac{K_2}{s + \alpha} \tag{3.114}$$

where K_1 and K_2 are constants which may be easily determined algebraically from Eq. 3.114, an identity. In this example

$$K_1 = -K_2 = K/\alpha \qquad (3.115)$$

If Eq. 3.114 is employed the inverse transformation of $X_0(s)$ may be found by taking the inverse transforms of the two individual terms

$$x_0(t) = K_1 + K_2\epsilon^{-\alpha t} \qquad (3.116)$$

The two constants K_1 and K_2 are important in determining the size and shape of the $x_0(t)$ curve. The relative magnitudes of these two constants determine, to a degree, the relative importance of the two components which comprise $x_0(t)$. Since K_1 and K_2 are of equal magnitude (but of opposite sign) in this example, it can be said that the term K_1 is as important as the term $K_2\epsilon^{-\alpha t}$ in determining the size and shape of $x_0(t)$. Furthermore, it is apparent that although the term $K_2\epsilon^{-\alpha t}$ is equal in magnitude to the term K_1 at time $t = 0$, it becomes smaller and smaller as t increases, until it approaches the vanishing point when $t \gg 1/\alpha$. The idea of the relative importance of the two terms may be expressed as follows: K_1 is "as important" as $K_2\epsilon^{-\alpha t}$, since the general form (size and shape) of $x_0(t)$ would be significantly changed if either of these terms were subtracted from $x_0(t)$ This is illustrated graphically in Fig. 3.30, which shows $x_0(t)$ to be the sum of the two "equally important" terms.

The two constants K_1 and K_2 are given special names. K_1 is called the *residue of* $X_0(s)$ *at the point* $s = 0$, and K_2 is called the *residue of* $X_0(s)$ *at the point* $s = -\alpha$. A discussion of the theory of complex variables would be necessary to make clear the significance of the term *residue*. Such a discussion requires more space than is available here, but fortunately a complete understanding of the origin of the term residue is only incidental to a useful development of the methods of

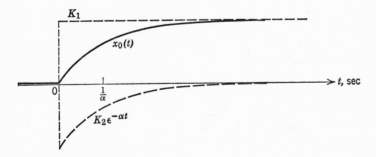

Fig. 3.30. $x_0(t)$ the sum of two terms, $K_1 + K_2\epsilon^{-\alpha t}$.

control system analysis.   Here K_1 and K_2 are regarded simply as the constants which result from a partial fraction expansion of $X_0(s)$.

Consider a second example of a first order system.   Let the transfer function for this system be

$$\frac{X_0(s)}{X_1(s)} = \frac{K(s + a)}{(s + \alpha)} \qquad (3.117)$$

If a unit step input is applied to this system the output response will be given by

$$X_0(s) = \frac{K(s + a)}{s(s + \alpha)} \qquad (3.118)$$

This may be expanded into partial fractions.

$$X_0(s) = \frac{K(s + a)}{s(s + \alpha)} = \frac{K_3}{s} + \frac{K_4}{s + \alpha} \qquad (3.119)$$

Here $K_3 = Ka/\alpha$ and $K_4 = K(\alpha - a)/\alpha$ in order that Eq. 3.119 be an identity.   The inverse transformation of Eq. 3.119 yields the dynamic response

$$x_0(t) = K_3 + K_4 \epsilon^{-at} \qquad (3.120)$$

The actual form of this response depends upon the relative magnitudes and algebraic signs of the two residues K_3 and K_4, and these in turn depend upon the two constants α and a.   Assuming that $\alpha > a$ and $a > 0$, the response $x_0(t)$ will be as shown in Fig. 3.31.

A comparison of the responses of these two first order systems is instructive.   The two system transfer functions have the same denominator $(s + \alpha)$ and the same multiplying constant K, but the second system has the term $(s + a)$ in its numerator as well.   Notice that the partial fraction expansions, Eqs. 3.114 and 3.119, are of exactly the same form, the only possible difference between the two being the values of the constants K_1, K_2 and K_3, K_4.   Notice also that the gen-

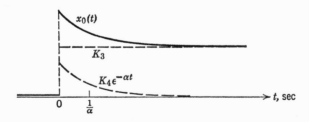

Fig. 3.31. $x_0(t)$ the sum of two terms, $K_3 + K_4\epsilon^{-\alpha t}$ $(\alpha > a > 0)$.

eral form for the first order response is determined by the denominator of $X_0(s)$, since in the partial fraction expansion one term occurs for each factor of the denominator. The numerator of $X_0(s)$ does not affect the general form of $x_0(t)$, but it does influence the values of the residues K_1, K_2, K_3, and K_4. This influence is quite important in determining the size and shape of $x_0(t)$.

3.5 CHARACTERISTIC EQUATION

In a linear system of the type studied in this book the response to a specified input may always be written in this form:

$$X_0(s) = \frac{KN(s)}{D(s)} \qquad (3.121)$$

Here both the numerator $KN(s)$ and denominator $D(s)$ are algebraic polynomials in s. In the previous section it was shown that when $D(s)$ is written in factored form

$$D(s) = (s + \alpha)(s + \beta)(s + \gamma) \cdots \qquad (3.122)$$

$X_0(s)$ can be expanded into partial fractions, each fraction having as its denominator one of the factors of $D(s)$. The general form of $x_0(t)$ is therefore determined by the factors of $D(s)$. Hence the equation

$$D(s) = 0 \qquad (3.123)$$

is sometimes called the characteristic equation because the roots of this equation determine the factors of $D(s)$. The first order systems with unit step inputs discussed in the previous section have in each case the characteristic equation

$$D(s) = s^2 + \alpha s = 0 \qquad (3.124)$$

the roots of which are $s = 0$ and $s = -\alpha$. The equation in which the denominator of the transfer function is set equal to zero is sometimes called the characteristic equation for the *system*, whereas Eq. 3.123 is called the characteristic equation for the *response*.

It should be noted here that the characteristic equation for the response $x_0(t)$ does not alone determine all the significant features of the response. The characteristic equation merely determines the *general form* for $x_0(t)$ and the time constants of the exponential factors. The actual size and shape of the response curve depends upon the coefficients of the individual terms as well as upon the time constants, and the coefficients are dependent upon the numerator of $X_0(s)$ as well as upon the denominator. Hence, two systems having in their transfer functions the same denominator but different numerators will have the same characteristic equation but may exhibit markedly different responses to the same input. Such a situation is illustrated in Figs. 3.30 and 3.31.

3.6 SECOND ORDER SYSTEMS

Consider as an example the familiar system composed of a spring, a mass, and a viscous damper (or dashpot) shown in Fig. 3.32. To derive a transfer function in which the applied force $f(t)$ is considered to be the input and the displacement of the mass from its rest position $x(t)$ is considered to be the response, we write the differential equation describing the dynamic behavior of the system, applying Newton's second law.

$$M \frac{d^2x}{dt^2} = f(t) - kx(t) - B \frac{dx}{dt} \qquad (3.125)$$

Here the friction force on the rollers is considered to be zero. If Eq. 3.125 is first Laplace transformed, the initial conditions $x(0)$ and $\dot{x}(0)$ being considered zero, and then rearranged, the transfer function is found to be

$$\frac{X(s)}{F(s)} = \frac{1}{Ms^2 + Bs + k} = \frac{1/M}{s^2 + (B/M)s + k/M} \qquad (3.126)$$

The dynamic character of this second order system may best be studied by computing its response to a step input. Let the applied force be a step of P pounds applied at time 0. Using pounds as a unit for force suggests slugs for mass, feet for displacement, and seconds for units of time. The spring constant k is in pounds per foot, and the

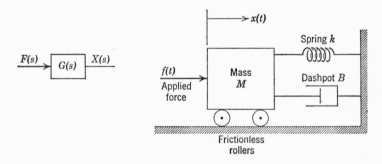

Fig. 3.32. Second order system.

damper coefficient B is in pounds per foot per second. The response to the step input is given as

$$X(s) = \frac{P/M}{s[s^2 + (B/M)s + k/M]} \qquad (3.127)$$

Now the denominator may be factored and the expression expanded into partial fractions as follows:

$$X(s) = \frac{P/M}{s(s + \alpha)(s + \beta)} = \frac{K_1}{s} + \frac{K_2}{s + \alpha} + \frac{K_3}{s + \beta} \quad (\alpha \neq \beta) \quad (3.128)$$

where α and β are given by the familiar quadratic rule of algebra

$$\alpha, \beta = \frac{B/M \pm \sqrt{B^2/M^2 - 4k/M}}{2} = \frac{B}{2M} \pm \frac{1}{2M} \sqrt{B^2 - 4kM}$$

$$(3.129)$$

The two roots α and β can bear one of three algebraic relationships to each other, depending upon the relative magnitudes of the parameters M, B, and k. If $B^2 > 4kM$, α and β will both be real and unequal numbers; if $B^2 = 4kM$, α and β will be real and equal numbers; and if $B^2 < 4kM$, α and β will be complex numbers having equal real parts and imaginary parts which are equal in magnitude but opposite in sign —that is, α and β will be complex conjugates. The responses for each of these three cases are computed in the following paragraphs.

Case 1. $B^2 > 4kM$, α and β real and unequal. In this case the response $x(t)$ may be determined directly from the inverse transform of Eq. 3.128.

$$x(t) = K_1 + K_2 \epsilon^{-\alpha t} + K_3 \epsilon^{-\beta t} \qquad (3.130)$$

α and β are given by Eq. 3.129, and the residues K_1, K_2, and K_3 are determined by the partial fraction expansion process as

$$K_1 = \frac{P}{k}, \qquad K_2 = \frac{P/M}{\alpha^2 - \alpha\beta}, \qquad K_3 = \frac{P/M}{\beta^2 - \alpha\beta} \qquad (3.131)$$

When plotted on a time scale $x(t)$ appears in Fig. 3.33, Case 1. This is called the *overdamped* case, for obvious reasons.

Case 2. $B^2 = 4kM$, α and β real and equal. In this case the response is given by

$$X(s) = \frac{P/M}{s(s + B/2M)^2} = \frac{P/M}{s(s + \sqrt{k/M})^2} \qquad (3.132)$$

which may be transformed by use of the Laplace transform table, pair 23.

$$x(t) = \frac{P}{k} \left(1 - \epsilon^{-(B/2M)t} - \frac{B}{2M} t\epsilon^{-(B/2M)t} \right) \qquad (3.133)$$

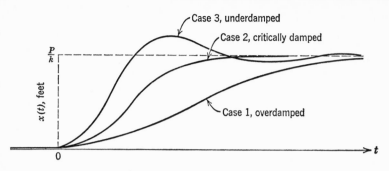

Fig. 3.33.   Response of second order system to step input of force, three cases.

This response, called a *critically damped response*, is plotted in Fig. 3.33 as Case 2.

Case 3. $B^2 < 4kM$, α and β complex conjugates.   In this case the response will be given by Eq. 3.128, which may be written in the partial fraction form as

$$X(s) = \frac{K_1}{s} + \frac{K_2}{s + a + jb} + \frac{K_3}{s + a - jb} \tag{3.134}$$

where

$$\alpha, \beta = a \pm jb$$

and

$$a = \frac{B}{2M}, \qquad b = \frac{\sqrt{4kM - B^2}}{2M} \tag{3.135}$$

j is the imaginary operator $\sqrt{-1}$.   An evaluation of the residues K_1, K_2, and K_3 shows that

$$K_1 = \frac{P}{k}$$

$$K_2 = -\frac{P}{2k}\left[1 + j\left(\frac{B}{\sqrt{4kM - B^2}}\right)\right]$$

$$K_3 = -\frac{P}{2k}\left[1 - j\left(\frac{B}{\sqrt{4kM - B^2}}\right)\right] \tag{3.136}$$

Notice that the two residues K_2 and K_3 are complex conjugates.   The time response is obtained by the inverse transformation of Eq. 3.134.

$$x(t) = \frac{P}{k} + K_2\epsilon^{(-a-jb)t} + K_3\epsilon^{(-a+jb)t} \tag{3.137}$$

By making use of the relationship

$$\epsilon^{(-a\pm jb)t} = \epsilon^{-at}(\cos bt \pm j \sin bt) \tag{3.138}$$

it is possible to write the response equation in this form:

$$x(t) = \frac{P}{k} + \frac{P}{k}\left(1 + \frac{B^2}{4kM - B^2}\right)^{\frac{1}{2}} \epsilon^{-(B/2M)t} \sin\left(\frac{\sqrt{4kM - B^2}}{2M} t + \psi\right)$$

(3.139)

where $$\psi = \tan^{-1}\left(\frac{-\sqrt{4kM - B^2}}{-B}\right)$$

Notice that the coefficient $[P/k][1 + B^2/(4kM - B^2)]^{\frac{1}{2}}$ is just twice the absolute value of the residue K_2, and the tangent of ψ is the ratio of the real part of K_2 to the imaginary part of K_2. The response $x(t)$ is plotted in Fig. 3.33 as *Case 3* and is called an underdamped response.

Several interesting things may be observed about this second order system. The initial displacement and the initial velocity of the mass are both zero. This is easily verified by applying the initial value theorem to Eq. 3.127.

$$x(0^+) = \lim_{s \to \infty} sX(s) = \lim_{s \to \infty} \frac{P/M}{s^2 + (B/M)s + k/M} = 0 \qquad (3.140)$$

$$\dot{x}(0^+) = \lim_{s \to \infty} s(sX(s)) = \lim_{s \to \infty} \frac{sP/M}{s^2 + (B/M)s + k/M} = 0 \qquad (3.141)$$

The initial acceleration must be the applied force divided by the mass; this may also be verified by the initial value theorem.

$$\ddot{x}(0^+) = \lim_{s \to \infty} s(s^2X(s)) = \lim_{s \to \infty} \frac{s^2P/M}{s^2 + (B/M)s + k/M} = \frac{P}{M} \qquad (3.142)$$

If the damping coefficient B is set equal to zero the response will be completely undamped and will oscillate indefinitely; this may be shown by making $B = 0$ in Eq. 3.139.

$$x(t) = \frac{P}{k} + \frac{P}{k} \sin\left(\sqrt{k/M}\, t + \frac{3\pi}{2}\right) = \frac{P}{k}\left(1 - \cos\sqrt{k/M}\, t\right) \quad (3.143)$$

This response is plotted in Fig. 3.34. The undamped natural frequency for the system is defined from this response.

$$\omega_n = \sqrt{k/M} \text{ rad/sec} = \text{undamped natural frequency} \quad (3.144)$$

Another quantity frequently used in describing a second order system is the *damping ratio* for the system. This term is defined as

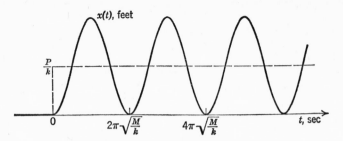

Fig. 3.34.   Undamped (B = 0) second order response.

the ratio of the damping coefficient B to that value of B which will give critical damping.

$$\text{Damping ratio} = \zeta = \frac{B}{B_{\text{crit.}}} = \frac{B}{2\sqrt{kM}} \qquad (3.145)$$

If the damping ratio is greater than unity the system is overdamped; if it is equal to unity the system is critically damped, and if it is less than unity the system is underdamped.

The damping ratio and undamped natural frequency parameters are conveniently used in writing the response expression for the second order system.   For example, Eq. 3.139, written in terms of ζ amd ω_n is

$$x(t) = \frac{P}{k}\left[1 + \frac{\epsilon^{-\zeta\omega_n t}}{\sqrt{1 - \zeta^2}}\sin\,(\omega_0 t + \psi)\right] \qquad (3.146)$$

where $\psi = \tan^{-1}\{(-\sqrt{1 - \zeta^2})/(-\zeta)\}$ and $\omega_0 = \omega_n\sqrt{1 - \zeta^2}$.

Notice that the frequency of oscillation* is lower than the undamped natural frequency, except for $\zeta = 0$.

$$\text{frequency of oscillation} = \omega_0 = \omega_n\sqrt{1 - \zeta^2} \qquad (3.147)$$

It is convenient to normalize Eq. 3.146 to a steady-state value of unity by dividing through by P/k.   After this is done $x(t)$ may be plotted against $\omega_n t$, rather than against t, as shown in Fig. 3.35. Several curves, each for a different value of ζ, are plotted in this diagram.   This set of curves is very useful in that it is normalized both with respect to the final value of the output and with respect to time. Any second order system whose transfer function has a constant numerator will have a step response corresponding to one of the curves

---

* In Chapter 8 a third characteristic frequency for the second order system, the resonant frequency, is defined.   The resonant frequency is lower than the oscillating frequency.

in Fig. 3.35 (or to a curve for an intermediate value for ζ not shown in this diagram). One need know only the ζ and ω_n of the system and the final value of the output to construct the step response from these curves.

Two other useful relationships may be derived from Eq. 3.146. When dx/dt is computed and set equal to zero it can be seen that

$$\text{Maximum overshoot, percent} = 100\epsilon^{-\pi\zeta/\sqrt{1-\zeta^2}}$$

$$\text{Instant of maximum overshoot} = t_p = \frac{\pi}{\omega_n \sqrt{1-\zeta^2}} \quad (3.148)$$

As an example, consider a system such as that shown in Fig. 3.32, where the mass M, spring constant k, and damping coefficient B are

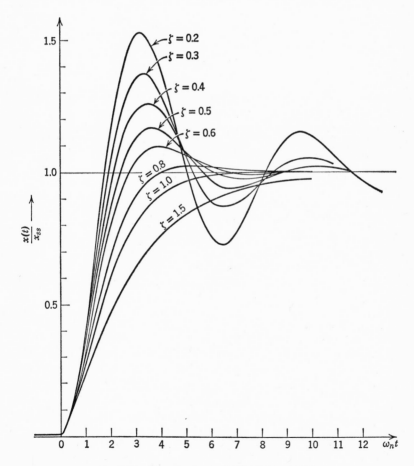

Fig. 3.35. Normalized second order response curves.

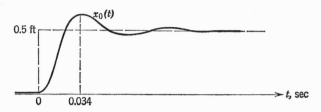

Fig. 3.36.   Response of the second order system to a 50-pound step input.

unknown.   These coefficients can be determined by making a simple transient test and comparing the result with the set of curves in Fig. 3.35.   Assume that a 50-pound force is applied to the system in a step-like manner and that the resulting response $x_0(t)$ looks like the curve shown in Fig. 3.36.   From the analysis of this system it is known that

$$X_0(s) = \frac{50}{s(Ms^2 + Bs + k)} \tag{3.149}$$

The final value theorem shows that

$$x_0(\infty) = \lim_{s \to 0} sX_0(s) = \frac{50}{k} \text{ feet} \tag{3.150}$$

Since the measured value for $x_0(\infty)$ is 0.5 ft, the spring constant must be 100 lb/ft.   The experimental curve shows the peak overshoot to be about 25 percent.   From the normalized curves in Fig. 3.35 it is seen that an overshoot of 25 percent corresponds to a damping ratio of 0.4, and that the peak overshoot occurs at the instant $\omega_n t = 3.4$.   The experimental data show the peak to occur at $t = 0.034$ sec; therefore, the ω_n for this system is 100 rad/sec.   We know that $\omega_n = \sqrt{k/M}$, so the mass in this system must be 0.01 slug.   Finally, B can be found by applying Eq. 3.145. B turns out to be 0.8 lb sec/ft for this system.

Many systems found in mechanical and electrical equipment closely approximate second order systems of the type discussed here, and the second order curves in Fig. 3.35 are found to be useful in analyzing these systems.   However, some second order systems are not of this type, and the curves in Fig. 3.35 should not be expected to apply to all second order systems.   Those second order systems whose transfer functions have a factor $(s + a)$ in the numerator are discussed more fully in Chapter 4.

3.7   HIGHER ORDER SYSTEMS

In the previous sections it has been shown that the time responses of first and second order systems are sums of rather simple functions of time—exponentials, damped sinusoids, constants, or powers of t. It will now be shown that the time responses of higher order systems are composed of larger numbers of the same basically simple functions as those found in first and second order systems.

The response of a linear system having lumped and constant parameters may always be computed in this manner:

$$X_0(s) = X_1(s)G(s) \qquad (3.151)$$

$X_0(s)$ and $X_1(s)$ are the output and input functions, and $G(s)$ is the transfer function. Now $X_0(s)$ may always be written in this form

$$X_0(s) = \frac{K(s + Z_1)(s + Z_2) \cdots (s + Z_m)}{(s + P_1)(s + P_2) \cdots (s + P_n)} \qquad (3.152)$$

that is, as a ratio of two algebraic polynomials in s, each polynomial appearing in factored form with the coefficient of s in each factor being unity. The numbers $-Z_1, -Z_2, \ldots$ and $-P_1, -P_2, \ldots$ are the roots of the two polynomials. These numbers are either real or complex, but for each complex Z (or P) there will occur another complex Z (or P) which is the conjugate of the first. If the factors of the polynomials are multiplied together, Eq. 3.152 will appear as

$$X_0(s) = \frac{K(s^m + a_1 s^{m-1} + a_2 s^{m-2} + \cdots + a_m)}{s^n + b_1 s^{n-1} + b_2 s^{n-2} + \cdots + b_n)} \qquad (3.153)$$

where the as and bs are all real numbers.*

The response $x_0(t)$ may be obtained by taking the inverse Laplace transform of $X_0(s)$. If $X_0(s)$ is of high order it may not be listed in available tables of Laplace transforms. In this case the inverse transform process may be facilitated by making a partial fraction expansion of $X_0(s)$. The first step in this operation is to check the order of the numerator, m, and that of the denominator, n.

If m is equal to or greater than n, $X_0(s)$ is said to be an improper fraction, and the denominator is divided into the numerator until the

---

* Two important relationships between polynomials in factored form occur in Eq. 3.152 and, in expanded form, in Eq. 3.153:

$$a_1 = Z_1 + Z_2 + \cdots + Z_m$$
$$b_1 = P_1 + P_2 + \cdots + P_n$$

and

$$a_m = Z_1 Z_2 \cdots Z_m$$
$$b_n = P_1 P_2 \cdots P_n$$

These relationships are useful later in connection with stability studies in feedback systems.

remainder is a proper fraction. In this case $X_0(s)$ will be of the general form

$$X_0(s) = K\left[\alpha_1 + \alpha_2 s + \cdots + s^{(m-n)}\right.$$
$$\left. + \frac{\beta(s^{n-1} + c_1 s^{n-2} + \cdots + c_{n-1})}{s^n + b_1 s^{n-1} + \cdots + b_n}\right] \quad (3.154)$$

where the αs, βs and cs are constants. It should be noted here that an $X_0(s)$ in this form, when transformed, yields in the time response impulses, doublets, triplets, etc. from the α_1, $\alpha_2 s$, $\alpha_3 s^2$, . . . terms. These functions do not correspond to physically realizable response functions of voltage, current, force, displacement, etc., and they occur when idealizations (such as resistanceless circuits or massless bodies) are assumed for convenience in analysis. The impulse functions which result can often be ignored, the realistic terms alone being retained as the significant ones.

In most analyses n will be greater than m, and no expansion such as that indicated in Eq. 3.154 will be necessary. Assuming that $n > m$, one may easily expand $X_0(s)$ into partial fractions. Two situations arise here: (1) The roots of the denominator $-P_1$, $-P_2$, . . . are either distinct (all different), or (2) some of the Ps may occur more than once (multiple roots).

If the roots are all distinct, the partial fraction expansion will be of the form

$$X_0(s) = \frac{K(s + Z_1)(s + Z_2) \cdots (s + Z_m)}{(s + P_1)(s + P_2) \cdots (s + P_n)} = \frac{K_1}{s + P_1} + \frac{K_2}{s + P_2}$$
$$+ \cdots + \frac{K_n}{s + P_n} \quad (3.155)$$

where the constants K_1, K_2, K_3 $\cdots$ are called residues (K_1 being the *residue of* $X_0(s)$ *at* $s = -P_1$). These may be evaluated algebraically as follows:

$$K_1 = (s + P_1)X_0(s)\Big|_{s=-P_1}$$

$$K_2 = (s + P_2)X_0(s)\Big|_{s=-P_2}$$

$$\cdot$$
$$\cdot$$
$$\cdot$$

$$K_n = (s + P_n)X_0(s)\Big|_{s=-P_n} \quad (3.156)$$

For example, consider the function

$$X_0(s) = \frac{24(s+1)(s+2)}{s(s+3)(s+4)(s^2+2s+4)} \qquad (3.157)$$

The quadratic term may be factored into two complex conjugate factors:

$$s^2 + 2s + 4 = (s+1+j\sqrt{3})(s+1-j\sqrt{3}) \qquad (3.158)$$

The partial fraction expansion for this function is

$$X_0(s) = \frac{K_1}{s} + \frac{K_2}{s+3} + \frac{K_3}{s+4} + \frac{K_4}{s+1+j\sqrt{3}} + \frac{K_5}{s+1-j\sqrt{3}}$$
$$(3.159)$$

The residues are evaluated, by Eq. 3.156, as

$$K_1 = \frac{24(1-0)(2-0)}{(3-0)(4-0)(4-0)} = \frac{48}{48} = 1$$

$$K_2 = \frac{24(1-3)(2-3)}{(-3)(4-3)(9-6+4)} = \frac{48}{-21} = -2.286$$

$$K_3 = \frac{24(1-4)(2-4)}{(-4)(3-4)(16-8+4)} = \frac{144}{48} = 3$$

$$K_4 = \frac{24(1-1-j\sqrt{3})(2-1-j\sqrt{3})}{(-1-j\sqrt{3})(3-1-j\sqrt{3})}$$
$$\qquad\qquad (4-1-j\sqrt{3})(1-j\sqrt{3}-1-j\sqrt{3})$$

$$= \frac{12(2\underline{/-60°})}{(2\underline{/-120°})(\sqrt{7}\underline{/-40.89°})(\sqrt{12}\underline{/-30°})}$$
$$= 1.309\underline{/130.89°} = -0.857 + j(0.990)$$

$$K_5 = \frac{24(1-1+j\sqrt{3})(2-1+j\sqrt{3})}{(-1+j\sqrt{3})(3-1+j\sqrt{3})}$$
$$\qquad\qquad (4-1+j\sqrt{3})(1+j\sqrt{3}-1+j\sqrt{3})$$

$$= \frac{12(2\underline{/60°})}{(2\underline{/120°})(\sqrt{7}\underline{/40.89°})(\sqrt{12}\underline{/30°})}$$
$$= 1.309\underline{/-130.89°} = -0.857 - j(0.990) \quad (3.160)$$

Notice that K_4 and K_5 are complex conjugates. Once the residues are computed, the time response may be written by inspection. In the general case (for distinct Ps)*

$$x_0(t) = K_1\epsilon^{-P_1 t} + K_2\epsilon^{-P_2 t} + K_3\epsilon^{-P_3 t} + \cdots + K_n\epsilon^{-P_n t} \quad (3.161)$$

In this example the response is

$$x_0(t) = 1 - 2.286\epsilon^{-3t} + 3\epsilon^{-4t} + (-0.857 + j0.990)\epsilon^{-(1+j\sqrt{3})t}$$
$$+ (-0.857 - j0.990)\epsilon^{-(1-j\sqrt{3})t} \quad (3.162)$$

The last two terms may be combined in the manner indicated in Eq. 3.138 so that all imaginary notation is eliminated from $x_0(t)$.

$$x_0(t) = 1 - 2.286\epsilon^{-3t} + 3\epsilon^{-4t} + 2.618\epsilon^{-t} \sin(\sqrt{3}\,t + \psi)$$

where
$$\psi = \tan^{-1}\left(\frac{-0.857}{0.990}\right) = -40.89° \quad (3.163)$$

Notice that the constant 2.618 in Eq. 3.163 is just twice the absolute value of the residue K_4, and the angle ψ is determined by the ratio of the real part of K_4 to the imaginary part. In general, the two complex terms may always be combined as they are in this example, that is:

$$\mathcal{L}^{-1}\left\{\frac{(a+jb)}{s+c+j\omega_0} + \frac{(a-jb)}{s+c-j\omega_0}\right\} = 2(a^2+b^2)^{\frac{1}{2}}\epsilon^{-ct}\sin(\omega_0 t + \psi)$$

$$(3.164)$$

where
$$\psi = \tan^{-1}\left(\frac{a}{b}\right)$$

Here $a + jb$ is the residue of the s function at $s = -c - j\omega_0$. In most systems it is desirable to express the quadratic factor in the general form $(s^2 + 2\zeta\omega_n s + \omega_n{}^2)$, in which case the c in Eq. 3.164 is $\zeta\omega_n$, and the ω_0 is $\omega_n\sqrt{1 - \zeta^2}$. The advantage of using this notation is brought out in Chapter 4.

If $X_0(s)$ has multiple roots in its denominator the partial fraction expansion becomes slightly more complicated. If one of the factors is repeated r times, $X_0(s)$ will be

$$X_0(s) = \frac{K(s + Z_1)(s + Z_2) \cdots (s + Z_m)}{(s + P_1)^r(s + P_2)(s + P_3) \cdots (s + P_n)} \quad (3.165)$$

* Here it is seen that the general form for $x_0(t)$ is determined by the denominator of $X_0(s)$—that is, by the Ps. The numerator of $X_0(s)$ has no influence upon the *general form* of $x_0(t)$. The Zs and K in the numerator do play a prominent role in determining the magnitudes and signs of the residues K_1, K_2, K_3 . . . , and these are important in determining the size and shape of the $x_0(t)$ response.

and the partial fraction expansion will be

$$X_0(s) = \frac{K_1}{(s + P_1)} + \frac{C_2}{(s + P_1)^2} + \frac{C_3}{(s + P_1)^3} + \cdots + \frac{C_r}{(s + P_1)^r}$$
$$+ \frac{K_2}{s + P_2} + \frac{K_3}{s + P_3} + \cdots + \frac{K_n}{s + P_n} \quad (3.166)$$

The constants $K_1, K_2, K_3 \cdots K_n$ are the residues, and the constants $C_2, C_3 \cdots C_r$ do not have special names. The residues $K_2, K_3, \ldots K_n$ are computed exactly as indicated in Eq. 3.156, but the residue K_1 and the constants $C_2, C_3, \ldots C_r$ are computed in the following fashion:

$$C_r = (s + P_1)^r X_0(s) \Big|_{s=-P_1}$$

$$C_{r-1} = \frac{1}{1!} \left\{ \frac{d}{ds} [(s + P_1)^r X_0(s)] \right\}_{s=-P_1}$$

$$C_{r-2} = \frac{1}{2!} \left\{ \frac{d^2}{ds^2} [(s + P_1)^r X_0(s)] \right\}_{s=-P_1}$$

.
.
.

$$C_2 = \frac{1}{(r-2)!} \left\{ \frac{d^{(r-2)}}{ds^{(r-2)}} [(s + P_1)^r X_0(s)] \right\}_{s=-P_1}$$

$$K_1 = \frac{1}{(r-1)!} \left\{ \frac{d^{(r-1)}}{ds^{(r-1)}} [(s + P_1)^r X_0(s)] \right\}_{s=-P_1} \quad (3.167)$$

Once the residues and constants are computed it is a simple matter to obtain the response function $x_0(t)$ by writing the inverse transform of $X_0(s)$. The only new term introduced by the multiple root is transformed in this manner:

$$\mathcal{L}^{-1} \left\{ \frac{A}{(s + P)^k} \right\} = \frac{A}{(k-1)!} t^{(k-1)} \epsilon^{-Pt} \quad (3.168)$$

An example will illustrate the application of Eq. 3.167 in the partial fraction expansion of a function having multiple roots in the denominator. Take

$$X_0(s) = \frac{(30)(s + 1)}{(s + 2)^3(s + 3)(s + 5)} \quad (3.169)$$

This is expandable to

$$X_0(s) = \frac{K_1}{s + 2} + \frac{C_2}{(s + 2)^2} + \frac{C_3}{(s + 2)^3} + \frac{K_2}{(s + 3)} + \frac{K_3}{(s + 5)} \quad (3.170)$$

Using the expressions for the residues and constants given in Eqs. 3.156 and 3.167, compute the following:

$$K_3 = (s + 5)X_0(s)\Big|_{s=-5} = \frac{30(1 - 5)}{(2 - 5)^3(3 - 5)} = -2.223$$

$$K_2 = (s + 3)X_0(s)\Big|_{s=-3} = \frac{30(1 - 3)}{(2 - 3)^3(5 - 3)} = 30$$

$$C_3 = (s + 2)^3 X_0(s)\Big|_{s=-2} = \frac{30(s + 1)}{(s + 3)(s + 5)}\Big|_{s=-2} = -10$$

$$C_2 = \frac{1}{1!}\left[\frac{d}{ds}\frac{(30)(s + 1)}{(s + 3)(s + 5)}\right]_{s=-2}$$

$$= 30\left\{\frac{(s + 3)(s + 5) - (s + 1)[(s + 3) + (s + 5)]}{(s + 3)^2(s + 5)^2}\right\}_{s=-2}$$

$$= 30\left[\frac{-s^2 - 2s + 7}{(s + 3)^2(s + 5)^2}\right]_{s=-2} = \frac{70}{3} = 23.332$$

$$K_1 = \frac{1}{2!}\left\{\frac{d^2}{ds^2}\left[\frac{30(s + 1)}{(s + 3)(s + 5)}\right]\right\}_{s=-2}$$

$$= \frac{30}{2}\left\{\frac{2[2(s^2 + 2s - 7)(s + 4) - (s + 1)(s + 3)(s + 5)]}{(s + 3)^3(s + 5)^3}\right\}_{s=-2}$$

$$= -\frac{250}{9} = -27.777 \tag{3.171}$$

The response is

$$x_0(t) = -27.777\epsilon^{-2t} + 23.332t\epsilon^{-2t} - 5t^2\epsilon^{-2t}$$
$$+ 30\epsilon^{-3t} - 2.223\epsilon^{-5t} \tag{3.172}$$

If the original expression $X_0(s)$ has a root repeated more than three times, or if the expression is more complicated than the example which is given here, the labor involved in computing the derivatives in the $K_1, C_2, C_3, \ldots C_{r-1}$ terms may become excessive. This labor may be reduced considerably by approximating the repeated roots by separate roots which have nearly the same value as the repeated roots. For example, if the $(s + 2)^3$ term in Eq. 3.169 is so replaced, the expression will be

$$X_0(s) = \frac{30(s + 1)}{(s + 1.9)(s + 2)(s + 2.1)(s + 3)(s + 5)} \tag{3.173}$$

This expression has no repeated roots; consequently, the calculation of the residues may be made very quickly without taking derivatives. Although the form of $x_0(t)$ derived in this manner differs from the form obtained by the more exact multiple root process, it will be found that the instantaneous values of $x_0(t)$ will be very nearly the same in both expressions. If greater accuracy than that obtained in Eq. 3.173 is desired, the triple root may be replaced by $(s + 1.99)(s + 2)$ $(s + 2.01)$.

3.8 SUMMARY

The derivation of transfer functions for electric networks, motors, and gear trains has served to acquaint the reader with the procedure for linearizing the physical system involved, (when this is permissable) obtaining from the linearized model the equations which describe its dynamic behavior, and, finally, using the Laplace transformation to obtain the transfer function, which is used to relate the variable defined as the input to the variable defined as the output.

The material in Sections 3.5 and 3.7 is essential to the understanding of the graphical procedures which permit the engineer to calculate, or at least to estimate, the residues of $X_0(s)$, and from this to determine, or at least to estimate, $x_0(t)$. These graphical procedures are developed in Chapter 4 and throughout the remainder of the book.

The dynamic properties of first order systems have been fully described in Sections 3.3 and 3.4, and most of the important aspects of second order systems have been introduced in connection with the simple mass-spring-damper system in Section 3.6. In the ensuing chapters the second order system is more fully described, and the usefulness of the ζ and ω_n notation is made apparent.

REFERENCES

1. Pfeiffer, *Linear Systems Analysis*, McGraw-Hill, 1961.
2. Scott, *Linear Circuits, Part 1, Time Domain Analysis*, Addison-Wesley, 1960.
3. Chestnut and Mayer, *Servomechanisms and Regulating Systems Design*, Vol. 1, 2nd ed., Wiley, 1959.
4. Murphy, *Basic Automatic Control Theory*, Van Nostrand, 1957.
5. Ahrendt, *Servomechanism Practice*, McGraw-Hill, 1954.
6. Gibson and Tuteur, *Control System Components*, McGraw-Hill, 1958.
7. Trimmer, *Response of Physical Systems*, Wiley, 1950.
8. Lauer, Lesnick, and Matson, *Servomechanism Fundamentals*, 2nd ed., McGraw-Hill, 1960.
9. Bruns and Saunders, *Feedback Control Systems*, McGraw-Hill, 1955.

4 Complex Plane Analysis

4.1 INTRODUCTION

In Chapter 3 the transfer function for a linear system having lumped and constant parameters was defined, and it was demonstrated that the dynamic response of the system for a specified input could be determined simply as follows:

$$F(s) = [G(s)] [Y(s)]$$

$$f(t) = \mathcal{L}^{-1}\{F(s)\} \tag{4.1}$$

where $f(t)$ is the response function, $F(s)$ is its Laplace transform, $G(s)$ is the transfer function of the system, and $Y(s)$ is the Laplace transform of the input function. Two restrictions are made upon Eq. 4.1: first, $y(t)$ must be Laplace transformable (a step, ramp, sinusoid, etc.), and second, the initial condition terms which appear in the transformed versions of the original system equations must be assumed to be zero. Section 3.7 showed that the inverse transformation process of obtaining $f(t)$ from $F(s)$ is made simpler when $F(s)$ is expressed as a partial fraction expansion in which each of the terms is a relatively simple one, the numerators being constants. $f(t)$, then, is a sum of relatively simple time functions, each multiplied by a constant. The relative values of the constants thus determine to a large degree the relative importance of the components which make up $f(t)$.

This chapter describes a technique for the graphical computation of $f(t)$ from $F(s)$—that is, the determination of the residues and other constants in the partial fraction expansion. The graphical method presented here has several advantages over the analytical technique of Chapter 3. A pictorial representation of the problem often points up mistakes in the analysis and also indicates ways in which the problem may be simplified through approximation, when this is permissible. Probably the greatest use of the graphical method is made in estimating the values of the residues, and from this, estimating the size and form of the response function $f(t)$. The control engineer is often more interested in obtaining a quick estimate of $f(t)$ than in determining, by a lengthy computation process, the exact expression for $f(t)$. Some practice in the methods developed in this chapter will give the reader considerable insight into this technique of estimation.

4.2   POLE-ZERO MAP OF F(s)

A zero of $F(s)$ is a value of s which makes $F(s) = 0$.   A pole of $F(s)$ is a value of s which makes $F(s) = \infty$.   For example, if

$$F(s) = \frac{15(s + 1)}{s(s^2 + 5s + 6)} \tag{4.2}$$

$s = -1$ is a zero of $F(s)$, since $F(-1) = 0$, and $s = 0$, $s = -2$, and $s = -3$ are poles of $F(s)$, since $F(0)$, $F(-2)$, and $F(-3)$ are infinite In general, $F(s)$ may be written as

$$F(s) = \frac{N(s)}{D(s)} = \frac{K(s + Z_1)(s + Z_2) \cdots (s + Z_m)}{(s + P_1)(s + P_2)(s + P_3) \cdots (s + P_n)} \tag{4.3}$$

where the roots of the equation $N(s) = 0$, $-Z_1$, $-Z_2$, etc. are zeros of $F(s)$, and the roots of the equation $D(s) = 0$, $-P_1$, $-P_2$, $-P_3$, etc., are poles of $F(s)$.

The numbers $-Z_1$, $-Z_2$, etc. and $-P_1$, $-P_2$, $-P_3$, etc. are not always the only zeros and poles of $F(s)$.   If the order of the denominator is different from that of the numerator, poles or zeros will occur at $s = \infty$.   For example, in Eq. 4.2 one zero of $F(s)$ occurs at $s = -1$, and three poles of $F(s)$ occur at $s = 0$, $s = -2$, and $s = -3$.   However, if s is allowed to approach infinity in this expression

$$\lim_{s \to \infty} [F(s)] \cong \lim_{s \to \infty} \left[\frac{15(s)}{s(s^2)} \right] = \lim_{s \to \infty} \left[\frac{15}{(s)(s)} \right] \tag{4.4}$$

$F(s)$ approaches 0; that is, $F(\infty) = 0$, so that $s = \infty$ must also be a zero of $F(s)$.   In fact, since two s factors occur in the denominator of the expression in Eq. 4.4, a more complete description of the poles and zeros of $F(s)$ is this: $F(s)$ has three zeros—one at $s = -1$ and two at infinity—and three poles—one each at $s = 0$, $s = -2$, and $s = -3$. Therefore, it may be said that any $F(s)$ of the general form indicated in Eq. 4.3 has the same number of zeros as poles, provided the poles or zeros at infinity are included in the count. It should be said of Eq. 4.2 that $F(s)$ has three finite poles and one finite zero.

The word singularity is a generic term for poles and zeros. For example, if

$$F(s) = \frac{K(s + a)}{(s - b)(s + c)} \tag{4.5}$$

$F(s)$ is said to have three finite singularities—one zero at $s = -a$, and two poles, at $s = b$ and $s = -c$. Another general term for pole or zero is critical frequency. (See Section 4.6.)

It is apparent from the general form for $F(s)$ (Eq. 4.3) that $F(s)$ is completely determined if its poles, zeros, and constant multiplier are specified. Since the constant multiplier determines only the magnitude and not the shape of $f(t)$, it is sometimes of minor importance in the analysis.

$F(s)$ may be represented graphically by making a pole-zero map of $F(s)$. As a first example, consider the function in Eq. 4.2 with a finite zero at $s = -1$ and poles at $s = 0$, $s = -2$, and $s = -3$. These singularities may be indicated by marks along a line representing all values of s, as in Fig. 4.1. Here the pole values are indicated by a small cross and the zero values by a small circle. The line on which they are plotted is called the s axis. The constant multiplier 15 is specified in the small box just to the right of the origin. Notice that the pole-zero map carries exactly the same information as the equation form for $F(s)$, and either may be constructed from the other. For example,

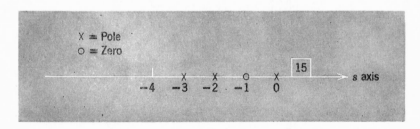

Fig. 4.1.   Pole-zero map of $F(s) = \dfrac{15(s + 1)}{s(s^2 + 5s + 6)}$.

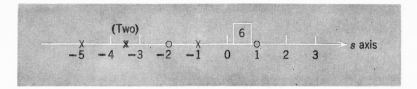

Fig. 4.2. Pole-zero map.

the pole-zero map shown in Fig. 4.2 may be interpreted as representing the function

$$F(s) = \frac{6(s-1)(s+2)}{(s+1)(s+3.5)^2(s+5)} \qquad (4.6)$$

Next consider the pole-zero map for a function which has complex poles. Let

$$F(s) = \frac{3(s+1)}{s(s^2+2s+2)} = \frac{3(s+1)}{s(s+1+j1)(s+1-j1)} \qquad (4.7)$$

To plot the poles and zeros of this function it is necessary to use two axes, one for the real component of the pole and one for the imaginary component. Thus the poles and zeros are plotted on a complex plane, the s plane, as illustrated in Fig. 4.3. The real axis of the s plane is

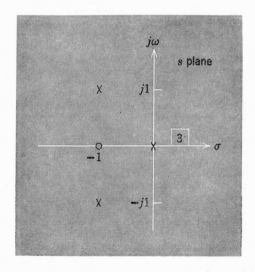

Fig. 4.3. Pole zero map for $F(s) = \dfrac{3(s+1)}{s(s+1+j1)(s+1-j1)}$.

labeled σ, and the imaginary axis is labeled $j\omega$; consequently, s is a complex variable, $s = \sigma + j\omega$. In Eq. 4.7 $F(s) = 0$ for $s = -1 + j0$, so a zero is indicated by the small circle at this point in the s plane. $F(s) = \infty$ for $s = 0 + j0$, $s = -1 + j1$, and $s = -1 - j1$, so poles are indicated at these three points in the s plane. The two zeros at $s = \infty$ are omitted! The constant multiplier 3 is noted in the box to the right of the origin.

In the following paragraphs four dynamic response problems are described by means of the pole-zero plots. These problems are of the general form indicated in Fig. 4.4, where a specified input function is

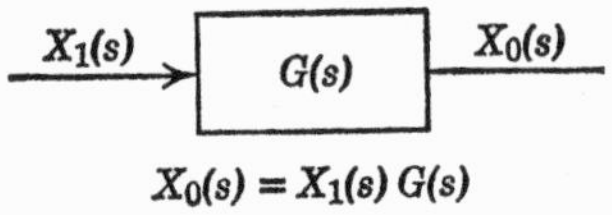

$$\xrightarrow{X_1(s)} \boxed{\ G(s)\ } \xrightarrow{X_0(s)}$$

$$X_0(s) = X_1(s)\,G(s)$$

Fig. 4.4. Dynamic response problem.

applied to a system whose transfer function is known, the output being the product $G(s)X_1(s)$.

Problem 1

Let the transfer function for the system be

$$G(s) = \frac{4(s + 2)(s + 3)}{(s + 1)(s + 5)} \tag{4.8}$$

and the input function $x_1(t)$ be the pulse shown in Fig. 4.5. The pulse duration is 1 msec, and since this is very much smaller than either of the two characteristic time constants of the system (1 sec and $\frac{1}{5}$ sec), the input function may be approximated by an impulse function. The area under the $x_1(t)$ curve is $(2000)(0.001) = 2$, so

$$x_1(t) \cong 2u_1(t) \tag{4.9}$$

where $u_1(t)$ is the unit impulse function. The Laplace transform of Eq. 4.9 is

$$\mathcal{L}\{2u_1(t)\} = 2 \tag{4.10}$$

so the response function $X_0(s)$ is

$$X_0(s) = \frac{8(s + 2)(s + 3)}{(s + 1)(s + 5)} \tag{4.11}$$

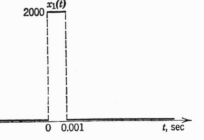

Fig. 4.5. Input function for Problem 1.

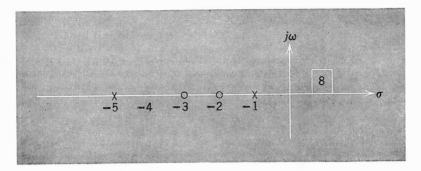

Fig. 4.6. Pole-zero map for $X_0(s)$, Problem 1.

A pole-zero map of $X_0(s)$ is drawn in Fig. 4.6. In this example an equal number of finite poles and zeros occur, so there are no poles or zeros at infinity, as shown by

$$X_0(s) \Big|_{s \to \infty} = 8 \tag{4.12}$$

Problem 2

Let the transfer function for this example be

$$G(s) = \frac{9(s + 2)}{(s + 1)(s^2 + 3s + 9)} \tag{4.13}$$

and the input function be a step as shown in Fig. 4.7. Then

$$X_1(s) = \frac{3}{s} \tag{4.14}$$

and
$$X_0(s) = \frac{27(s + 2)}{s(s + 1)(s^2 + 3s + 9)} \tag{4.15}$$

Here $X_0(s)$ has a pair of complex poles at the points $s = -1.5 \pm j1.5 \sqrt{3}$, real poles at the points $s = 0$, $s = -1$, and a finite zero at $s = -2$. Three

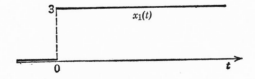

Fig. 4.7. Input function for Problem 2.

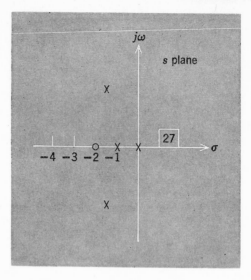

Fig. 4.8.   Pole-zero map for $X_0(s)$, Problem 2.

zeros of $X_0(s)$ occur at $s = \infty$, since the denominator is of the fourth order and the numerator of the first order. $X_0(s)$ is plotted in Fig. 4.8.

Problem 3

Assume the transfer function for the system to be

$$G(s) = \frac{(s^2 + 3s + 4)}{(s^2 + 3s + 2)} \tag{4.16}$$

and the input function to be a ramp as shown in Fig. 4.9.   Thus

$$X_1(s) = \frac{6}{s^2} \tag{4.17}$$

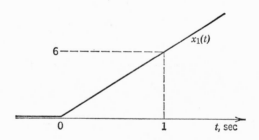

Fig. 4.9.   Input function for Problem 3.

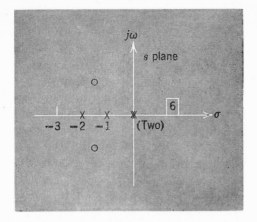

Fig. 4.10. Pole-zero map for $X_0(s)$, Problem 3.

The output response is given by the product $X_1(s)G(s)$:

$$X_0(s) = \frac{6(s^2 + 3s + 4)}{s^2(s^2 + 3s + 2)} \qquad (4.18)$$

When the numerator and denominator of $X_0(s)$ are factored, a pair of complex zeros and two real poles appear in the transfer function. A map of the finite poles and zeros of $X_0(s)$ is shown in Fig. 4.10.

Problem 4

Take the transfer function for the system as

$$G(s) = \frac{14}{(s + 1)(s^2 + 5s + 6)(s^2 + 4s + 5)} \qquad (4.19)$$

and the input as the sinusoidal function shown in Fig. 4.11. The transform of $x_1(t)$ is

$$X_1(s) = \frac{6}{s^2 + 4} \qquad (4.20)$$

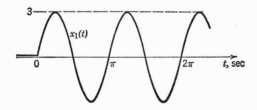

Fig. 4.11. Input function for Problem 4.

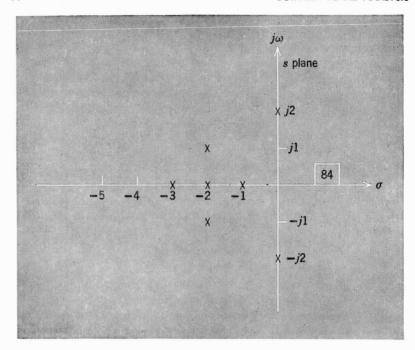

Fig. 4.12. Pole-zero map of $X_0(s)$, Problem 4.

so the output is

$$X_0(s) = \frac{84}{(s^2 + 4)(s + 1)(s^2 + 5s + 6)(s^2 + 4s + 5)} \qquad (4.21)$$

as plotted in Fig. 4.12. Since no finite zeros occur in $X_0(s)$, there must be seven zeros at infinity.

These four examples have illustrated the manner in which the pole-zero map for $X_0(s)$ is drawn for a given system having a specified input. The problem of determining the time response, $x_0(t)$, by making a graphical computation of the residues of $X_0(s)$ from the pole-zero map of $X_0(s)$ is considered in the next section.

4.3 GRAPHICAL CALCULATION OF RESIDUES ON THE s PLANE

In Chapter 3 it was shown that the inverse Laplace transformation of a function of the form

$$F(s) = \frac{K(s + Z_1)(s + Z_2) \cdot \cdot \cdot (s + Z_m)}{(s + P_1)(s + P_2) \cdot \cdot \cdot (s + P_n)} \qquad (4.22)$$

may be computed by making a partial fraction expansion of $F(s)$. If no multiple poles of $F(s)$ occur, this takes the form

$$F(s) = \frac{K_1}{s + P_1} + \frac{K_2}{s + P_2} + \frac{K_3}{s + P_3} + \cdots + \frac{K_n}{s + P_n} \quad (4.23)$$

where K_1, K_2, K_3, . . . K_n are the residues of $F(s)$ at the poles $-P_1$, $-P_2$, $-P_3$, . . . P_n, respectively. The residues K_1, K_2, K_3, . . . K_n are evaluated in Eq. 3.156. A graphical method of evaluating Eq. 3.156, which is illustrated in the following three examples, makes it possible to judge very quickly the relative values of the various residues, and from this to assess the relative importance of each of the terms in the partial fraction expansion of $F(s)$.

Example 1. Evaluate the residues of the function

$$F(s) = \frac{18(s + 1)}{s(s + 3)(s + 6)} \quad (4.24)$$

$$= \frac{K_1}{s} + \frac{K_2}{s + 3} + \frac{K_3}{s + 6}$$

The residues are determined from Eq. 3.156 to be

$$K_1 = \frac{18(s + 1)}{(s + 3)(s + 6)}\Big|_{s=0} = \frac{18(1)}{(3)(6)} = 1$$

$$K_2 = \frac{18(s + 1)}{s(s + 6)}\Big|_{s=-3} = \frac{18(-3 + 1)}{(-3)(-3 + 6)} = 4 \quad (4.25)$$

$$K_3 = \frac{18(s + 1)}{s(s + 3)}\Big|_{s=-6} = \frac{18(-6 + 1)}{(-6)(-6 + 3)} = -5$$

Now consider the pole-zero plot for $F(s)$ shown in Fig. 4.13. A vector drawn from the point $s = -1$ to the origin is designated as $(s + 1)$, the vector

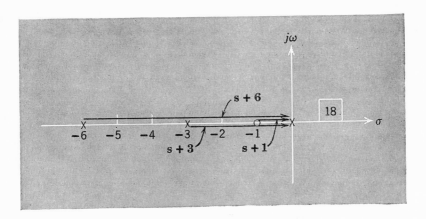

Fig. 4.13. Pole-zero map for $F(s) = \dfrac{18(s + 1)}{s(s + 3)(s + 6)}$.

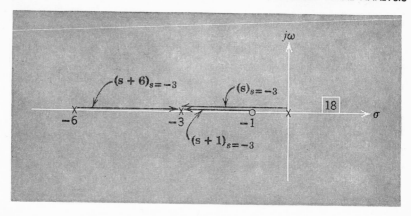

Fig. 4.14.   Pole-zero map for computing K_2, Example 1.

from $s = -3$ to the origin is $(s + 3)$, and, similarly, the vector from $s = -6$ to the origin is $(s + 6)$.*   The vector $(s + 1)$ in this instance has a value of $+1$, since its length is 1 and it is directed along the real axis with a reference angle (or argument) of zero degrees.   In other words, the vector $(s + 1)$ in Fig. 4.13 is equivalent to $(s + 1) \Big|_{s=0}$, since it is the vector drawn from the point $s = -1$ to the point $s = 0$.   Similarly, the other two vectors are

$$(s + 3) = (s + 3) \Big|_{s=0}$$
$$(s + 6) = (s + 6) \Big|_{s=0}$$

(4.26)

The calculation in Eq. 4.25 for the residue K_1 may therefore be described graphically as

$$K_1 = \frac{18(s + 1)}{(s + 3)(s + 6)} \quad = \frac{18(+1)}{(+3)(+6)} = 1 \tag{4.27}$$

Here the residue K_1, corresponding to the pole of $F(s)$ at the origin ($s = 0$), is evaluated by drawing vectors from all the other poles and zeros to the pole at $s = 0$ and computing the ratio

$$K_1 = (18) \left(\frac{\text{Product of vectors drawn from zeros to } s = 0}{\text{Product of vectors drawn from poles to } s = 0} \right) \tag{4.28}$$

Equation 4.28 may be abbreviated as follows:

$$K_1 = 18 \left[\frac{\Pi Z}{\Pi P} \right]_{s=0} \tag{4.29}$$

To compute K_2, the residue of $F(s)$ at the pole $s = -3$, draw vectors to the point $s = -3$ from each of the poles and the zero, as shown in Fig. 4.14.

* The term *vector* is used rather loosely here. $(s + 6)$ is handled as a vector when it is added or subtracted in computation, but it is handled as a complex number (or a "phasor") in multiplication and division.   We do not use the dot product or cross product here.

The direction of each vector is determined by the arrowhead, which shows each vector terminating at the point $s = -3$.

$$K_2 = 18 \left[\frac{\Pi Z}{\Pi P} \right]_{s=-3} = \frac{18(-2)}{(-3)(+3)} = +4 \qquad (4.30)$$

where $(s+1)\big|_{s=-3} = -2$, $(s)\big|_{s=-3} = -3$, and $(s+6)\big|_{s=-3} = +3$.

Finally, to compute K_3, the residue of $F(s)$ at $s = -6$, draw vectors from the poles and zero to the point $s = -6$ and take the ratio of the product of vectors from zeros to the product of vectors from poles,

$$K_3 = 18 \left[\frac{\Pi Z}{\Pi P} \right]_{s=-6} = \frac{18(-5)}{(-6)(-3)} = -5 \qquad (4.31)$$

which gives the same result as the numerical evaluation in Eq. 4.25.

Example 2. Consider a function which has a pair of complex poles. Let

$$\begin{aligned} F(s) &= \frac{(s+2)}{(s+1)(s+5)(s^2+3s+9)} \\ &= \frac{K_1}{s+1} + \frac{K_2}{s+5} + \frac{K_3}{s+1.5+j2.6} + \frac{K_4}{s+1.5-j2.6} \end{aligned} \qquad (4.32)$$

The four residues K_1, K_2, K_3, and K_4 may be evaluated in exactly the same manner as that shown above. Fig. 4.15 shows the pole-zero plot for evaluating

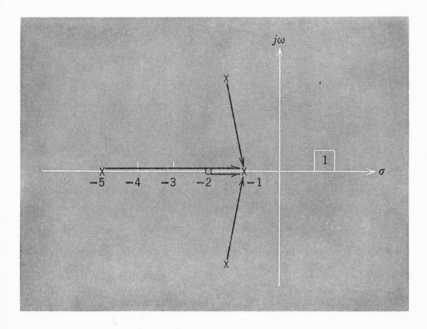

Fig. 4.15. Pole-zero map for computing K_1, Example 2.

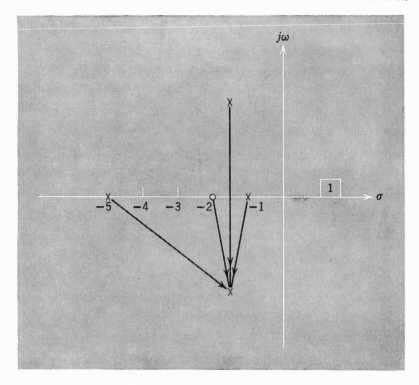

Fig. 4.16.   Pole-zero map for computing K_3, Example 2.

K_1.   Here

$$K_1 = \left[\frac{\Pi Z}{\Pi P}\right]_{s=-1} = \frac{(1)}{(4)(2.645\ @\ 79.1°)(2.645\ @\ -79.1°)} = \frac{1}{28} \quad (4.33)$$

where $(2.645\ @\ 79.1°)$ is the notation used for the value of the vector drawn
to the point $s = -1$ from the point $s = -1.5 - j2.6$.   Similarly

$$K_2 = \frac{(-3)}{(-4)(4.39\ @\ 143.4°)(4.39\ @\ -143.4°)} = 0.039 \quad (4.34)$$

Notice that the vectors drawn from the complex conjugate poles have complex conjugate values, which, when multiplied together, give a real product.
Hence, both K_1 and K_2 are pure real numbers.   However, an evaluation of
K_3 shows all the vectors drawn from the zero and the poles to the point $s =
-1.5 - j2.6$ to be complex and to have no conjugate pairs in their product;
consequently, K_3 is a complex number having a nonzero imaginary part.   A
pole-zero vector map for this calculation is drawn in Fig. 4.16.   From this

map it is seen that

$$K_3 = \frac{(2.645 \ @ \ -79.1°)}{(2.645 \ @ \ -100.9°)(4.39 \ @ \ -36.6°)(5.2 \ @ \ -90°)}$$

$$= 0.04385 \ @ \ +148.4° = -0.03735 + j0.023 \qquad (4.35)$$

Now, the residue K_4 is computed by drawing the vectors from the poles and zero to the point $s = -1.5 + j2.6$. Because this point is the complex conjugate of the point used for the computation of K_3, K_4 becomes the complex conjugate of K_3.

$$K_4 = \frac{(2.645 \ @ \ +79.1°)}{(2.645 \ @ \ +100.9°)(4.39 \ @ \ +36.6°)(5.2 \ @ \ +90°)}$$

$$= 0.04385 \ @ \ -148.4° = -0.03735 - j0.023$$

$$= \bar{K}_3 \qquad (4.36)$$

$\bar{K}_3$ is the notation for the complex conjugate of K_3.

Whenever a pair of complex poles appears in a function such as that in Eq. 4.32, the two terms having complex residues may be combined into a single term in which no complex numbers occur. In this example the K_3 and K_4 terms may be combined as follows:

$$\frac{(-0.03735 + j0.023)}{s + 1.5 + j2.6} + \frac{(-0.03735 - j0.023)}{s + 1.5 - j2.6}$$

$$= \frac{2[s(-0.03735) + (-0.03735)(1.5) + (0.023)(2.6)]}{s^2 + 3s + 9} \qquad (4.37)$$

If the inverse Laplace transform of this term is evaluated, it is found to be

$$2(0.04385)\epsilon^{-1.5t} \sin (2.6t + \psi) \qquad (4.38)$$

where $\qquad \psi = \tan^{-1}\dfrac{(-0.03735)}{0.023} = -58.4° = 90° - \underline{/K_3}$

Equations 4.37 and 4.38 illustrate clearly the relationships which exist between the real and imaginary components of the residues of $F(s)$ at the complex poles and the coefficients and angle ψ in the damped sinusoidal term. These relationships were also defined in Chapter 3, Eq. 3.164, and are listed as Pair 17 in Appendix 1.

Example 3. If a given function has no finite zeros, the ΠZ term (as in Eq. 4.29) is considered to be unity. Let

$$F(s) = \frac{3}{s(s + 1)(s + 2)} = \frac{K_1}{s} + \frac{K_2}{s + 1} + \frac{K_3}{s + 2} \qquad (4.39)$$

Then the pole-zero vector plot will show

$$K_1 = \frac{3}{\Pi P}\bigg|_{s=0} = \frac{3}{2}$$

$$K_2 = \frac{3}{\Pi P}\bigg|_{s=-1} = -3$$

$$K_3 = \frac{3}{\Pi P}\bigg|_{s=-2} = \frac{3}{2} \tag{4.40}$$

A special instrument called a Spirule is sometimes used to compute the residues from the pole-zero plot. The Spirule is designed to measure and multiply (or divide) vector lengths and to measure and add (or subtract) their angles in much the same way in which an ordinary slide rule multiplies and divides numbers. The Spirule* is also used in making root locus plots (see Chapter 6), which require the measuring and multiplying of vector lengths and angles on the s plane.

If a given $F(s)$ has a double pole, the partial fraction expansion of $F(s)$ takes the form

$$F(s) = \frac{K(s + Z_1) \cdots (s + Z_m)}{(s + P_1)^2(s + P_2)(s + P_3) \cdots (s + P_n)}$$

$$= \frac{C}{(s + P_1)^2} + \frac{K_1}{s + P_1} + \frac{K_2}{s + P_2} + \frac{K_3}{s + P_3} + \cdots$$

$$+ \frac{K_n}{s + P_n} \tag{4.41}$$

where $-P_1$ is a double pole and $-P_2, -P_3, \ldots$ are all separate poles, and $K_1, K_2, K_3, \ldots$ are the residues of $F(s)$ at their respective poles, $-P_1, -P_2, -P_3, \ldots$. C is a constant which bears no special name. The residues at the single poles, $K_2, K_3, \ldots$, may all be evaluated by the s plane vector method.

$$K_j = K\left(\frac{\Pi Z}{\Pi P}\right)_{s=-P_j} \qquad j \neq 1 \tag{4.42}$$

K_1 and C may also be evaluated by graphical means. When the partial fraction expansion formula for functions with multiple poles is applied (Eqs. 3.165, 3.166, 3.167), C is seen to be

$$C = \left(\frac{K\Pi Z}{\Pi P}\right)_{s=-P_1} \tag{4.43}$$

*Obtainable from the Spirule Company, 9728 El Venado Drive, Whittier, California.

but K_1 is

$$K_1 = \left\{ \frac{d}{ds} [(s + P_1)^2 F(s)] \right\}_{s=-P_1}$$

$$= \left\{ \frac{d}{ds} \left[\frac{K(s + Z_1) \cdots (s + Z_m)}{(s + P_2)(s + P_3) \cdots (s + P_n)} \right] \right\}_{s=-P_1} \quad (4.44)$$

By performing the differentiation indicated in Eq. 4.44, we may write K_1 as

$$K_1 = \left\{ \left[\frac{K(s + Z_1) \cdots (s + Z_m)}{(s + P_2)(s + P_3) \cdots (s + P_n)} \right] \left[\frac{1}{s + Z_1} + \frac{1}{s + Z_2} \right. \right.$$

$$+ \cdots + \frac{1}{s + Z_m} - \frac{1}{s + P_2} - \frac{1}{s + P_3} - \cdots$$

$$\left. \left. - \frac{1}{s + P_n} \right] \right\}_{s=-P_1}$$

$$= C \left[\frac{1}{s + Z_1} + \frac{1}{s + Z_2} + \cdots + \frac{1}{s + Z_m} - \frac{1}{s + P_2} \right.$$

$$\left. - \frac{1}{s + P_3} - \cdots - \frac{1}{s + P_n} \right]_{s=-P_1} \quad (4.45)$$

The graphical evaluation of Eq. 4.45 is

$$K_1 = C \left(\frac{1}{\mathbf{Z}_1} + \frac{1}{\mathbf{Z}_2} + \cdots + \frac{1}{\mathbf{Z}_m} - \frac{1}{\mathbf{P}_2} - \frac{1}{\mathbf{P}_3} - \cdots - \frac{1}{\mathbf{P}_n} \right)_{s=-P_1}$$

$$= C \left(\sum \frac{1}{\mathbf{Z}} - \sum \frac{1}{\mathbf{P}} \right)_{s=-P_1} \quad (4.46)$$

The residue K_1 may be computed graphically by drawing the vectors from each of the zeros to the point $s = -P_1$, summing their reciprocals, subtracting from this sum the sum of the reciprocals of the vectors drawn from the poles to the point $s = -P_1$, and multiplying the difference by C. As an example, consider the function

$$F(s) = \frac{48(s + 2)}{(s + 1)(s + 3)(s + 4)^2} \quad (4.47)$$

This may be expanded to

$$F(s) = \frac{C}{(s + 4)^2} + \frac{K_1}{(s + 4)} + \frac{K_2}{(s + 3)} + \frac{K_3}{(s + 1)} \quad (4.48)$$

The s plane vector method is used to compute K_2, K_3, and C.

$$K_2 = (48)\frac{(-1)}{(1)^2(-2)} = 24$$

$$K_3 = (48)\frac{(1)}{(3)^2(2)} = \frac{8}{3}$$

$$C = (48)\frac{(-2)}{(-3)(-1)} = -32 \qquad (4.49)$$

K_1 is calculated from Eq. 4.46.

$$K_1 = (-32)\left[\frac{1}{(-2)} - \frac{1}{(-1)} - \frac{1}{(-3)}\right] = -\frac{80}{3} \qquad (4.50)$$

The advantage of the graphical method over the analytical method of computing K_1 in this example is obvious.

If the expression $F(s)$ has no finite zeros, the term $\Sigma(1/Z)$ in Eq. 4.46 is taken to be zero in the computation, since no such term would appear in the result when the derivation indicated by Eq. 4.44 is performed.

If the expression $F(s)$ has more than two poles at the same point in the s plane, the graphical procedure outlined above may not be used conveniently to compute the residue at the multiple pole. A second (or higher order) derivative would have to be computed to evaluate the residue. The term resulting from the higher derivative operation is more complex than that in Eq. 4.45, and, although it could be interpreted graphically, it is usually easier to compute the residue analytically, as in Eq. 3.167.

If a function has a multiple pole of order r it may usually be approximated by a function which has r distinct poles, all very close to the original multiple poles. For example

$$\frac{7(s+1)}{(s+2)(s+3)^3(s+4)} \cong \frac{7(s+1)}{(s+2)(s+2.9)(s+3)(s+3.1)(s+4)} \qquad (4.51)$$

An inverse Laplace transform of the right side of Eq. 4.51 will give a time function which for most engineering purposes is essentially the same as the inverse transform of the left side.

It is useful to know the relative values of the residues (and, in the case of multiple poles, the other constants in the partial fraction expansion) in order to determine the relative importance of the terms corresponding to each residue. For example, a term in the expanded form of $F(s)$ having a very small residue can often be ignored in the analysis because its contribution to $f(t)$ is small. A pole-zero plot of $F(s)$ is useful in assessing the relative values of the residues.

The graphical expression for the residue at the pole $s = -P_n$ (all distinct poles) is

$$K_n = K \left[\frac{\Pi Z}{\Pi P} \right]_{s=-P_n} \tag{4.52}$$

The multiplying constant K is unimportant insofar as the *relative* values of the various residues are concerned. It determines only the magnitude or "scale factor" of the function and is often left unspecified until the magnitude must actually be determined. A solution is often normalized by changing K to make the initial or final value of $f(t)$ unity. Notice that K_n may be made small either by decreasing the size of the numerator ΠZ, or by increasing the size of the denominator ΠP.

Consider the pole-zero plot shown in Fig. 4.17. The residue at the pole $s = -P_n$ will be relatively small here because of the nearness of the zero. Since the vector drawn from the near zero is very short, the product ΠZ is small. No other pole has a zero near it, so the residue

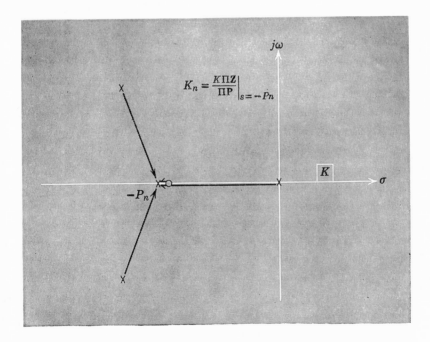

Fig. 4.17.   Residue at a pole near a zero is relatively small.

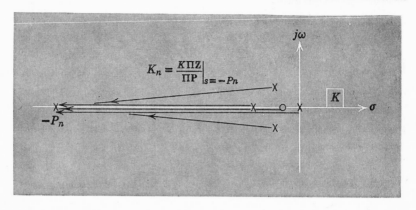

Fig. 4.18.   Residue at a remote pole is relatively small.

at each of the other poles will be large compared to that at $s = -P_n$. If the pole and zero were at the same point they would cancel each other, and the residue would be zero.

Consider next the pole-zero plot in Fig. 4.18.   Here a single pole is located far to the left in the s plane, and the product ΠP is large because the vectors drawn from the other singularities are all long.   Hence the residue at the remote pole is relatively small when compared to those at the other poles, each of which has only a single long vector coming from the remote pole.   More poles than zeros must exist in the group near the origin for the residue at the remote pole to be significantly smaller, and the greater the excess of poles over zeros, the more significant will be the relative smallness of the "remote" residue (see page 152).

Section 4.4 describes both the practical use of this quality of residues at poles near zeros or at remote poles and the criteria for neglecting such poles.   It should be noted here, however, that a small residue at a pole does not always mean that the term corresponding to that pole is insignificant for the purpose at hand.   For example, a pole at the origin corresponds to a constant in the time function, and if all other poles are in the left-half s plane, indicating that they correspond to functions which decay exponentially with increasing time, they will eventually become negligible with respect to the constant, no matter how small the constant!   Moreover, if a pole is located in the right-half s plane, it corresponds to an exponentially increasing (or unstable) time function, and no matter how small the residue is at this pole, the time function will eventually grow to overwhelming proportions. Unstable functions of this sort are discussed more completely in Section 4.5 and in later chapters.

4.4 TRANSIENT RESPONSE OBTAINED FROM POLE-ZERO MAP

For the purpose of this section the transient response is defined as the response of the linear system to a step input applied at time zero. The function of s which is of concern here then, is,

$$F(s) = \frac{A}{s} \times G(s) \tag{4.53}$$

where A/s is the Laplace transform of the step input with magnitude A, and $G(s)$ is the transfer function of the system. $F(s)$ is therefore the Laplace transform of $f(t)$, the transient response of the system. The work in this section is directed toward computing $f(t)$ from the pole-zero plot of $F(s)$. The techniques employed here are applicable in computing the system response to input functions other than the step, but the step is used almost exclusively to provide a uniform basis for comparison of the dynamic responses of the various systems studied here. Furthermore, the step response represents the unforced or natural motion of the system; that is, it is essentially the same response which will result if the system is started from rest with zero input and a nonzero initial value of $f(t)$, the two responses differing only by a constant. In other words, the pole-zero map for $F(s)$ is almost the same as that for $G(s)$, the only difference being the single pole at the origin introduced by the step input.

First order systems

Example 1. R-C network. Consider the R-C network in Fig. 4.19. The step input is obtained by closing switch S at time zero, making $E_1(s) = E/s$, and the output voltage is given by

$$E_0(s) = \frac{E}{s} \times \left[\frac{\alpha(s + 1/\alpha RC)}{(s + 1/RC)} \right] \tag{4.54}$$

where α is the ratio of the displacement of the potentiometer arm from the

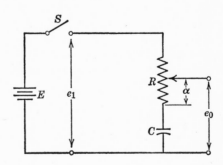

Fig. 4.19. R-C network with changeable parameters.

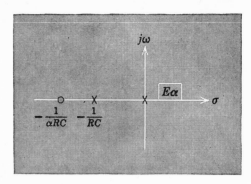

Fig. 4.20.   Pole-zero map for $E_0(s)$.

capacitor side of the potentiometer to the maximum possible displacement. The pole-zero plot for $E_0(s)$ is that shown in Fig. 4.20, from which it is apparent that the pole location at $s = -1/RC$ is fixed and will not change if the potentiometer arm is moved from one position to another. It is also apparent that the zero location at $s = -1/\alpha RC$ depends upon the position of the arm, but that the zero will always lie to the left of the pole for all values of α except $\alpha = 1$, in which instance the pole and zero will lie on the same point.

The transient response, $e_0(t)$, is simply the inverse Laplace transform of $E_0(s)$. In this simple example the inverse transform can be found directly from a table of transform pairs, but for the sake of illustrating the technique of analysis let us find the inverse transform by constructing it from a partial fraction expansion of $E_0(s)$.

$$E_0(s) = \frac{K_1}{s} + \frac{K_2}{s + 1/RC} \tag{4.55}$$

where K_1 is the residue of $E_0(s)$ at $s = 0$, and K_2 is the residue at $s = -1/RC$. K_1 and K_2 may be computed quickly by using the vector method developed in Section 4.3.

$$K_1 = E\alpha \left(\frac{1/\alpha RC}{1/RC} \right) = E$$

$$K_2 = E\alpha \left(\frac{1/\alpha RC - 1/RC}{-1/RC} \right) = -E(1 - \alpha) \tag{4.56}$$

Now the inverse transform of Eq. 4.55 may be taken term by term, each of which may be handled from memory without reference to a table of Laplace transforms. The transient response is

$$e_0(t) = E - E(1 - \alpha)\epsilon^{-t/RC} \tag{4.57}$$

$e_0(t)$ is plotted in Fig. 4.21. It is possible to study the effect of a change in α on each component of the response, E and $-E(1 - \alpha)\epsilon^{-t/RC}$, and also on the total response.

First, it is obvious from both the analytical and physical aspects that the position of the potentiometer arm has no effect upon the final value of the out-

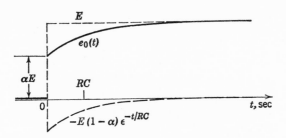

Fig. 4.21. $e_0(t)$ corresponding to pole-zero map in Fig. 4.20.

put E.   The residue E at $s = 0$ is independent of the position of the zero. For any α setting the capacitor will charge toward E volts, and the current through the resistor will decay toward zero as time increases.   The initial value of the output $e_0(0^+)$, however, depends upon the value of the residue at $s = -1/RC$, and this in turn depends upon α.

Consider the effect of a change in α upon the residue $E(1 - \alpha)$.   When $\alpha \cong 0$ the location of the zero is far to the left in the s plane and the residue $E(1 - \alpha)$ is close to its maximum value E.   Here the exponential component of $e_0(t)$ is fully as important as the constant component; that is, the size and shape of the $e_0(t)$ curve is influenced significantly by the exponential component, and the total response will be like that shown in Fig. 4.22a.   Now,

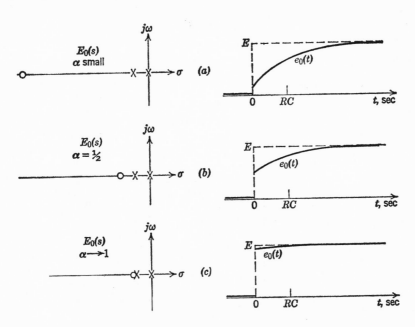

Fig. 4.22.   Effect of α on the transient response of the R-C network.

if the potentiometer arm is moved up to make $\alpha \cong \frac{1}{2}$, the zero will move in from its previous remote location to the position shown in Fig. 4.22b. The residue at $s = -1/RC$ will be about half its former value, making the influence of the exponential component of $e_0(t)$ less. This is seen in the transient response drawn in Fig. 4.22b; the exponential component is now significant, but less so, in its effect upon the total response. Finally, if the potentiometer arm is moved close to the top, $\alpha \cong 1$. The proximity of the zero to the pole at

$s = -1/RC$ makes the residue, as given by the $\Pi Z/\Pi P\Big|_{s=-1/RC}$ method, very small. Now, because of the extremely small residue at $s = -1/RC$, the exponential term is virtually an insignificant part of the total response $e_0(t)$. The response curve in Fig. 4.22c shows this to be true. Because the pole and zero are so close to one another they almost cancel each other. $e_0(t)$ may be computed approximately by omitting the pole and zero from the analysis. The result, in this case, is that $e_0(t)$ will be a step of E volts at time zero, a response very nearly the same as that in Fig. 4.22c.

The purpose of this section is to provide the reader with practice in relating the physical properties of a system to the pole-zero map of its transient response s function and to study the effect of the physical parameters upon the transient response. This has been done in the example above by expanding the transient response s function into a sum of simple partial fractions and then transforming this sum inversely to obtain the time response. Since the time response is also a sum of simple functions, the relationship between the coefficient of each term and the physical parameters of the system is easily determined.

Example 2. R-L network. An R-L network similar to the R-C network in Example 1 is shown in Fig. 4.23. In this system the transient response is found to be

$$E_0(s) = \frac{E}{s} \times \left(\frac{s + \alpha R/L}{s + R/L}\right) \tag{4.58}$$

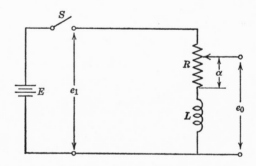

Fig. 4.23.   R-L network with changeable parameters.

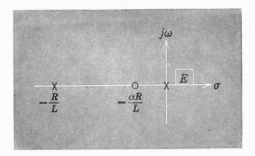

Fig. 4.24. Pole-zero map of $E_0(s)$ for R-L network.

as represented on the s plane in Fig. 4.24. Here the pole location $s = -R/L$ is independent of the potentiometer setting, but the zero location, which is always to the right of the pole (except for $\alpha = 1$), is dependent upon α. The transient response is calculated by expanding Eq. 4.58 into partial fractions and finding the residues in the manner described in Example 1.

$$e_0(t) = E\alpha + E(1 - \alpha)\epsilon^{-(R/L)t} \qquad (4.59)$$

This equation is plotted as the sum of two components in Fig. 4.25. Here the initial value of the output $e_0(0^+)$ is E, regardless of the potentiometer setting, but the final value is directly proportional to α. An inspection of the circuit itself bears this out, since the current is initially zero and increases exponentially toward the value E/R.

Consider now the effect of a change in α upon the transient response. For α nearly equal to 1 the zero and pole will be very close together, the residue at $s = -R/L$ very small, and the contribution of the exponential term to the total response almost insignificant, as shown in Fig. 4.26a. As α is changed to $\frac{1}{2}$, the zero moves closer to the origin to a point midway between the two poles, as shown in Figure 4.26b. Now the residues at both poles are equal, and therefore both the constant and the exponential components are significant in determining the size and shape of $e_0(t)$. As the potentiometer arm is

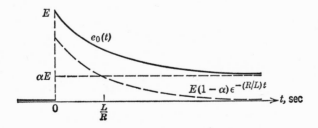

Fig. 4.25. $e_0(t)$ corresponding to pole-zero map in Fig. 4.24.

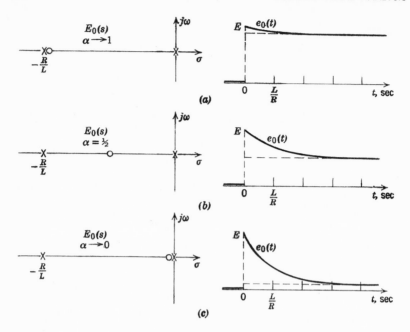

Fig. 4.26. Effect of α on the transient response of the R-L network.

moved to a point very close to the bottom, the zero moves in very close to the origin.   This makes the constant term very small compared to the residue at the pole $s = -R/L$.   The constant term contributes an insignificant amount to the whole transient response during the initial part of the transient. Of course, as time increases, the constant term becomes a larger and larger portion of $e_0(t)$ until finally the exponential term dies out to complete insignificance.   Therefore, $e_0(t)$ may be approximated, except for the small final value, by omitting from the analysis the pole and zero near the origin.*

The algebraic sign of the residue of the exponential term has a significant effect upon the general character of the transient response.   In both the examples above, the sign of the constant term is positive, since all the poles and zeros used to define the vectors in the $\Pi Z/\Pi P$ term lie to the left of the pole at the origin (the point at which the constant term is computed), making the signs of all the vectors positive. In the R-C network the sign of the residue of the exponential term is

---

* A pole and zero close to one another on the s plane are sometimes called a dipole.   In Fig. 4.26a a dipole occurs at $s = -R/L$.   Another occurs at the origin in Fig. 4.26c.

negative, because the pole at $s = -1/RC$ lies to the left of an odd number (one) of poles, making the sign of $\Pi Z/\Pi P$ negative. Because of the negative residue of the exponential term the total response $e_0(t)$ approaches its final value *from below*. On the other hand, in the *R-L* network example, the pole at $s = -R/L$ lies to the left of an even number (two) of poles and zeros, so that the negative vectors in $\Pi Z/\Pi P$ give a net positive value to the residue. Because of the positive residue of the exponential term the total response $e_0(t)$ approaches its final value *from above*. The *R-C* response might be said to be an *undershooting* response, while the *R-L* response would *overshoot*. Later in this book the algebraic signs of the residues are used to estimate the general character of transient responses of more complex systems which *overshoot* or *undershoot* their final value.

Second order systems

In Chapter 3 the spring-mass-damper system studied was found to have a transfer function whose denominator was a second order polynomial in s, showing it to be a second order system. In this section several other second order systems are studied to show some significant characteristics of this important class of system.

Consider as a first example the *R-L-C* circuit shown in Fig. 4.27. A step input is obtained by closing switch S at time zero, so that $E_1(s) = E/s$. The transfer function is derived, and the expression for the system output is arranged.

$$E_0(s) = \frac{E}{s}\left[\frac{1}{LCs^2 + RCs + 1}\right] \tag{4.60}$$

It is convenient to rearrange the transfer function algebraically so that the coefficient of the s^2 term in the denominator is unity, since the transfer function may then be expressed in the standard form, using the undamped natural frequency and damping ratio notation. In

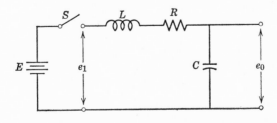

Fig. 4.27. R-L-C circuit.

this system, then,

$$E_0(s) = \frac{E}{s} \left[\frac{1/LC}{s^2 + (R/L)s + 1/LC} \right] = \frac{E}{s} \left[\frac{\omega_n^2}{s^2 + 2\zeta\omega_n s + \omega_n^2} \right] \quad (4.61)$$

where the damping ratio and undamped natural frequency may be determined by equating the coefficients of the s terms and the constant terms in the denominators of Eq. 4.61.

$$\omega_n = \sqrt{1/LC} = \text{Undamped natural frequency}$$

$$\zeta = \frac{R}{2} \sqrt{C/L} = \text{Damping ratio} \quad (4.62)$$

As an exercise the reader may verify these two relationships by computing the transient response of this system for several different values of R, ranging from zero to, say, $8\sqrt{L/C}$. This range of variation in R will take the system from an undamped condition to an underdamped condition, to critical damping, and finally to an overdamped condition.

Now consider a pole-zero plot for $E_0(s)$ made to determine the relationship among the damping ratio and undamped natural frequency and the pole locations. No finite zeros occur in this particular system, so the pole-zero plot will consist of three finite poles. Because of the step input, one of these will be at the origin of the s plane, and the other two, corresponding to the transfer function, will lie at positions determined by ζ and ω_n. If the system is overdamped the poles will be real and unequal, lying on the negative real axis of the s plane. The product of the two pole values is ω_n^2. If the system is critically damped the poles will be real and equal, the double pole lying at the point $s = -\omega_n$. The underdamped condition is the one of greatest importance in engineering, and in this state the poles will be complex conjugates.

If $\zeta < 1$ the denominator of Eq. 4.61 may be factored in the following manner:

$$E_0(s) = \frac{E}{s} \left[\frac{\omega_n^2}{(s + \zeta\omega_n + j\omega_n\sqrt{1 - \zeta^2})(s + \zeta\omega_n - j\omega_n\sqrt{1 - \zeta^2})} \right]$$

$$(4.63)$$

This can easily be verified by multiplying the two complex factors and comparing the product with the denominator of Eq. 4.61. The pole locations for the underdamped case are related to the ζ and ω_n of the system in a rather simple way, as shown in Fig. 4.28. The pole

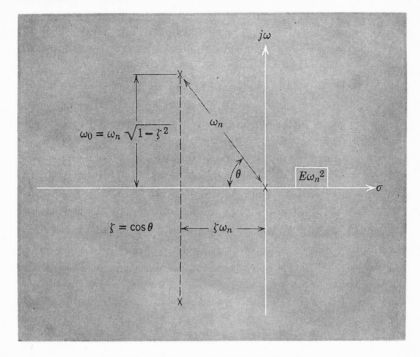

Fig. 4.28. Pole locations for $E_0(s)$ in R-L-C circuit.

locations, $-\zeta\omega_n \pm j\omega_n \sqrt{1-\zeta^2}$, indicate that the damping ratio is equal to the cosine of the angle θ shown in Fig. 4.28 and that the undamped natural frequency is equal to the distance between the origin and one of the poles. In dynamic analysis these simple geometrical relationships make it possible to visualize the values of ω_n and ζ from the pole-zero plot and to determine, with the aid of the generalized second order transient response curves in Fig. 3.35, the entire transient response for the system, including the proper time scale and the final value of the output.

Two other important geometrical relationships between the pole-zero plot and the dynamic behavior of the system are apparent in a calculation of the transient response. A partial fraction expansion of Eq. 4.63 is made.

$$E_0(s) = \frac{K_1}{s} + \frac{K_2}{s + \zeta\omega_n + j\omega_n \sqrt{1-\zeta^2}}$$
$$+ \frac{\bar{K}_2}{s + \zeta\omega_n - j\omega_n \sqrt{1-\zeta^2}} \quad (4.64)$$

An evaluation by the s plane vector method of the residues at each of the three poles shows that

$$K_1 = E\omega_n{}^2 \left[\frac{1}{(\omega_n/-\theta)(\omega_n/+\theta)} \right] = E$$

$$K_2 = E\omega_n{}^2 \left[\frac{1}{(\omega_n/-(180° - \theta))(2\omega_n \sqrt{1 - \zeta^2}/-90°)} \right]$$

$$= \frac{E}{2\sqrt{1 - \zeta^2}} \, /270° - \theta$$

$$\bar{K}_2 = \frac{E}{2\sqrt{1 - \zeta^2}} \, /\theta - 270° \qquad\qquad (4.65)$$

The transient response $e_0(t)$ is found by taking the inverse Laplace transform of Eq. 4.64. The first term in this expression, K_1/s, transforms into the constant K_1 (the residue of $E_0(s)$ at the origin of the s plane) in the time domain. The second and third terms will transform into an exponentially damped sinusoidal function in the time domain, as shown in Eq. 3.164. The whole transient response for this system is

$$e_0(t) = E + \frac{E}{\sqrt{1 - \zeta^2}} \, \epsilon^{-\zeta\omega_n t} \sin(\omega_n \sqrt{1 - \zeta^2}\, t + \psi) \qquad (4.66)$$

where $\qquad \psi = \tan^{-1}\left(\frac{-\sqrt{1 - \zeta^2}}{-\zeta} \right) = 90° - /K_2$

The set of response curves in Fig. 3.35 describes this function plotted for several different values of damping ratio. Notice that the time constant of the exponentially decaying term is the reciprocal of $\zeta\omega_n$, the distance between the $j\omega$ axis and the complex poles in Fig. 4.28. The decay time for the envelope of the sinusoidal term may be determined very quickly, then, from the magnitude of $\zeta\omega_n$—the farther the poles from the $j\omega$ axis, the faster the decay of the exponential envelope. Equation 4.66 shows the frequency of the sinusoidal term to be

$$\omega_0 = \omega_n \sqrt{1 - \zeta^2} = \text{Frequency of oscillation, rad/sec} \quad (4.67)$$

which is just the distance from the real axis to the complex poles in Fig. 4.28. Thus the frequency of oscillation may also be read directly from the pole-zero plot—the farther the poles lie from the real axis the higher the frequency of oscillation. Notice that the ω_0 and $\zeta\omega_n$ distances determine the angle θ, indicating the interdependence of the damping ratio, the decay time of the sinusoidal term, and the frequency of oscillation.

Because the dynamic response of the second order system is used extensively in control system engineering it is essential for the reader to familiarize himself with the above analysis and that in Chapter 3 which deals with second order systems. Numerous references to complex pole locations are made in the succeeding chapters, and it is assumed that the reader understands the significance of the real and imaginary parts of the pole positions in determining the distinguishing characteristics of the time response, such as damping ratio, decay time, and frequency of oscillation.

It should be clear from the above analysis that the transient response of the R-L-C second order system is completely described by the pole-zero plot of $E_0(s)$ and that the transient response may be described equally well, either in terms of the pole locations on the s plane or in terms of the curve $e_0(t)$, which shows directly the distinguishing characteristics of the response. Therefore, the effect of a change in one of the physical parameters, R, L, or C, upon the actual transient response of the system may be determined by studying the change in the complex pole locations which occur with a change in the parameter.

For example, consider the effect of a change in R upon the transient response of this network. Assume that R is set to make the system critically damped.

$$\zeta = 1$$

so

$$R = R_{crit} = 2 \sqrt{L/C} \tag{4.68}$$

R is then decreased from this value to zero. Equation 4.62 indicates that the damping ratio is proportional to R, but that the undamped natural frequency is independent of R. Therefore, as R is decreased from the value given in Eq. 4.68, the two system poles will move from the position indicating a critically damped pair at $s = -1/\sqrt{LC}$ along a semicircle, indicating that ω_n is constant, as shown in Fig. 4.29. Finally, for $R = 0$, the poles will reside on the $j\omega$ axis. Notice that for values of R which make the damping ratio near unity the frequency of oscillation is very much less than ω_n, but as R (and ζ) is decreased, the frequency of oscillation increases, and for $\zeta < 0.2$ little difference exists between the magnitudes of ω_n and ω_0. For $R = 0$ no difference exists between the frequency of oscillation and the undamped natural frequency. Also, as R decreases the time constant of the exponentially damped sinusoidal term increases. The transient oscillation

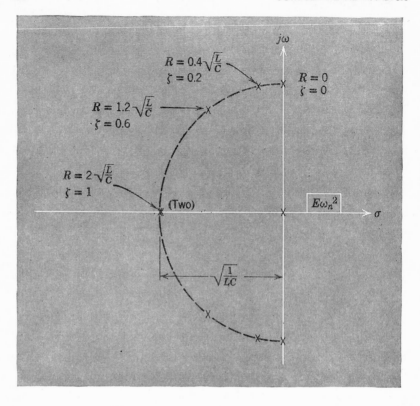

Fig. 4.29. Change in system pole locations as R changes.

persists for a longer period of time when R is small than when R is large.

With the aid of the curves in Fig. 3.35 the transient responses for the four cases shown in Fig. 4.29 are sketched in Fig. 4.30 to indicate the way in which the changes in R shown above affect the dynamic response of the network.

Consider next the changes in transient response which result from a change in C. Assume that R and L are fixed and that C is set at the value which gives a unity damping ratio, so

$$C = \frac{4L}{R^2} \tag{4.69}$$

Now C is reduced from this value toward zero, and the resulting changes in the pole positions are noted. Equation 4.62 shows that the undamped natural frequency will increase and the damping ratio will decrease as the capacitance is reduced. However, the product of ζ and ω_n will remain fixed, as it depends only upon R and L.

$$\zeta\omega_n = \frac{R}{2L} \tag{4.70}$$

Therefore, as C is reduced the poles will move from the critically damped position at $s = -R/2L$ along a straight line parallel to the $j\omega$ axis, as shown in Fig. 4.31. With the aid of Fig. 3.35, the transient responses for the three different conditions indicated in Fig. 4.31 may be sketched. These are shown in Fig. 4.32, in which it is apparent that the time constant of the exponential envelope for each of the underdamped responses is constant at $2L/R$.

If R and C are held fixed and L is increased from the value which gives critical damping, the system will become underdamped, the poles will move along a semicircular trajectory which, as shown by Eq. 4.62, gives a continuously decreasing natural frequency and a continuously decreasing damping ratio. The calculation of this trajectory is left as an exercise for the reader. It turns out to be that shown in Fig. 4.33, which summarizes the effects of decreasing R or C and of increasing L from the values which give a unity damping ratio.

If R or C is increased or L is decreased from the values which give a unity damping ratio, the system will become overdamped. The poles will be real and unequal, and their positions on the s plane may be easily computed by factoring the denominator of Eq. 4.61.

Now, if the elements of the R-L-C circuit are rearranged slightly by placing the resistor in shunt with the capacitor (Fig. 4.34), the transfer

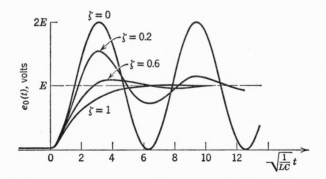

Fig. 4.30.   Transient response of R-L-C circuit for various values of R.

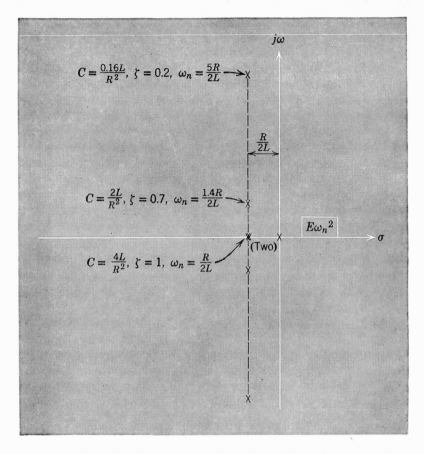

Fig. 4.31. Change in system pole locations as C is decreased.

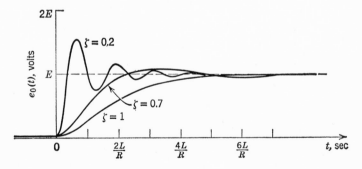

Fig. 4.32. Transient response of R-L-C circuit for the three conditions shown in Fig. 4.31.

function, considering the capacitor voltage as the output, will be

$$\frac{E_0(s)}{E_1(s)} = \frac{1/LC}{s^2 + (1/RC)s + 1/LC} \qquad (4.71)$$

This may be written in the standard second order form:

$$\frac{E_0(s)}{E_1(s)} = \frac{\omega_n{}^2}{s^2 + 2\zeta\omega_n s + \omega_n{}^2} \qquad (4.72)$$

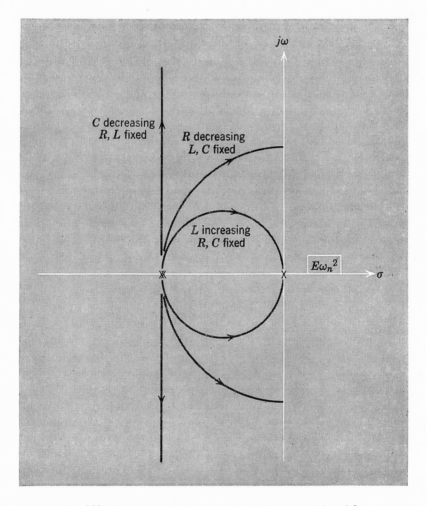

Fig. 4.33. Trajectories of pole movements with changes in R, L, and C.

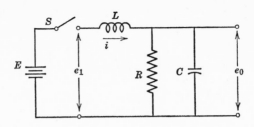

Fig. 4.34.   R-L-C circuit.

where
$$\zeta = \frac{\sqrt{L}}{2R\sqrt{C}}$$

$$\omega_n = \frac{1}{\sqrt{LC}} \tag{4.73}$$

Notice that the resistor R now plays a role just opposite to that which it played in the series circuit of Fig. 4.27; that is, an increase in the resistance will bring about a *decrease* in damping ratio in this circuit. Similarly, the effects of both L and C in this circuit are the inverse of what they were in the series circuit.   The product $\zeta\omega_n$ is insensitive to changes in L here, whereas in the series circuit it was insensitive to changes in C.   As an exercise the reader may derive pole position trajectories for this circuit like those appearing in Fig. 4.33.

Using the definitions and s plane geometries established in Chapter 3 and also in the paragraphs above it is possible to compute the dynamic response of any second order system, whether it be electrical or mechanical.   If the transfer function of the system has a constant numerator, the curves in Fig. 3.35 will give the normalized transient response of the system directly.   These curves are extremely useful in making quick evaluations of the transient response because the rise time, amount of overshoot, settling time, and general character of the response are evident at a glance.   If the particular system under study has a damping ratio other than those included in Fig. 3.35, some interpolation or extrapolation will be necessary.

If the second order system under study has a term in s in the numerator of the transfer function—that is, if a finite zero and two poles occur in the transfer function—the curves in Fig. 3.35 will not give the transient response.   An example of such a system is the L-R-C circuit in Fig. 4.34, in which the output quantity is taken to be the current delivered by the battery.   The transfer function for the circuit viewed in this light is

$$\frac{I(s)}{E_1(s)} = \frac{(1/L)(s + 1/RC)}{s^2 + (1/RC)s + 1/LC} = \frac{(1/L)(s + a)}{s^2 + 2\zeta\omega_n s + \omega_n^2} \quad (4.74)$$

where $a = 1/RC = 2\zeta\omega_n$, and ζ and ω_n are given by Eq. 4.73. For the step input the output $I(s)$ is given by

$$I(s) = \frac{(E/L)(s + a)}{s(s^2 + 2\zeta\omega_n s + \omega_n^2)} \quad (4.75)$$

A pole-zero map of $I(s)$ is given in Fig. 4.35 for the underdamped case. It is interesting to study the effect of the finite zero on the transient response of this second order system. A partial fraction expansion of Eq. 4.75 shows that $I(s)$ has exactly the same form as that of $E_0(s)$ in Eq. 4.64 for the second order system having no finite zero. The presence of the zero in the second order system does not affect the form of the output expression; however, it does affect the magnitude of the residues, and this in turn affects the nature of the transient response. Consequently, the presence of a zero in the transfer function of a second order system means that the response of the system will be distinctly different from that of the simple second order

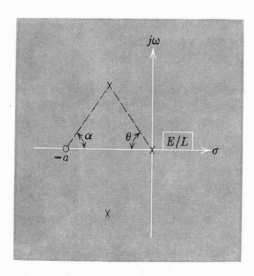

Fig. 4.35. Pole-zero map for $I(s)$.

system. In this system, for example, the expanded form for $I(s)$ is

$$I(s) = \frac{K_1}{s} + \frac{K_2}{s + \zeta\omega_n + j\omega_n \sqrt{1 - \zeta^2}} + \frac{\bar{K}_2}{s + \zeta\omega_n - j\omega_n \sqrt{1 - \zeta^2}}$$
(4.76)

where the residues K_1, K_2, and $\bar{K}_2$ depend upon ζ, ω_n, and a, and, of course, the multiplying constant E/L. These terms are now evaluated.

$$K_1 = \frac{E}{L} \times \frac{a}{\omega_n{}^2}$$

$$K_2 = \frac{E}{L} \times \left[\frac{\sqrt{a^2 - 2a\zeta\omega_n + \omega_n{}^2}}{2\omega_n{}^2 \sqrt{1 - \zeta^2}} \right] @ \underline{/-\alpha - \theta - 90°}$$

$$\bar{K}_2 = \frac{E}{L} \times \left[\frac{\sqrt{a^2 - 2a\zeta\omega_n + \omega_n{}^2}}{2\omega_n{}^2 \sqrt{1 - \zeta^2}} \right] @ \underline{/\alpha + \theta + 90°} \qquad (4.77)$$

θ and α are defined in the diagram in Fig. 4.35. If the last two terms in Eq. 4.76 are combined and the inverse transform is taken, the transient response is found to be

$$i(t) = \frac{E}{L} \left[\frac{a}{\omega_n{}^2} + \frac{\sqrt{a^2 - 2a\zeta\omega_n + \omega_n{}^2}}{\omega_n{}^2 \sqrt{1 - \zeta^2}} \epsilon^{-\zeta\omega_n t} \sin(\omega_0 t + \psi) \right] \qquad (4.78)$$

where $\omega_0 = \omega_n \sqrt{1 - \zeta^2}$, and $\psi = 180° + \alpha + \theta$.

For $\zeta < 1$ in this particular system the position of the zero is dependent upon the pole positions because of the way in which the physical parameters appear in the transfer function. The zero is always located just two times farther from the $j\omega$ axis than are the poles.

$$a = 2\zeta\omega_n \qquad (4.79)$$

Because of this

$$\alpha = \theta \qquad (4.80)$$

and Eq. 4.78 may be rearranged to give the transient response as a function of ζ, ω_n, and the steady state value E/R.

$$i(t) = \frac{E}{R} \left[1 + \frac{\epsilon^{-\zeta\omega_n t}}{2\zeta \sqrt{1 - \zeta^2}} \sin(\omega_0 t + \psi) \right] \qquad (4.81)$$

where $\omega_0 = \omega_n \sqrt{1 - \zeta^2}$, and $\psi = 180° + 2\theta$.

The transient response of this R-L-C network is plotted in Fig. 4.36 for several different values of ζ. These curves all show the same steady state value, and each one is plotted for the same ω_n. In the circuit the steady state would be held at the same level by using the same R for each curve, but if the ω_n is to be kept constant while the ζ is changed, both L and C must be different for each curve, while their product remains constant.

A comparison of Fig. 4.36 with Fig. 3.35 shows one of the basic differences between a second order system having a zero in the transfer function and one without a zero. The slope of the curves shown in Fig. 4.36 is not zero at $t = 0^+$, whereas in the second order system having no zero in its transfer function (Fig. 3.35) the slope of the curve at $t = 0^+$ is always zero.

The differences between the transient responses of these two types of second order systems will now be explored more generally. Let us return to Eq. 4.78 and allow a to take on values independent of ζ and ω_n. The transfer function is not now to be associated with any particular physical system. It is also useful to normalize the transfer function to a steady state value of unity. In other words, the study will now be concentrated on the transfer function

$$\frac{X_0(s)}{X_1(s)} = \frac{(\omega_n^2/a)(s + a)}{s^2 + 2\zeta\omega_n s + \omega_n^2} \tag{4.82}$$

where $x_0(t)$ and $x_i(t)$ are the general output and input variables.

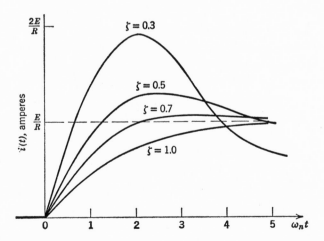

Fig. 4.36. Transient response, $i(t)$, of R-L-C circuit in Fig. 4.34 for various values of ζ; ω_n fixed

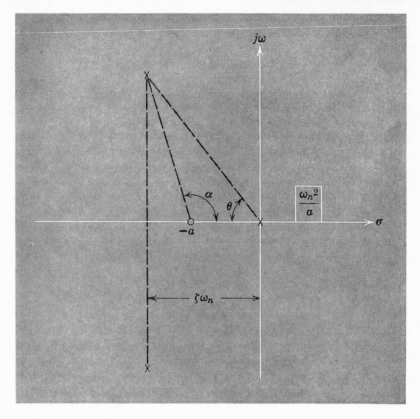

Fig. 4.37. Pole-zero map for $X_0(s)$, general second order system having a finite zero in its transfer function; $\zeta < 1$.

A comparison of the second order system having a zero in its transfer function with the "pure" second order system may be made by studying their respective step responses. If $x_1(t)$ is a unit step at $t = 0$, the output response for the second order system having a zero is

$$X_0(s) = \frac{(\omega_n{}^2/a)(s + a)}{s(s^2 + 2\zeta\omega_n s + \omega_n{}^2)} \tag{4.83}$$

A pole-zero plot for $X_0(s)$ is drawn in Fig. 4.37.

$X_0(s)$ may be written as two terms

$$X_0(s) = \frac{\omega_n{}^2}{s(s^2 + 2\zeta\omega_n s + \omega_n{}^2)} + \frac{(1/a)s\omega_n{}^2}{s(s^2 + 2\zeta\omega_n s + \omega_n{}^2)} \tag{4.84}$$

If the first of these two terms is called $X_a(s)$, Eq. 4.84 becomes

$$X_0(s) = X_a(s) + \left(\frac{1}{a}\right) s X_a(s) \qquad (4.85)$$

Now, $X_a(s)$ is the transform of a pure second order step response, and $(1/a)sX_a(s)$ is $1/a$ times the transform of the derivative of the pure second order step response. Hence

$$x_0(t) = x_a(t) + \frac{1}{a}\left(\frac{dx_a}{dt}\right) \qquad (4.86)$$

$x_a(t)$ is a pure second order step response which has the form, determined by ζ and ω_n, indicated in Fig. 3.35. The total response, $x_0(t)$, may therefore be constructed as shown in Fig. 4.38. Notice that at times 0, t_1, t_2, etc. the slope of $x_a(t)$ is zero, and the total response curve $x_0(t)$ passes through the $x_a(t)$ curve at these points. Also, the slope of the $x_a(t)$ curve is positive for $0 < t < t_1$, negative for $t_1 < t < t_2$, and so forth. The total response curve $x_0(t)$, therefore, has more initial overshoot and more undershoot than has $x_a(t)$, so the oscillations in $x_0(t)$ are more pronounced than are those in $x_a(t)$.

The magnitude of the derivative term depends upon a. For large

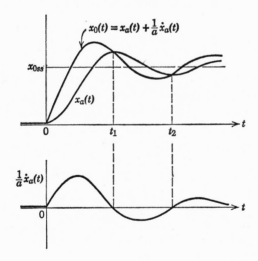

Fig. 4.38. $x_0(t)$ constructed as sum of $x_a(t)$ and $\frac{1}{a}\dot{x}_a(t)$.

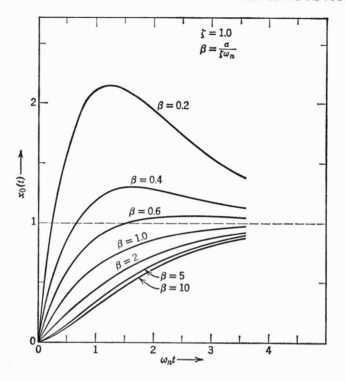

Fig. 4.39. Normalized response curves, second order system having a finite zero.

values of a (the zero located far to the left in the s plane) the derivative term will be very small, and the total response will approach that of a pure second order response. On the other hand, when the zero is located close to the origin the derivative term is very large compared to $x_a(t)$, so that the total response is approximately $(1/a)\dot{x}_a(t)$, except for large values of t when the steady state component of $x_a(t)$ predominates.

The time response $x_0(t)$ can also be computed in the conventional way simply by taking the inverse transform of Eq. 4.83.

$$x_0(t) = 1 + \frac{\sqrt{a^2 - 2a\zeta\omega_n + \omega_n{}^2}}{a\sqrt{1 - \zeta^2}}\,\epsilon^{-\zeta\omega_n t}\sin(\omega_0 t + \psi) \quad (4.87)$$

$\psi = 180° + \alpha + \theta$; α and θ are defined in Fig. 4.37. Equation 4.87 is plotted accurately in Figs. 4.39–43 for various values of ζ and a.

The time scale in these plots is normalized with respect to ω_n in the manner shown in Fig. 3.35. The parameter β is $a/\zeta\omega_n$. The percentage overshoot of $x_0(t)$ for a wide range of ζ and a values has been calculated accurately and is presented in Fig. 4.44. These curves, together with Eq. 4.86, indicate that in the second order system described by a

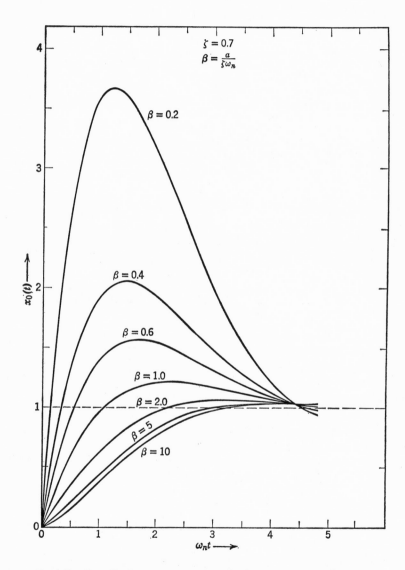

Fig. 4.40.   Normalized response curves, second order system having a finite zero.

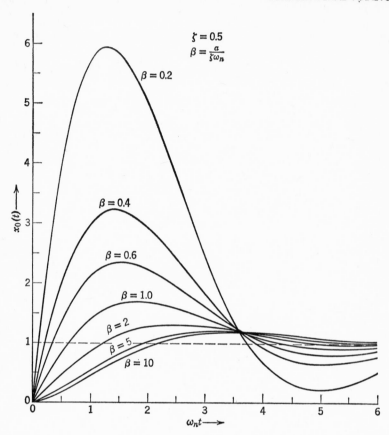

Fig. 4.41. Normalized response curves, second order system having a finite zero.

transfer function of the form given by Eq. 4.82 the percentage over-shoot in response to a step input can be much larger than 100 percent, which is the maximum percentage overshoot possible in the "pure" second order system.

Another difference between the two systems becomes apparent with a calculation of the slope of the response curve.   This is

$$\frac{dx_0}{dt} = \frac{\omega_n \sqrt{a^2 - 2a\zeta\omega_n + \omega_n{}^2}}{a \sqrt{1 - \zeta^2}} \, \epsilon^{-\zeta\omega_n t} \sin(\omega_0 t + \alpha) \qquad (4.88)$$

where α is defined in Fig. 4.37; $\alpha = 180° - \tan^{-1}\left(\dfrac{\omega_n \sqrt{1 - \zeta^2}}{\zeta\omega_n - a}\right)$.

When $t = 0$ in Eq. 4.88,

$$\frac{dx_0}{dt}\bigg|_{t=0} = \frac{\omega_n{}^2}{a} \tag{4.89}$$

This shows the initial slope of $x_0(t)$ to be nonzero and independent of ζ.
Two statements will summarize the points made in the above analy-

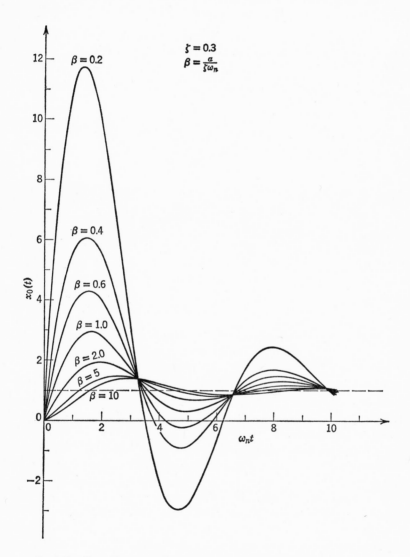

Fig. 4.42.   Normalized response curves, second order system having a finite zero.

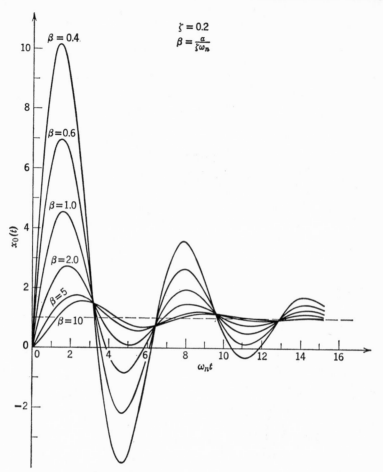

Fig. 4.43.   Normalized response curves, second order system having a finite zero.

sis.   First, the dynamic response of the second order system depends upon both the pole locations *and* the zero location.   It is erroneous therefore to assume that the dynamic response of a linear system may be determined completely from the roots of the characteristic equation of the system—that is, from locations of the poles of the transfer function.   It is true that the general *form* of the expression for the response is determined by the pole locations; however, the actual *shape* of the response curve depends upon the coefficients of the terms in the expression for $x_0(t)$ as well as upon the general form of the expression.

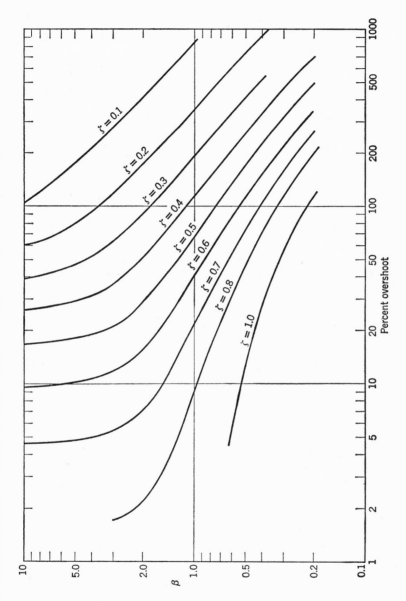

Fig. 4.44. Percent overshoot as a function of β and ζ for the second order system having a finite zero.

123

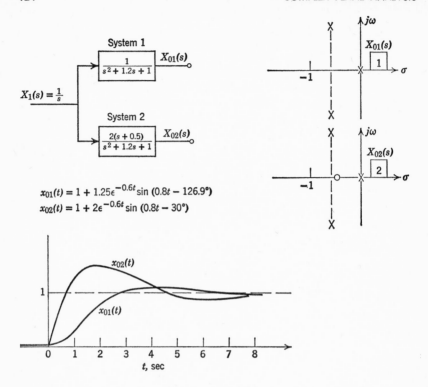

Fig. 4.45. Comparison of step responses of two second order systems having identical characteristic equations.

The zeros of the transfer function can have a strong effect upon these coefficients; consequently the zeros can have a strong effect upon the nature of the dynamic response. For example, the two systems shown in Fig. 4.45 are both second order systems having the same characteristic equation (the same poles in the transfer function), and the general form of the expressions for the two outputs are the same. However, the actual step responses of the two systems are very much different in some respects, as illustrated by the response curves in Fig. 4.45. Therefore, it must be concluded that while the poles of the transfer function convey a considerable amount of information concerning the dynamic response of the system, the exact character of the response (including the initial value of the output and its time derivatives and the maximum overshoot) is determined by both the poles *and* zeros of the transfer function.

Second, while curves such as those in Figs. 4.39–43 will help to determine the pole-zero configuration required to obtain a desired response from a physical system, in general it is impossible to obtain the desired pole-zero configuration for the transfer function of the system simply by adjusting the parameter values of the system. In the R-L-C circuit in Fig. 4.34, for instance, the zero in the transfer function (Eq. 4.74) is restricted to the point $s = -2\zeta\omega_n$ by the physical arrangement of the components in the network. Any value for ζ or ω_n may be obtained, in principle, by a suitable selection of the values of R, L, and C, but the resulting value for a will always be $2\zeta\omega_n$ for this network configuration. If one desires a pole-zero configuration other than this one he will have to use a different network.

The process by which one arrives at a design for a network having a given pole-zero configuration is called network synthesis. This is a topic of considerable importance in the design of automatic control systems and one about which a considerable body of technical literature has been developed. The topic cannot be covered adequately in this volume. The emphasis here is on the *analysis* of a given system rather than on the *synthesis* of the system to satisfy a given dynamic response requirement. Actually, with a good background in analysis it is possible to develop a useful capacity for design work, but additional training in synthesis gives a more comprehensive view of the design problem.

Rate gyroscope

A small physical system of considerable importance in automatic control is the gyroscope, which is used in many different ways for making inertial measurements in control systems. Only one particular type of gyroscope is treated here—the rate gyroscope, so called because it is used to measure the angular rate of change of the base on which it is mounted with respect to an inertial reference. In many practical applications such as short term ship or airplane stabilization the inertial reference can be assumed to be the earth.

A single axis rate gyroscope is sketched in Fig. 4.46. A massive wheel is mounted in a gimbal frame and driven at a high speed. The gimbal frame is, in turn, mounted to the base through low friction pivots, so that the gimbal assembly rotates with respect to the base around the z axis. The gimbal assembly is restrained with respect to the base by a spring with constant k and is damped by a dashpot with coefficient B. When the sign conventions defined by Fig. 4.46 are used the rate gyroscope functions in the following manner. It can be shown using Newton's laws of mechanics that if the gimbal is locked

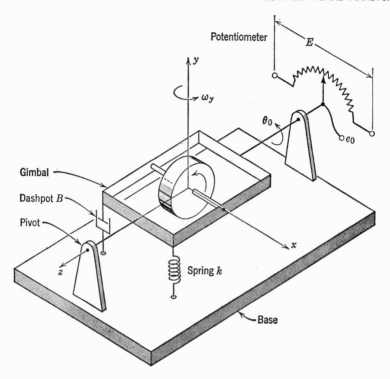

Fig. 4.46. Single axis rate gyroscope.

with respect to the base, by replacing the spring with a rigid link, for example, and if the base should rotate around the y axis at an angular velocity ω_y with respect to the earth* a torque will be developed around the z axis in the direction indicated by the arrow labeled θ_0. This torque will be directly proportional to the angular velocity ω_y, the constant of proportionality being the angular momentum of the rotating wheel.

$$T = H\omega_y$$

$$H = I\Omega \tag{4.90}$$

T is the torque developed around the z axis, H is the angular momentum of the wheel, ω_y is the angular rate of rotation of the base, I the polar moment of inertia of the wheel about its spin axis, and Ω is the spin speed, usually held constant and at as high a value as is

* More correctly, with respect to an inertial reference frame.

practical. If T is measured in dyne-centimeters and ω_y in radians per second, I will be labeled gram-(centimeters)^2, Ω will be radians per second, and H will be gram-(cm)^2 per second.

Now, if the gimbal is not locked rigidly to the base but is restrained by the spring and dashpot, as shown in Fig. 4.46, the torque which is developed around the z axis in response to an angular rate around the y axis will cause a movement of the gimbal assembly around the z axis. If the amplitude of this motion remains very small, the motion will be governed approximately by this equation:

$$T = J\ddot{\theta}_0 + B\dot{\theta}_0 + k\theta_0 + T_f \qquad (4.91)$$

where J is the polar moment of inertia of the gimbal assembly about the z axis, θ_0 is the angular displacement of the gimbal assembly from its neutral position, and T_f is the frictional torque in the pivots. T, B, and k are defined above. If T_f is assumed to be zero, a transfer function relating ω_y and θ_0 can be derived. A Laplace transformation of Eqs. 4.90 and 4.91 follows:

$$\frac{T(s)}{\omega_y(s)} = H \qquad (4.92)$$

$$\frac{\theta_0(s)}{T(s)} = \frac{1/J}{s^2 + (B/J)s + k/J} \qquad (4.93)$$

The angular displacement θ_0 is sensed by a transducer, such as a potentiometer (see sketch), which produces a voltage proportional to the angular displacement.

$$e_0 = K\theta_0 \qquad (4.94)$$

These three equations combined give an overall transfer function relating $\omega_y(s)$ and $E_0(s)$.

$$\frac{E_0(s)}{\omega_y(s)} = \frac{H(K/J)}{s^2 + (B/J)s + k/J} \qquad (4.95)$$

This second order transfer function describes the dynamic behavior of the rate gyroscope, where the angular velocity ω_y is considered to be the input, and the voltage e_0 is considered to be the output. It has a constant numerator, so the curves in Fig. 3.35 may be applied to determine the response to a step input of angular velocity.

Assume that the base on which the rate gyroscope is mounted is suddenly rotated, beginning from rest, at a constant angular velocity about the y axis. The input rate is then a step function, and the out-

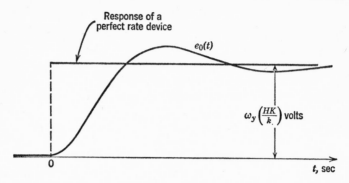

Fig. 4.47.   Response of the rate gyroscope to a velocity step input.

put response would be something like that shown in Fig. 4.47, assuming the dashpot coefficient were adjusted to give an underdamped response. It is apparent from this sketch that the rate gyroscope, because of the inertia of the gimbal frame, is an imperfect rate-measuring device, inasmuch as the response of a perfect rate measuring device to a step input would be simply a step output, as indicated in the sketch.

It is usually desirable to have the dynamic response of the rate gyroscope match, as closely as possible, the perfect response curve. This ideal response will be approached if the speed of response of the instrument is made to be very short.   This means the undamped natural frequency, ω_n, should be as high as possible, as shown by the abscissa of Fig. 3.35.   As ω_n is increased the time of response is decreased.

In addition to the speed of response, at least three other performance characteristics are important in the design of the rate gyroscope. These are: sensitivity, threshold, and output axis angular deflection. Sensitivity is defined as the calibration of the instrument in volts output per radian per second input.   Equation 4.95 shows this to be

$$\text{Sensitivity} = \frac{HK}{k} \qquad (4.96)$$

Of course, it is desirable to have as high a sensitivity as possible.

Threshold, which is dependent upon the friction level of the pivots, is the angular rate input required to produce a torque which will just overcome the frictional torque of the pivots.   Any angular rates below the threshold level will be undetected by the instrument.   Hence it is desirable to place this level as low as possible. If the pivots are characterized by pure coulomb friction, the last term in Eq. 4.91 becomes

$$T_f = K_c(\text{sgn } \dot\theta_0) \tag{4.97}$$

where K_c is a constant and sgn $\dot\theta_0$ means "algebraic sign of the angular velocity $\dot\theta_0$." Hence the frictional torque is always a decelerating torque. The threshold is then

$$\omega_T = \frac{K_c}{H} \tag{4.98}$$

The angular deflection θ_0 should be kept as low as possible because of the cross-coupling problem. (When $\theta_0 = 0$ the instrument is sensitive only to angular rates about the y axis, but as the gimbal assembly rotates away from the neutral position the instrument becomes sensitive to angular rates about the x axis as well.) In many practical situations the cross-coupling is insignificant if θ_0 does not exceed 5 degrees. For a given angular velocity input, ω_y, the gimbal deflection (from Eqs. 4.92, 4.93) is found to be

$$\theta_0 = \omega_y \left(\frac{H}{k}\right) \tag{4.99}$$

A summary of the four performance characteristics in terms of the physical parameters of the instrument follows.

Natural frequency of gimbal assembly $= \sqrt{k/J}$

Sensitivity $= \dfrac{HK}{k}$

Threshold $= \dfrac{K_c}{H}$

Angular deflection per unit velocity input $= \dfrac{H}{k}$ $\qquad$ (4.100)

A study of these four equations reveals some of the simpler compromises which the gyroscope designer must make in arriving at the final configuration for his design. For example, the spring constant k should be large for a high natural frequency, but it should be low for a high sensitivity, all other quantities remaining constant. The reader may wish to develop this idea of design compromises further by expressing the parameters H, J, and K_c in terms of the mass and speed of the wheel, and the parameter K in terms of the voltage and power rating of the potentiometer. This will indicate the way in which the final design dimensions for the instrument are determined.

Third order systems

The dynamic response of higher order systems may usually be represented, by means of the partial fraction expansion, as a sum of first and second order terms. A knowledge of the relationships between the s plane pole-zero map and the residues, time constants, and natural frequencies of only first and second order terms makes it possible to compute the dynamic response of higher order systems. This technique is illustrated here in the analysis of the transient response of a third order system. The extension of this technique to fourth and higher order systems should be obvious to the reader.

The electro-hydraulic valve shown in Fig. 4.48 is analyzed as an example of a third order system. This valve is typical of the early developments in the electro-hydraulic servomechanism field, but it has been largely superseded by other types of valves such as the nozzle and flapper variety. The valve and ram system operates as follows: Suppose the ram is to be driven toward the right. A voltage e_i is applied to the grid of the amplifier tube shown at the left of the drawing, producing a current i in the tractive magnet, the winding of which is in the plate circuit of the tube. This current produces a magnetic flux in the air gap of the magnet, thus producing a tractive force on the armature of the magnet and causing it to move toward the left. The armature is rigidly attached to the spool of the valve, so that the spool is also displaced toward the left, uncovering port a. Hydraulic fluid under high pressure is conducted from the supply at P through port a and into the left chamber of the ram cylinder. The ram, along with the attached load, will move toward the right, and the fluid from the

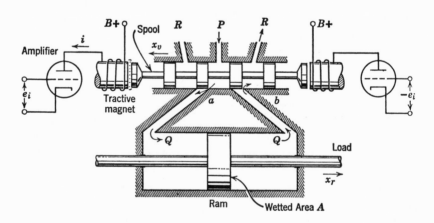

Fig. 4.48.   Electro-hydraulic valve.

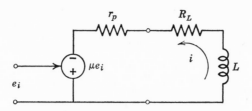

Fig. 4.49. Equivalent circuit for amplifier and magnet.

right chamber will flow through port b and out of the valve to the exhaust line R. If the ram is to be driven to the left, the spool is displaced by the tractive magnet at the right hand side of the drawing, all of the action being similar to that described above but in the opposite direction.

In order to make a quantitative analysis of the valve-ram system some simplifying assumptions must be made to permit the use of linear equations. First, the vacuum tube amplifier and magnet circuit are represented by the equivalent circuit shown in Fig. 4.49. Here μ is the amplification factor, r_p is the plate resistance of the tube, R_L is the resistance of the magnet, and L is its inductance. If the right and left amplifier tubes are operated in push-pull fashion and i_D is defined as the *differential current*—the difference between the two plate currents—the transfer function relating $I_D(s)$ to $E_i(s)$ is

$$\frac{I_D(s)}{E_i(s)} = \frac{2\mu/L}{s + (r_p + R_L)/L} \tag{4.101}$$

With the tubes operating in push-pull, the force developed on the spool is proportional to the differential current; thus

$$F = K_M i_D \tag{4.102}$$

where F is the net force on the spool and K_M is the magnetic force constant. Actually, the force developed in the magnet also depends upon the air gap length; the effect of a change in air-gap length is taken into account below.

The force developed on the spool will cause the spool to move in accordance with this equation

$$F = M\ddot{x}_v + B\dot{x}_v + kx_v + F_R \tag{4.103}$$

where M is the mass of the spool-armature assembly and B is an equivalent viscous friction coefficient which includes not only the actual viscous drag occurring by virtue of the immersion of the spool in fluid but also the effect of certain forces—proportional to the velocity of the spool—which exist on the spool due to the flow of fluid through the valve. k is a spring coefficient including any centering springs (not shown in Fig. 4.48) which may be used, the effect of certain flow forces proportional to spool displacement, and the effect of a change in F due to the change in air-gap length as the spool is displaced. This latter effect acts as a "negative spring" in that the decentering force increases with spool displacement. For this reason a centering spring is often used to make the total force-displacement characteristic a positive one—that is, to make the total centering force increase with spool displacement. In some special types of valves there occurs also a spring-like effect due to either a positive or negative pressure imbalance on the moving member. x_v is the spool displacement, and F_R is the friction force on the spool. F_R determines the threshold level of the valve and can present a serious problem in valve design, but for the purpose of deriving a transfer function it is neglected. The transfer function relating spool displacement to applied force is derived from Eq. 4.103.

$$\frac{X_v(s)}{F(s)} = \frac{1/M}{s^2 + (B/M)s + k/M} \qquad (4.104)$$

This is a second order transfer function, the natural frequency and damping ratio of which depend upon M, B, and k. These in turn are dependent upon the several properties of the valve and magnet discussed above, and, depending upon the design of the system, they can make the natural frequency and damping ratio vary over a wide range. The effects of these variations are discussed below.

Next, the flow Q must be related to the valve displacement x_v. The flow of fluid through an orifice is proportional to the area of the orifice and the square root of the pressure drop across the orifice.

$$Q = K_1 A_0 \sqrt{P} \qquad (4.105)$$

Q is the flow, A_0 is the area of the orifice, P is the pressure drop across the orifice, and K_1 is a flow coefficient. If the area of the orifice is proportional to the displacement, and if the pressure drop across the orifice is constant, Eq. 4.105 becomes

$$Q = K_v x_v \qquad (4.106)$$

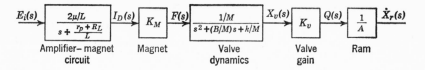

Fig. 4.50. Block diagram for electro-hydraulic valve system.

where K_v is a constant depending upon K_1, P, and the geometry of the orifice. The fluid is considered to be incompressible; hence the velocity of the ram must be proportional to the flow Q, provided there is no leakage of fluid from one side of the piston to the other. Thus

$$\dot{x}_r = \frac{Q}{A} \tag{4.107}$$

where $\dot{x}_r$ is the ram velocity, and A is the wetted area of the piston face.

Each of the transfer functions in Eqs. 4.101–4.107 may be represented as blocks and arranged in the chain-like fashion indicated in Fig. 4.50. Notice that in this diagram a one-to-one correspondence does not exist between the individual blocks and particular pieces of the physical system. The first block, for example, represents the last stage of the amplifier plus the magnet resistance and inductance. The second block represents only the force-current property of the magnet. Similarly, the valve is represented by two blocks, each describing a salient characteristic of the valve. All five blocks in this diagram may be combined to form a single block, as in Fig. 4.51. The physical parameters μ, r_p, R_L, L, B, k, and M have been combined so that the transfer function may be written in the standard form, using α, ζ and

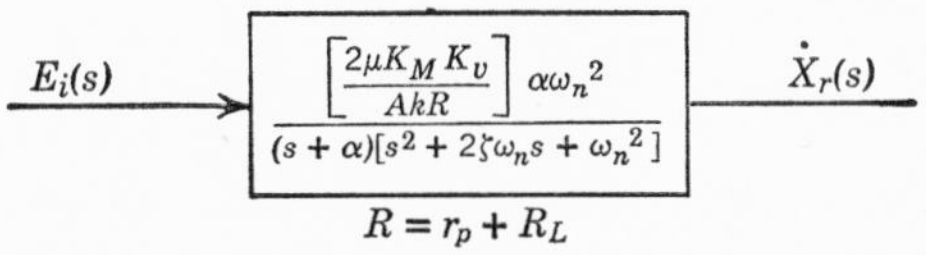

$$E_i(s) \longrightarrow \boxed{\dfrac{\left[\dfrac{2\mu K_M K_v}{AkR}\right]\alpha\omega_n^2}{(s+\alpha)[s^2 + 2\zeta\omega_n s + \omega_n^2]}} \longrightarrow \dot{X}_r(s)$$

$$R = r_p + R_L$$

Fig. 4.51. Composite block diagram for electro-hydraulic valve system where: $\alpha = \dfrac{r_p + R_L}{L}$,

$$\omega_n^2 = \frac{k}{M}, \zeta = \frac{B}{2\sqrt{kM}}.$$

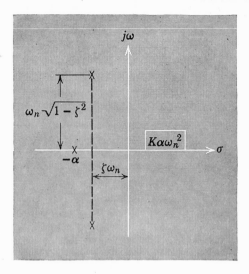

Fig. 4.52. Pole zero map for electro-hydraulic valve system transfer function;
$K = (2\mu K_M K_v)/(AkR)$.

ω_n. The constant $2(\mu K_M K_v)/AkR$ is sometimes called the "system gain" because the steady-state relationship between ram velocity $\dot{x}_r$ and input voltage e_i is this number.

$$2\frac{\mu K_M K_v}{AkR} = \frac{\left(\dfrac{\text{volts}}{\text{volt}}\right)\left(\dfrac{\text{dynes}}{\text{amp}}\right)\left(\dfrac{\text{cm}^3/\text{sec}}{\text{cm}}\right)}{\text{cm}^2\left(\dfrac{\text{dynes}}{\text{cm}}\right)(\text{ohms})} = \frac{\text{cm/sec}}{\text{volt}} \quad (4.108)$$

A pole-zero plot of the transfer function of the electro-hydraulic system is drawn in Fig. 4.52. The transfer function has three finite poles and no finite zeros. The quadratic factor $(s^2 + 2\zeta\omega_n s + \omega_n{}^2)$ is a pair of poles which may be either complex, as shown in the plot, or real if the damping ratio is unity or higher. Because the transfer function is of odd order, it always has at least one real pole, and in this case it appears at $s = -\alpha$.

Assume that a step voltage is applied at the input at time $t = 0$. Then

$$E_1(s) = \frac{E}{s} \quad (4.109)$$

where E is the magnitude of the applied voltage. The output is

$$\dot{X}_r(s) = \frac{EK\alpha\omega_n^2}{s(s + \alpha)(s^2 + 2\zeta\omega_n s + \omega_n^2)} \quad (4.110)$$

where K is the "system gain" defined in Fig. 4.52 and Eq. 4.108. Now Eq. 4.110 may be expanded into partial fractions.

$$\dot{X}_r(s) = \frac{K_1}{s} + \frac{K_2}{s + \alpha} + \frac{K_3}{s + \zeta\omega_n + j\omega_0} + \frac{\bar{K}_3}{s + \zeta\omega_n - j\omega_0} \quad (4.111)$$

where K_1, K_2, K_3, and $\bar{K}_3$ are the residues of $\dot{X}_r(s)$ at the poles of $\dot{X}_r(s)$, and $\omega_0 = \omega_n \sqrt{1 - \zeta^2}$.

The inverse Laplace transform of Eq. 4.111 is taken term by term to obtain the transient response.

$$\dot{x}_r(t) = K_1 + K_2\epsilon^{-\alpha t} + 2|K_3|\epsilon^{-\zeta\omega_n t} \sin(\omega_0 t + \psi) \quad (4.112)$$

where, if $K_3 = a + jb$, $\psi = \tan^{-1} a/b = 90° - \underline{/K_3}$.

The residues in this example are evaluated:

$$\dot{x}_r(t) = EK\left[1 - \frac{\omega_n^2}{\alpha^2 - 2\zeta\omega_n\alpha + \omega_n^2}\epsilon^{-\alpha t}\right.$$
$$\left. + \frac{\alpha\epsilon^{-\zeta\omega_n t}\sin(\omega_0 t + \psi)}{\sqrt{1 - \zeta^2}(\alpha^2 - 2\zeta\alpha\omega_n + \omega_n^2)^{1/2}}\right] \quad (4.113)$$

where

$$\psi = -\tan^{-1}\frac{\sqrt{1 - \zeta^2}}{-\zeta} - \tan^{-1}\frac{\omega_0}{\alpha - \zeta\omega_n} \text{ and } \omega_0 = \omega_n \sqrt{1 - \zeta^2}.$$

It is interesting to observe the change in $\dot{x}_r(t)$ which occurs when one of the physical parameters in the system is changed. Assume for the sake of illustration that the system parameters are as follows:

$M = 5$ g
$k = 45 \times 10^4$ dynes/cm
$B = 600$ dynes/cm/sec
$L = 10$ henries
$R_L = 100$ ohms
$r_p =$ Variable from 100 to 3900 ohms
$K_M = 10^6$ dynes/amp
$K_v = 8000$ cm^3/sec/cm
$A = 8$ cm^2
μ varies as r_p is varied so that μ/R is always constant at 0.01

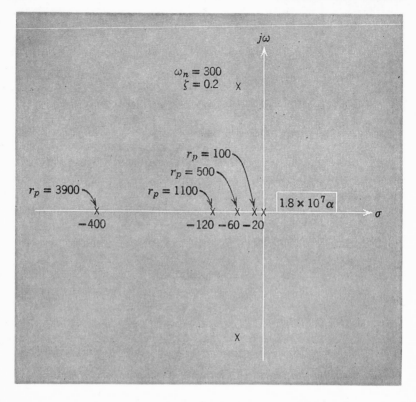

Fig. 4.53.   Pole-zero map for $\dot{X}_r(s)$, r_p varying from 100 to 3900.

With these numbers the transfer function is

$$\frac{\dot{X}_r(s)}{E_1(s)} = \frac{44.4(\alpha \times 9 \times 10^4)}{(s + \alpha)(s^2 + 120s + 9 \times 10^4)} \qquad \frac{\text{cm/sec}}{\text{volt}} \qquad (4.114)$$

where
$$\alpha = \frac{100 + r_p}{10}.$$

Assume that the magnitude of the applied voltage is 4.5 v, giving a steady state ram velocity of 200 cm/sec for any value of r_p. (The ratio μ/R is assumed to remain constant.)   If r_p is 100 ohms, α will be 20, and the pole zero plot for $\dot{X}_r(s)$ will be that shown in Fig. 4.53. The response $\dot{x}_r(t)$ may be computed by substituting the following values in Eq. 4.113:

$$E_1 = 4.5 \qquad K = 44.4 \qquad \zeta = 0.2 \qquad \omega_n = 300 \qquad \alpha = 20$$

Then

$$\dot{x}_r(t) = 200[1 - 1.023\epsilon^{-20t} + 0.069\epsilon^{-60t} \sin (294t - 199.5°)] \quad (4.115)$$

This is plotted in Fig. 4.54.   In this expression the residues K_1 and K_2 (Eq. 4.112) are significantly larger than K_3.   Also, the time constant of the first order exponential term, $1/\alpha$, is three times greater than the time constant of the damped sinusoidal term $1/\zeta\omega_n$.   Consequently, the damped sinusoidal term in Eq. 4.115 is small and decays rapidly when compared to the constant and first order exponential term.   The damped sinusoidal component in $\dot{x}_r(t)$ is significant only during the initial part of the transient, contributing some small oscillations which are superimposed upon the larger, slower first order curve.

Now assume that we increase r_p from 100 to 500 ohms by changing

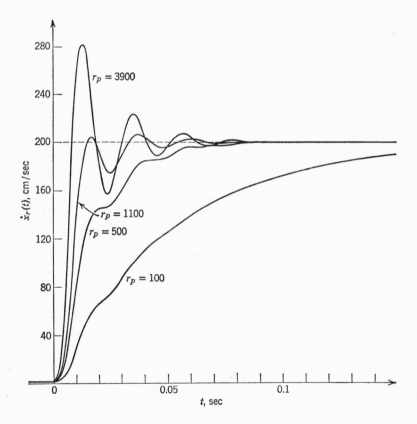

Fig. 4.54.   Transient response of electro-hydraulic system for various values of r_p corresponding to Fig. 4.53.

vacuum tubes in the amplifier. Now $\alpha = 60$, a threefold increase over the previous value because the total resistance in the plate circuit has been increased by a factor of three. In Fig. 4.53 this change would be reflected by a change in the position of the pole on the real axis to $s = -60$. Notice that this places all three system poles on the same line, namely, $s = -60$. The time response is computed by substituting $\alpha = 60$ into Eq. 4.113.

$$\dot{x}_r(t) = 200[1 - 1.04\epsilon^{-60t} + 0.21\epsilon^{-60t} \sin(294t - 191°)] \quad (4.116)$$

The change in the real pole position from $s = -20$ to $s = -60$ has produced a significant change in $\dot{x}_r(t)$. While the value of the residue K_2 (Eq. 4.112) has increased by only about 2 percent over its previous value, $|K_3|$ has increased over 300 percent. The oscillatory component in $\dot{x}_r(t)$ is now more pronounced than it is when $\alpha = 20$. The time constants of the first order term and the damped sinusoidal term are now equal; this increases the significance of the damped sinusoidal term relative to the first order term, since now they both decay at the same rate. (This rate, incidentally, is three times greater than the rate of decay of the first order term in the previous case.) The total effect of the change in α is seen in Fig. 4.54. The response is faster, and the oscillating component is more pronounced, although there is no overshoot.

Continuing this analysis, one may increase r_p to 1100 ohms, making $\alpha = 120$, as indicated in Fig. 4.53. Now the time constant of the first order term in $\dot{x}_r(t)$ is just half that of the damped sinusoidal term. An evaluation of Eq. 4.113 follows:

$$\dot{x}_r(t) = 200[1 - \epsilon^{-120t} + 0.41\epsilon^{-60t} \sin(294t - 180°)] \quad (4.117)$$

Notice that here K_2 has nearly the same magnitude as it had in the two previous cases, but that $|K_3|$ has again increased by about a factor of two. It is now clear that as the real pole is moved to the left in the s plane the magnitude of K_3 increases so that the damped sinusoidal term becomes more and more significant in the total response. When $\alpha = 120$ the damped sinusoidal term is large enough and the first order term decays fast enough for the response to overshoot slightly. Incidentally, the first peak in the curve occurs when t equals about 0.017 sec and the overshoot is only about 1.5 percent. The second peak, at $t \cong 0.037$, has about 3 percent overshoot. This interesting property of the third order system cannot occur in a second order system.

As the final step in this example, let $r_p = 3900$ ohms, and $\alpha = 400$, as indicated in Fig. 4.53. Now the real pole is far enough toward the left to cause a significant decrease in K_2 to less than half its former values and a corresponding increase in $|K_3|$. $\dot{x}_r(t)$ for this case is

$$\dot{x}_r(t) = 200[1 - 0.45\epsilon^{-400t} + 0.91\epsilon^{-60t} \sin (294t - 143°)] \quad (4.118)$$

Now the oscillatory term is definitely more significant in the total response, since the first order term is smaller in magnitude and decays much faster than does the damped sinusoid. In fact, the response resembles that of a pure second order system having a damping ratio of 0.2.

This example illustrates the importance of including in the analysis every physical parameter in the system which can conceivably affect the dynamic response of the system. Here the plate resistance of the amplifier tube, an obscure parameter which might go unnoticed by one unfamiliar with electronics, is seen to exert a considerable influence on the dynamic performance of the system. If this parameter is not set at the proper value an undesirable response will result. For example, if $r_p = 100$ ohms the transient response is quite sluggish, while an $r_p = 3900$ ohms gives a response which has a large overshoot with oscillations considered to be excessive for most control applications. A response corresponding to that shown in Fig. 4.54 for $r_p = 1100$ would be considered the best of the four shown for most purposes, for it is relatively fast but has only a small percentage overshoot.

One important characteristic of the third order system can be deduced from the above analysis. In this type of system no overshoot can occur in response to a step input if the real pole lies on or to the right of a line joining the two complex poles—that is, if the time constant of the first order exponential term is equal to or greater than the time constant of the envelope of the damped sinusoidal term. This can be shown most easily by computing the unit impulse response of the system, which is the time derivative of the unit step response, and by proving that for $\alpha \leqq \zeta\omega_n$ the derivative of the step response is always equal to or greater than zero. It follows that the step response, which is the time integral of the impulse response, is a monotonically increasing function; i.e., it does not overshoot. It can then be shown that if $\alpha > \zeta\omega_n$ the step response will overshoot. The amount of overshoot, the number of oscillations, and the time required for the transient to die out to a negligibly small amount all depend upon the ratio $\alpha:\zeta\omega_n$ and, of course, upon ζ and ω_n themselves. Figure 4.54 indicates the way in which the step response varies for changes in the ratio $\alpha:\zeta\omega_n$, where ζ and ω_n are held fixed at 0.2 and 300, respectively.

A more complete description of the transient response of the third order system having no zeros in its transfer function is given in Figs. 4.55 to 4.60. Here the time axes have been normalized with respect

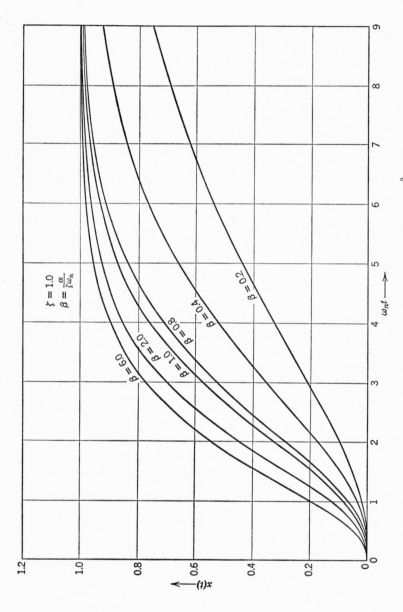

Fig. 4.55 through Fig. 4.59. Transient response, $x(t)$, where $X(s) = \dfrac{\alpha \omega_n{}^2}{s(s+\alpha)(s^2 + 2\zeta\omega_n s + \omega_n{}^2)}$ and $\beta = \dfrac{\alpha}{\zeta\omega_n}$.

$\zeta = 1.0$
$\beta = \dfrac{\alpha}{\zeta\omega_n}$

$\beta = 0.2$
$\beta = 0.4$
$\beta = 0.8$
$\beta = 1.0$
$\beta = 2.0$
$\beta = 6.0$

140

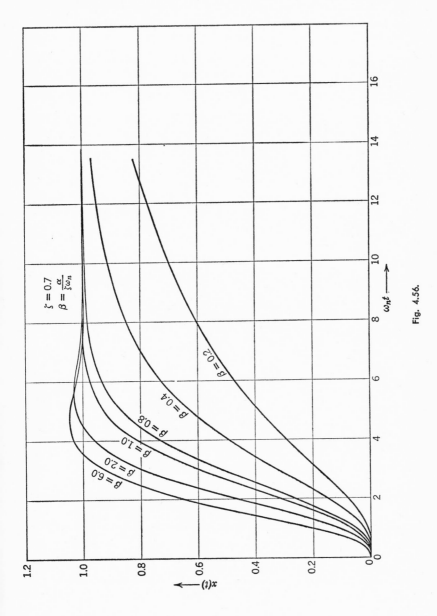

Fig. 4.56.

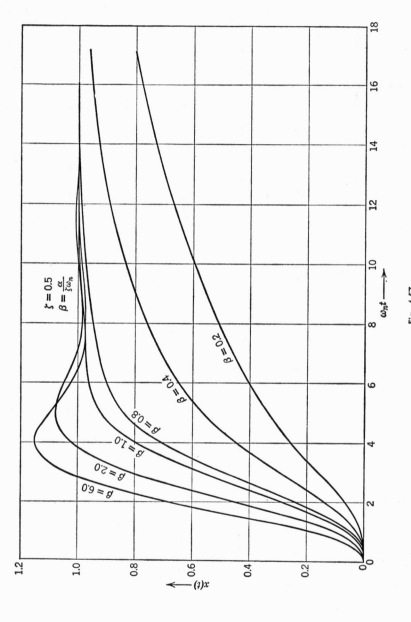

$\zeta = 0.5$

$\beta = \dfrac{\alpha}{\zeta \omega_n}$

$\beta = 0.2$

$\beta = 0.4$

$\beta = 0.8$

$\beta = 1.0$

$\beta = 2.0$

$\beta = 6.0$

$x(t) \longrightarrow$

$\omega_n t \longrightarrow$

Fig. 4.57.

142

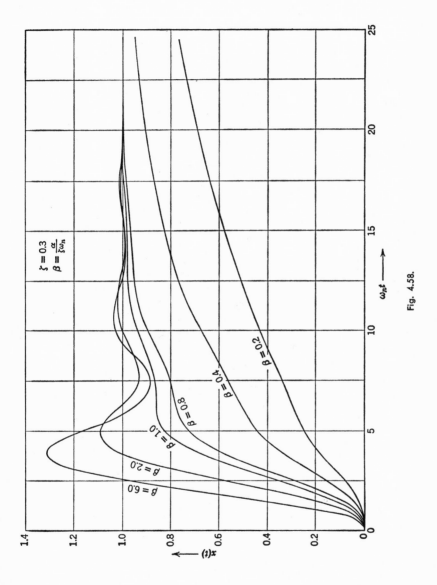

Fig. 4.58.

143

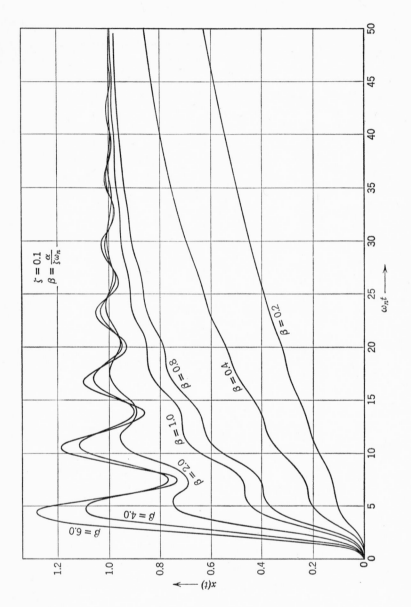

Fig. 4.59.

144

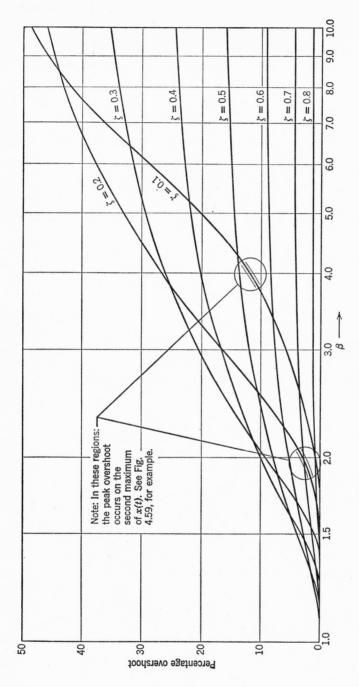

Note: In these regions: the peak overshoot occurs on the second maximum of $x(t)$. See Fig. 4.59, for example.

Fig. 4.60. Percentage overshoot in the third order system as a function of ζ and β.

145

to ω_n in the same way as were those in Figs. 3.35 and 4.39 to 4.43. In Fig. 4.60 a graph shows how the percentage overshoot in the third order system depends upon the ratio $\alpha:\zeta\omega_n(=\beta)$ and ζ. Notice that the overshoot is zero for $\alpha \leqq \zeta\omega_n(\beta \leqq 1)$. For large values of β the real pole is far to the left in the s plane and the residue at the real pole is very small, so that the overshoot here is practically the same as it would be in a pure second order system having the same damping ratio which the complex poles have in this system.

Higher order systems

The principles discussed in the above sections and also in Chapter 3 are easily applied to the analysis of fourth, fifth and higher order systems. The output of one of these systems may be calculated, provided only that the system transfer function is known and the input is specified (Fig. 4.4). The dynamic analysis then centers around the problem of finding the inverse Laplace transform of the output function. If $x_0(t)$ is the dynamic response of a linear system, then $X_0(s)$ will be of this form:

$$X_0(s) = \frac{K(s + Z_1)(s + Z_2) \cdots (s + Z_m)}{(s + P_1)(s + P_2)(s + P_3) \cdots (s + P_n)} \quad (4.119)$$

Several observations may be made about this expression. First, the initial value and the final value for $x_0(t)$ can be quickly determined from Eq. 4.119 by applying the initial and final value theorems. The initial value is

$$x_0(t) \Big|_{t=0^+} = \lim_{s \to \infty} sX_0(s) \quad (4.120)$$

Hence, if the initial value of the response $x_0(t)$ is to be finite, the order of the denominator in Eq. 4.119 must be higher than the order of the numerator. $X_0(s)$ must have more finite poles than finite zeros. If the numerator is of equal or higher order than the denominator, impulse functions will occur in $x_0(t)$. Since it is impossible for impulse functions of voltage, current, force, displacement, etc. to occur in a physical system, the denominator of $X_0(s)$—representing the response of a physical system—will necessarily be of higher order than the numerator, unless some of the physical characteristics of the system have been neglected in order to simplify the problem, or unless a non-physical type of input has been assumed. If the number of finite poles of $X_0(s)$ exceeds the number of zeros by two or more, the initial value of $x_0(t)$ will be zero.

The final value of $x_0(t)$ is

$$x_0(t)\Big|_{t\to\infty} = \lim_{s\to 0} sX_0(s) \qquad (4.121)$$

provided all the poles of $sX_0(s)$ lie in the left-half s plane. Notice that the final value of $x_0(t)$ will be zero unless one pole (and no zero) of $X_0(s)$ occurs at the origin of the s plane. If there is one pole at the origin, say $P_1 = 0$, the final value of $x_0(t)$ will be

$$x_0(t)\Big|_{t\to\infty} = \frac{KZ_1Z_2\cdots Z_m}{P_2P_3P_4\cdots P_n} \qquad (4.122)$$

In most examples treated so far the single pole at the origin has come from the step input function, and the output response has assumed a nonzero, finite, final value.

A second and more important observation concerning Eq. 4.119 is that K is a real number, and all Zs and Ps either are real numbers or, if complex, appear in conjugate pairs. This occurs because $x_0(t)$ is a real valued, physical quantity in a linear system having lumped parameters. When Eq. 4.119 is written in this form

$$X_0(s) = \frac{K(s^m + a_1s^{m-1} + \cdots + a_{m-1}s + a_m)}{(s^n + b_1s^{n-1} + \cdots + b_{n-1}s + b_n)} \qquad (4.123)$$

it is apparent that the as and the bs are all coefficients of the differential equation which describes the behavior of $x_0(t)$, and, consequently, they are all real numbers. Since the as and bs are real, the Ps and Zs must either be real or appear in conjugate pairs. If there are no multiple poles, Eq. 4.119 may be expanded in partial fractions.

$$X_0(s) = \frac{K_1}{s + P_1} + \frac{K_2}{s + P_2} + \cdots + \frac{K_n}{s + P_n} \qquad (4.124)$$

K_1 is the residue of $X_0(s)$ at $s = -P_1$, K_2 is the residue at $s = -P_2$, and so forth. With $X_0(s)$ written in expanded form the inverse Laplace transform of $X_0(s)$ may be written immediately by inspection.

$$x_0(t) = K_1\epsilon^{-P_1t} + K_2\epsilon^{-P_2t} + \cdots + K_n\epsilon^{-P_nt} \qquad (4.125)$$

In the event that a pair of complex poles in $X_0(s)$ occurs at the points $s = -\zeta\omega_n \pm j\omega_n\sqrt{1 - \zeta^2}$, the two terms in $x_0(t)$ which correspond to these two poles may be combined to form a single damped sinusoidal term

$$2|K_3|\epsilon^{-\zeta\omega_n t}\sin(\omega_n\sqrt{1 - \zeta^2}\,t + \psi) \qquad (4.126)$$

where K_3 is the residue of $X_0(s)$ at the point $s = -\zeta\omega_n - j\omega_n\sqrt{1 - \zeta^2}$.

K_3 will be a complex number

$$K_3 = a + jb \qquad (4.127)$$

so that $\qquad\qquad 2|K_3| = 2(a^2 + b^2)^{1/2} \qquad (4.128)$

The angle ψ in Eq. 4.126 is

$$\psi = \tan^{-1}\frac{a}{b} = 90° - \underline{/K_3} \qquad (4.129)$$

Thus in order to compute the inverse Laplace transform of any order function which has no multiple poles it is necessary simply to remember the two transform pairs listed as numbers 6 and 17 in the table in Appendix 1.

It is also useful to remember the s plane vector method for computing the residues, as outlined in Section 4.3. If double poles appear in $X_0(s)$, the procedure for finding the inverse Laplace transform is only slightly more complicated than that summarized above. In this case the partial fraction expansion contains an additional term, as in the example in Eq. 4.41. The constant C and the residue K_1 are evaluated by the procedure indicated in Eqs. 4.43, 4.44, 4.45, and 4.46. This procedure is easily memorized, and it, together with the procedure for the simpler case plus the transform pair number 8 in Appendix 1, makes it possible to take the inverse Laplace transform of any function having single or double poles without reference to tables, charts, or rule books of any sort. Roughly 95 percent of the functions we encounter in linear control system analysis may be handled in this fashion.

If multiple poles having a multiplicity of three or higher occur in $X_0(s)$, the constants and residues in the partial fraction expansion may be calculated by reference to Eqs. 3.165, 3.166, 3.167, or the function may be approximated by one which has all distinct poles, as in Eq. 4.51.

When $x_0(t)$ is written as a sum (Eq. 4.125) it is possible to make a graph of $x_0(t)$ by sketching each of its components and adding them graphically. Each first order component has an initial value equal to the residue and a time constant equal to the reciprocal of the pole value. For each pair of complex poles there is an exponentially damped sinusoidal term contained in an envelope whose initial value is $2|K_3|$ (see Eq. 4.126) and which decays with a time constant $1/\zeta\omega_n$. The frequency of oscillation of this term is ω_0, and the initial value is $2K_3 \sin \psi$, which is also equal to $2a$, a being the real part of the residue K_3. A double pole in $X_0(s)$ will produce two terms in $x_0(t)$, one a simple exponential, the other an exponential multiplied by t. It is usually possible to make an approximate sketch of each of the components of $x_0(t)$ from the pole-zero plot of $X_0(s)$, since the time constants and periods of oscillation of each of the components may be determined immediately by inspection, and the residues may be computed quickly, or at least estimated, by use of the s plane vector method described in Section 4.3.

A control system designer finds these simple relationships between the pole and zero locations of $X_0(s)$ and the corresponding terms of $x_0(t)$ to be extremely useful when it is necessary in an analysis to determine the way in which each of the physical parameters in the system affects the dynamic response. Several examples of this kind of analysis have already been presented in previous sections of this chapter and in Chapter 3. The next few paragraphs will develop a few important points which come out of the $X_0(s)$—$x_0(t)$ transformation just discussed.

Very often, and particularly in a high order system, it is possible to ignore some of the poles or zeros of $X_0(s)$ without causing a significant change in $x_0(t)$. For example, consider the function

$$X_0(s) = \frac{30}{s(s + 1)(s + 2)(s + 15)} \tag{4.130}$$

A pole-zero map for $X_0(s)$ is drawn to scale in Fig. 4.61. Equation

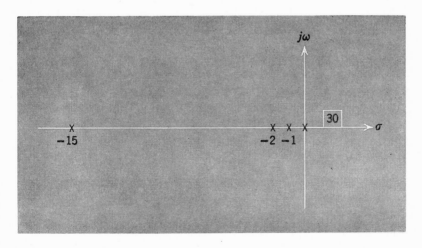

Fig. 4.61. Pole-zero map for $X_0(s) = \dfrac{30}{s(s + 1)(s + 2)(s + 15)}$.

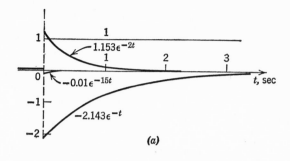

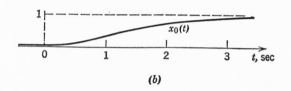

Fig. 4.62.   Components of $x_0(t)$, and $x_0(t)$.

4.130 can be expanded easily into partial fractions and the residues computed by the vector method.   The resulting equation is

$$X_0(s) = \frac{1}{s} - \frac{2.143}{s+1} + \frac{1.153}{s+2} - \frac{0.01}{s+15} \qquad (4.131)$$

Notice that the algebraic sign of each term is determined by the sign of the residue, and this sign may in turn be determined by inspection of the pole-zero plot.   The residue at the pole $s = -1$ is negative, since the vector drawn to this pole from the pole at $s = 0$ has the value -1, and the other two vectors from $s = -2$ and $s = -15$ are both positive.   In general, the residue at a pole will be negative if the pole lies to the left of an odd number of poles and zeros, and it will be positive if the pole lies to the left of an even number of poles and zeros. From Eq. 4.131 $x_0(t)$ may be written directly as

$$x_0(t) = 1 - 2.143\epsilon^{-t} + 1.153\epsilon^{-2t} - 0.01\epsilon^{-15t} \qquad (4.132)$$

A sketch of each of the components of $x_0(t)$ is drawn in Fig. 4.62a and the sum of these, $x_0(t)$, is sketched in Fig. 4.62b.   Several observations can be made about this particular response function.   The final value of $x_0(t)$ is unity.   This can be predicted from $X_0(s)$ by use of the final value theorem.   The initial values of $x_0(t)$ and its first and second time derivatives are all zero, while the initial value of the third time derivative is nonzero. These may also be determined from $X_0(s)$ by use of the initial value theorem, as follows:

$$x_0(0^+) = \lim_{s \to \infty} sX_0(s) = 0$$

$$\dot{x}_0(0^+) = \lim_{s \to \infty} s(sX_0(s)) = 0$$

$$\ddot{x}_0(0^+) = \lim_{s \to \infty} s(s^2 X_0(s)) = 0$$

$$\dddot{x}_0(0^+) = \lim_{s \to \infty} s(s^3 X_0(s)) = 30 \qquad (4.133)$$

The component $(-.01\epsilon^{-15t})$, which is very much smaller than the other three components in $x_0(t)$, corresponds to the pole at $s = -15$. Since this pole is located a relatively long distance from the other three poles it is called a *remote* pole, and by virtue of its location in the remote part of the s plane the residue at this pole is very small compared to the other residues. The vector method of calculating residues shows this; the residues in this example are computed by the vector method in the following form:

$$K = \frac{30}{\Pi \mathbf{P}} \qquad (4.134)$$

For each of the three poles in the region near the origin the order of magnitude of the residue may be determined as follows:

$$|K_{\text{near}}| = \frac{30}{(\text{short})(\text{short})(\text{long})} \qquad (4.135)$$

Consequently, the residues at each of these three poles are all of the same order of magnitude, 1.0, -2.143, and 1.153. At the remote pole, however, the order of magnitude of the residue is given by

$$|K_{\text{far}}| = \frac{30}{(\text{long})(\text{long})(\text{long})} \qquad (4.136)$$

In addition, the time constant in the component of $x_0(t)$ corresponding to this pole is very short when compared to the other time constants. The time component corresponding to the remote pole is therefore initially small and short lived.

For many practical purposes the contribution of the $(-0.01\epsilon^{-15t})$ term to the total response function $x_0(t)$ is negligibly small. The pole at $s = -15$ could be deleted from $X_0(s)$ without changing $x_0(t)$ significantly. The proper way to delete is to approximate the original $X_0(s)$ with one which has the same poles except for the one at $s = -15$.

In this instance the approximation would be

$$\frac{30}{s(s+1)(s+2)(s+15)} \cong \frac{2}{s(s+1)(s+2)} \qquad (4.137)$$

The constant 30 must be changed to 2 in the approximate function in order to keep the steady-state value of $x_0(t)$ unity, as in the original equation. The approximate $x_0(t)$ is then

$$x_0(t) \cong 1 - 2\epsilon^{-t} + \epsilon^{-2t} \qquad (4.138)$$

The error which results from the approximation may be calculated easily by subtracting the right side of Eq. 4.138 from the right side of Eq. 4.132. This error is

$$\text{Approximation error} = -0.143\epsilon^{-t} + 0.153\epsilon^{-2t} - 0.01\epsilon^{-15t} \qquad (4.139)$$

which has a maximum instantaneous magnitude of less than 4 percent of the final value of $x_0(t)$. For many engineering purposes this small instantaneous error is negligible.

The question of whether a pole is sufficiently removed from the other poles and zeros to be considered remote and therefore negligible can be determined only when all the poles and zeros of the function are located and some specifications on the accuracy of the analysis are established. Provided that the desired accuracy is known, computations similar to those in the above example will yield an answer. It should be observed here that the residue at a remote pole becomes smaller and smaller in comparison to the others as the number of poles in the near region of the origin increases, or more correctly, as the excess number of near poles over near zeros increases. For example, the exponential term in $y(t)$ corresponding to the pole at $s = -15$ in this function

$$Y(s) = \frac{45}{s(s+1)(s^2+s+1)(s+1.5)(s+2)(s+15)} \qquad (4.140)$$

is much less significant to $y(t)$ than the exponential term in $z(t)$ corresponding to the pole at $s = -15$ in this function

$$Z(s) = \frac{45}{s(s+1.5)(s+2)(s+15)} \qquad (4.141)$$

is to $z(t)$. A consideration of Eqs. 4.135 and 4.136 will show why a larger number of near poles will make a smaller residue at the remote pole.

It is necessary in every case, however, to have an excess of two or more near poles over near zeros before a remote pole can be neglected.

For example, in the function

$$X(s) = \frac{7.5(s + 2)}{s(s + 1)(s + 15)} \tag{4.142}$$

which has two near poles and one near zero, making an excess of only one near pole over near zero, the residue at $s = -15$ is not significantly smaller than the others. A partial fraction expansion of Eq. 4.142 reveals that

$$X(s) = \frac{1}{s} - \frac{0.536}{s + 1} - \frac{0.464}{s + 15} \tag{4.143}$$

where the residue of $X(s)$ at $s = -15$, -0.464, is not negligibly small when compared with the other two residues, 1 and -0.536.

No single rule can be made to state the conditions under which a remote pole may be neglected. A knowledge of the degree of accuracy desired in the analysis, a consideration of the principles described above, and the exercise of a little judgment will enable the engineer to estimate quickly which poles may be neglected without sacrificing more than the degree of accuracy desired in his analysis.

The approximate $x_0(t)$ in Eq. 4.138 is different from the exact $x_0(t)$ in Eq. 4.132 in one other respect; the second time derivative of the approximate function is nonzero at the origin. The table in Fig. 4.63 compares the values of the time derivatives of the two functions at the origin. Notice that the deletion of one pole in $X_0(s)$ decreases by one the order of the highest nonzero time derivative. This may, in some instances, constitute a significant difference between the exact function and the approximate function. Whether it does or not depends upon the particular system under study and the particular properties of the system important to the purpose at hand.

It is possible for the residue of $X_0(s)$ at a pole to be negligibly small even if the pole is not remotely located in the left-hand s plane. This will occur if there is a zero of $X_0(s)$ very close to the pole at which the

	Exact Function Eq. 4.132	Approximate Function Eq. 4.138
$x_0(0^+)$	0	0
$\dot{x}_0(0^+)$	0	0
$\ddot{x}_0(0^+)$	0	2
$\dddot{x}_0(0^+)$	30	∞

Fig. 4.63. Comparison of the initial value of $x_0(t)$ and its derivatives with those of the approximate $x_0(t)$.

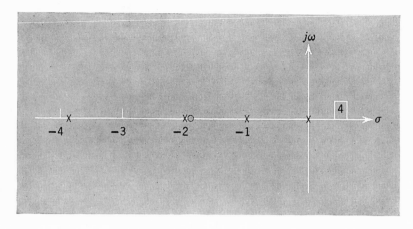

Fig. 4.64. Pole-zero map for $X_0(s) = \dfrac{4(s + 1.9)}{s(s + 1)(s + 2)(s + 3.8)}$.

residue is measured.   Consider the function

$$X_0(s) = \frac{4(s + 1.9)}{s(s + 1)(s + 2)(s + 3.8)} \tag{4.144}$$

which has the pole-zero plot shown in Fig. 4.64. $X_0(s)$ may be
expanded in partial fractions to

$$X_0(s) = \frac{1}{s} - \frac{1.286}{s + 1} - \frac{0.111}{s + 2} + \frac{0.397}{s + 3.8} \tag{4.145}$$

Notice here that the residues at each of the poles which lie to the left
of an odd number of poles and zeros are negative, while those which lie
to the left of an even number are positive.   Equation 4.145 transformed gives the dynamic expression

$$x_0(t) = 1 - 1.286\epsilon^{-t} - 0.111\epsilon^{-2t} + 0.397\epsilon^{-3.8t} \tag{4.146}$$

Since a zero occurs very close to the pole at $s = -2$, the residue -0.111
has a somewhat smaller magnitude than do the other three residues.
Remember that the residue, as calculated by the vector method is, in
this example,

$$K = \frac{(4)\Pi Z}{\Pi P} \tag{4.147}$$

and at $s = -2$ the (ΠZ) term is very small.   Since the zero is so close
to the pole at $s = -2$, it is said to *cancel* the pole, so that Eq. 4.144
is approximated as follows:

$$X_0(s) = \frac{4(s + 1.9)}{s(s + 1)(s + 2)(s + 3.8)} \cong \frac{3.8}{s(s + 1)(s + 3.8)} \tag{4.148}$$

This approximate expression may be evaluated and the error of approximation determined in the same manner as in Eqs. 4.132, 4.138, and 4.139. In this example the error of approximation is

$$\text{Approximation error} = 0.071\epsilon^{-t} - 0.111\epsilon^{-2t} + 0.040\epsilon^{-3.8t} \quad (4.149)$$

which has a maximum instantaneous value of less than 2 percent of the final value of $x_0(t)$.

The two examples above illustrate the way in which the response of a high order system is sometimes approximated by a simpler function when a pole in $X_0(s)$ is to be neglected, either because it is sufficiently remote from the origin or because it is sufficiently close to a zero to keep the error introduced by neglecting it within the bounds allowed by the problem at hand. This approximation technique often permits a systems engineer to estimate the response of a high order system without actually carrying out any exact calculation of residues.

Sometimes, however, the engineer is given the *response* $x_0(t)$ (from experimental data, for example), and from this he must carry out the reverse procedure of estimating the location of the poles and zeros of $X_0(s)$. To do this he makes use of the same relationships between the poles, zeros, and residues and the salient features of $x_0(t)$, as shown in the following example.

Assume that the dynamic response of a linear system is known to be that in Fig. 4.65. Several important facts about the poles and zeros of $X_0(s)$ may be deduced by inspection of this curve.

(1) Since the response is stable, no poles of $X_0(s)$ occur in the right-half s plane.

(2) The steady-state value of $x_0(t)$ is 1; consequently, there is a single pole in $X_0(s)$ at the origin, and, by the final value theorem

$$\lim_{s \to 0} sX_0(s) = 1 \quad (4.150)$$

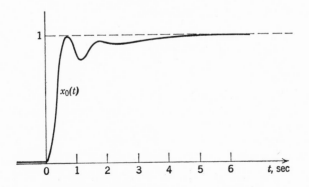

Fig. 4.65. Dynamic response of a linear system.

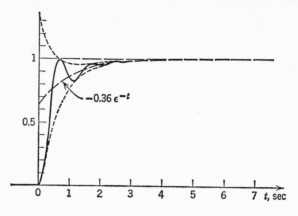

Fig. 4.66.   Dissection of $x_0(t)$.

This will determine the proper multiplying constant for $X_0(s)$ after the poles and zeros are found.

(3) $x_0(t)$ is continuous at $t = 0$, and the first derivative of $x_0(t)$ is zero there.   By the initial value theorem

$$\lim_{s \to \infty} s[sX_0(s)] = 0 \qquad (4.151)$$

which shows that $X_0(s)$ has a *net* order of 3 or more—that is, $X_0(s)$ has at least three more poles than zeros.   If the values of the second and higher order derivatives at the origin were all known, the exact *net* order of $X_0(s)$ could be determined.   However, derivatives higher than the first are usually difficult to determine by inspection of the graph.

A close inspection of the graph reveals other properties of $x_0(t)$ from which an approximate pole-zero plot for $X_0(s)$ may be constructed. $x_0(t)$ is a response curve which has a *long tail*.   The term *long tail* describes the character of $x_0(t)$ for large values of t, that is, for the time after which the oscillation in $x_0(t)$ is substantially completed.   In this example *large* values of t are those for which $t > 2$ sec.   During these later portions of the transient response $x_0(t)$ is approaching its final value somewhat slowly, indicating that there is probably in $x_0(t)$ an exponential term having a long time constant—long, that is, as compared with the oscillating terms which seem to be nearly dissipated at $t = 2$.   From this first clue a dissection of $x_0(t)$ may be started by sketching on the graph an exponential curve which appears to fit the *long tail* part of $x_0(t)$.   This curve is extended, exponentially, back to $t = 0$, as indicated by the dashed line in Fig. 4.66.   The dashed line represents the first order exponential component of $x_0(t)$, and this exponential term has an initial value of about -0.36 and a time constant of about 1 sec. At this point it is possible to write down two of the terms in $x_0(t)$.

$$x_0(t) = 1 - 0.36\epsilon^{-t} + \cdots \qquad (4.152)$$

The 1 comes from the final value of $x_0(t)$.

Now, to find the remaining unknown terms in $x_0(t)$, refer again to Fig. 4.66. From this graph it appears that the oscillation is an exponentially damped sinusoid, the envelope of which converges to the dashed line. Therefore, the remaining terms in $x_0(t)$ can probably be closely approximated by a single, lightly damped, second order term. The period of the oscillation can be found approximately by measuring the peak-to-peak interval, which in this case is about 1 sec.* The oscillating frequency is approximately

$$\omega_0 = \frac{2\pi}{T} \cong 6.3 \text{ rad/sec} \qquad (4.153)$$

This determines the imaginary part of the complex poles of $X_0(s)$.

Next, the time constant of the exponential damping term can be estimated by sketching the envelope of the oscillations, as shown by the dotted lines in Fig. 4.66. The time constant appears to be about $\frac{1}{2}$ sec from this sketch, so the real part of the complex poles, $\zeta\omega_n$, is 2. ω_0 and $\zeta\omega_n$ are sufficient to spot the complex poles on the s plane. These are shown in Fig. 4.67, along with the two real poles which have been previously determined. We now know that the complete expression for $x_0(t)$ has the form

$$x_0(t) \cong 1 - 0.36\epsilon^{-t} + K_2\epsilon^{-2t} \sin (6.3t + \psi) \qquad (4.154)$$

where K_2 and ψ remain to be found.

K_2 and ψ will depend upon the location of the poles and zeros of $X_0(s)$. The poles of $X_0(s)$ have been determined by the dissection of $x_0(t)$—from the time constants, final values, and frequency of oscillation of each of its components. The zeros of $X_0(s)$, if any occur, can also be found by making certain observations upon the information already derived. That there *is* a zero in $X_0(s)$ can be deduced as follows: $x_0(t)$ may be thought of as the step response of a third order system, the poles of which are known. Our study of the third order

---

* Since the second order term is lightly damped, the peak-to-peak time is a good approximation to the period. If it were well damped, the period of oscillation should be measured at the points at which $x_0(t)$ crosses the dashed exponential curve.

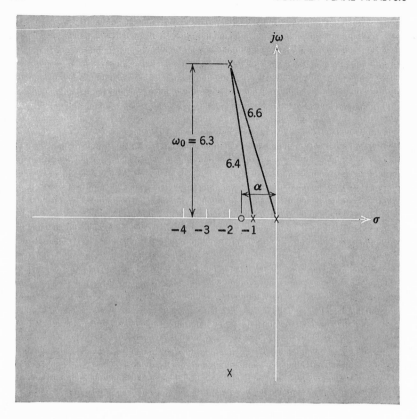

Fig. 4.67. Pole-zero map for $X_0(s)$.

system having no zeros showed that the step response of the system cannot exhibit an overshoot unless the real pole is farther from the $j\omega$ axis than are the complex poles. The damping ratio of the complex poles in this system is about 0.3. Using Fig. 4.58 we see that the response of this system, in which $\beta = 0.5$, would lie in between the $\beta = 0.4$ and 0.8 curves, giving a heavily damped response. Since the response of this system has a much higher amplitude oscillation ($x_0(t)$ nearly overshoots) than that indicated by Fig. 4.58, there must be a zero in $X_0(s)$ at a place which makes the coefficient of the real exponential term smaller than the coefficient of the damped sinusoidal term, namely, in the neighborhood of $s = -1$. We already have enough information to determine the number and locations of the zeros. From the fact that the derivative of $x_0(t)$ at $t = 0$ is zero we determined that there are at least three more poles than zeros in $X_0(s)$ (Eq. 4.151).   But since there are only four poles in $X_0(s)$ there can be only one zero.   Since only one zero occurs, it must lie on the real axis. It is known to be in the vicinity of the real pole at $s = -1$, and since we know that the residue of $X_0(s)$ at this pole is negative (-0.36), we can tell that the zero must lie to the left of $s = -1$.   If it were at the right of this point the residue at $s = -1$ would be positive.   If the zero in Fig. 4.67 is spotted at an undetermined distance, α, from the origin, α may be evaluated from a knowledge of the residues of $X_0(s)$ which are already known, as follows:

$$\text{Residue of } X_0(s) \text{ (at } s = 0) = 1 = \frac{K\alpha}{(1)(6.6)(6.6)}$$

$$\text{Residue of } X_0(s) \text{ (at } s = -1) = -0.36 = \frac{K(\alpha - 1)}{(-1)(6.4)(6.4)} \qquad (4.155)$$

These two equations, solved simultaneously, give the zero location, $\alpha \cong 1.5$.

Now, K_2 and ψ may be computed by a straightforward evaluation of $x_0(t)$ from $X_0(s)$.   We have, from the approximate measurements and estimates made on the graph of $x_0(t)$,

$$X_0(s) = \frac{(\frac{8.8}{3})(s + 1.5)}{s(s + 1)(s^2 + 4s + 44)} \qquad (4.156)$$

The exact inverse transformation of this function is

$$x_0(t) = 1 - 0.357\epsilon^{-t} + 0.692\epsilon^{-2t} \sin(6.32t + 248.4°) \qquad (4.157)$$

This checks closely with the estimates made in the dissection of the graph of $x_0(t)$.

As a final verification of this estimate for $x_0(t)$ we may plot Eq. 4.157 on top of the original curve in Fig. 4.65 to see how much the estimated $x_0(t)$ function is in error.   If the error is significant, a new estimate can be made by adjusting the time constants or frequency of oscillation by appropriate amounts, or by introducing additional poles and zeros into $X_0(s)$, if this is necessary.

The above example illustrates the way in which an engineer uses the simple relationships between the poles and zeros of $X_0(s)$, the magnitudes and signs of the residues of $X_0(s)$ at its poles, and the time constants and periods of oscillation of the terms in $x_0(t)$ to solve the problem of finding the poles and zeros of $X_0(s)$ from the transient response, $x_0(t)$.   This useful analytical procedure enables him to determine certain physical parameters in a system from test data when the physical parameters are related to the pole and zero locations in a known manner. Of course, in a high order system a larger number of significant poles and zeros may occur, and in this event the dissection procedure would require more extensive computations. However, in many practical situations the system under study can be approximated well enough by a first, second, or third order system having none, one, or two zeros, and the computation required to estimate $X_0(s)$ from $x_0(t)$ is no more complicated than that in this example.

Alternate method for regarding zeros

The role of the zeros in a given function of s is evident from the examples considered in this chapter. They do not determine the time constants and natural frequencies which appear in the time function— this is done by the poles—but they do have a significant effect on the magnitudes and signs of the residues; hence they influence the coefficients of the terms in the time function. The effect of the zeros of $X_0(s)$ on the time response $x_0(t)$ may always be determined simply by using the partial fraction expansion method to obtain the inverse transform of $X_0(s)$ and then inspecting the results.

An alternate method for assessing the influence of the zero sometimes provides more insight into the analysis problem. This method has already been introduced in the discussion of second order systems in this section, and it involves a slightly different point of view from that of the inverse transform by partial fraction expansion technique.

Assume that $X_0(s)$ has two zeros:

$$X_0(s) = \frac{K(s + a)(s + b)}{D(s)} = \frac{K[s^2 + (a + b)s + ab]}{D(s)} \quad (4.158)$$

$D(s)$ is a polynomial of the usual form. $X_0(s)$ may also be written in this form:

$$X_0(s) = \left[\frac{Kab}{D(s)}\right] + \left(\frac{a + b}{ab}\right) s \left[\frac{Kab}{D(s)}\right] + \frac{1}{ab} s^2 \left[\frac{Kab}{D(s)}\right] \quad (4.159)$$

Make the following definition:

$$F(s) = \frac{Kab}{D(s)}$$

so that $\qquad\qquad f(t) = \mathcal{L}^{-1}\left\{\frac{Kab}{D(s)}\right\} \qquad\qquad (4.160)$

$F(s)$ is a function which has no finite zeros. $f(t)$ is then relatively easy to compute, as no zeros need be included in the computation. Furthermore, if $D(s)$ is of the second or third order, the standard forms for $f(t)$ available in this book may be utilized (Figs. 3.35, 4.55 to 4.60). Notice that $f(t)$ has the same steady state value as $x_0(t)$.

Equations 4.159 and 4.160 indicate that $x_0(t)$ may be written as a sum of $f(t)$ and its first two derivatives, each weighted by a simple coefficient which depends upon the two zero values:

$$x_0(t) = f(t) + \left(\frac{a+b}{ab}\right)\frac{df}{dt} + \left(\frac{1}{ab}\right)\frac{d^2f}{dt^2} \qquad (4.161)$$

Once $f(t)$ is computed and sketched, the first and second derivatives may also be sketched (in a manner similar to that illustrated in Fig. 4.38) and the total response curve $x_0(t)$ formed. The zeros, then, may be considered to contribute first and second derivative terms to the basic function $f(t)$, which, except for its steady state value, is independent of the zero values. This idea may be extended to functions having three or more zeros. If m zeros occur in $x_0(t)$ there will be m terms involving derivatives in addition to the basic $f(t)$ term.

4.5 NONMINIMUM PHASE SYSTEMS

A system is said to be a nonminimum phase system if its transfer function has one or more poles or zeros in the right-half s plane. (Some authors restrict the definition of nonminimum phase systems to those whose transfer functions have one or more *zeros* in the right-half s plane.) All other systems are minimum phase systems. The following two transfer functions, for example, represent nonminimum phase systems.

$$H(s) = \frac{2(s-2)}{(s+1)(s^2+2s+4)}$$

$$G(s) = \frac{8(s+1)}{s^3+s^2+2s+8} \qquad (4.162)$$

$H(s)$ has a single zero in the right-half s plane at $s = 2$, and $G(s)$ has two complex poles in the right-half s plane at the points $s = \frac{1}{2} \pm j\,\sqrt{15}/2$.

The term *nonminimum phase* describes the phase shift characteristics of these systems when the input and output are steady state sinusoidal functions. This definition is discussed further in Chapter 8.

Consider first the nonminimum phase systems which have one or more poles in the right-half s plane. These are unstable systems. An unstable system is one whose output in response to an impulse (or step) input diverges, instead of converging toward a finite value. Figure 4.68 shows the impulse responses of four different systems. Figure

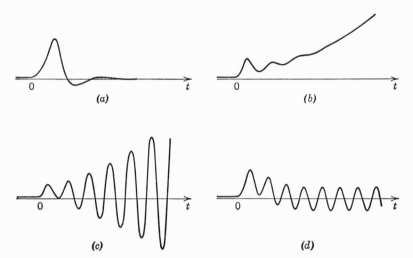

Fig. 4.68. Impulse responses of four systems: *a* Stable system; all poles in left half plane, *b* unstable system; real poles in right half plane, *c* unstable system; complex poles in right half plane, *d* neutrally stable system; complex poles on *jω* axis.

4.68*b* and *c* are examples of unstable systems. Figure 4.68*b* is easily recognized as one in which only real poles exist in the right-half plane, since the divergent term is apparently of the form $K_1\epsilon^{+at}$, where a is a positive real number. There is apparently a pair of complex poles in the left half s plane in system b, inasmuch as a positively damped term of the form $K\epsilon^{-bt}\sin(\omega_0 t + \psi)$, where b is positive, occurs in the response function. In system c a pair of complex poles must occur in the right-half plane to produce a negatively damped response term of the form $K\epsilon^{+ct}\sin(\omega_0 t + \psi)$, where c is positive. In system d, a neutrally stable system, an undamped term of the form $K\sin(\omega_0 t + \psi)$ in its response is due to a pair of pure imaginary poles lying exactly on the imaginary axis of the s plane.

An unstable automatic control system is ordinarily considered to be useless and may be extremely dangerous as well.* A system may become unstable when feedback is introduced unless the parameters of the system—amplifier gains, gear ratios, damping ratios, time constants, and so forth—are all adjusted to avert it. Much of the work which is done in the design of automatic feedback control systems is stability analysis—determining what must be done to the system

---

* If the useful life of the system is short compared to the period of the unstable oscillation, as sometimes occurs in a short term navigation problem, the instability may not be serious.

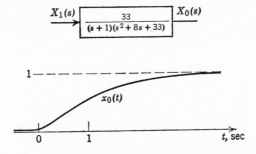

Fig. 4.69. Third order system with a troublesome pole.

parameters to keep all the poles of its transfer function out of the right-half s plane. A major part of the material remaining in this book is directed toward this problem.

In some systems the transfer function may have a pole or zero which affects the dynamic behavior of the system in an undesirable way. It is often possible to compensate for this deficiency by placing a second system in series with the original system, the poles and zeros of the compensating system being adjusted to *cancel* the troublesome poles or zeros of the original system. For example, in the third order system in Fig. 4.69 the real pole is located relatively close to the origin, and the step response is strongly influenced by this pole. If the step response is considered too slow, a series compensating element might be employed, as shown in Fig. 4.70. Y_1 is now the input to the com-

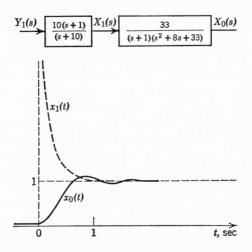

Fig. 4.70. Series compensator used with third order system to improve response.

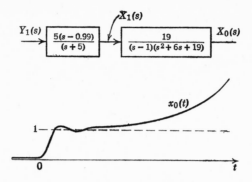

Fig. 4.71.   Attempt to series compensate a nonminimum phase system with an inexact compensator.

plete system.   The zero at $s = -1$ *cancels* the pole of the original
system, and the pole at $s = -10$ is far enough out in the s plane to
have only a minor influence on the step response, which now is seen
to be much faster than the step response of the original system.   A
disadvantage of this scheme is that the introduction of the element
containing a zero near the origin will cause the amplitude of rapidly
fluctuating signals to be very large at the input of the original system.
This may force the original system into its nonlinear state, thereby
rendering the analysis inexact.

If the troublesome pole in the original system lies in the right half
s plane, the series compensation scheme demonstrated above should
not be employed, since it is not possible to build a physical compensating element with a precise zero location, or, for that matter, to know
the exact location of the troublesome pole.   Consider, for example,
the compensation scheme illustrated in Fig. 4.71.   The pole in the
right half plane is not exactly canceled by the compensator zero at
$s = 0.99$.   Hence the step response will have a term $K_1\epsilon^{+t}$.   The
residue K_1 will be very small because of the nearness of the compensating zero to the troublesome pole, but this term grows with time and
eventually dominates the response, as shown in Fig. 4.71.*

The series compensation scheme in which troublesome poles or zeros
of the fixed element are canceled is quite widely used in minimum phase
systems.   The difficulty pointed out in Fig. 4.71 will not arise in these
systems, since the residues at the nearly canceled poles will be small.
Furthermore, since the poles are in the left-half s plane, the transient
terms in the time response corresponding to these poles will eventually
die out.

---

* Feedback schemes may be used to stabilize systems which have poles in the
right-half s plane.   Such a scheme is discussed in Chapter 7.

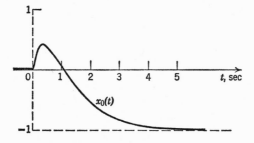

$$x_1(t) = u(t)$$
$$x_0(t) = -1 + 4\epsilon^{-t} - 3\epsilon^{-2t}$$

Fig. 4.72.   Step response of nonminimum phase system.

Nonminimum phase systems which have only zeros in the right-half s plane are stable.   They present special problems in system stability when they are used in feedback systems; these problems are considered in later chapters.   Here only one property of this type of system is pointed out.   Since the zeros of a system affect only the magnitudes and signs of the residues of the response expression, any special effect which zeros in the right half s plane exhibit can be traced to the residues.   If a stable system has an odd number of zeros in the right-half s plane, the step response will have a negative steady state value. Hence, step responses of the type shown in Fig. 4.72 are possible; the output starts out in a positive direction but settles eventually at a negative value.

Nonminimum phase systems with zeros in the right-half s plane can be formed physically by combinations of simpler subsystems.   The system shown in Fig. 4.72, for example, would result if two first order systems were connected in the manner described by Fig. 4.73.   Here

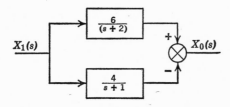

Fig. 4.73.   Formation of nonminimum phase system from two minimum phase systems.

the overall system transfer function is derived by writing the equation of the system as indicated by the summation point at the output.

$$X_0(s) = X_1(s)\left(\frac{6}{s+2}\right) - X_1(s)\left(\frac{4}{s+1}\right) \qquad (4.163)$$

4.6 COMPLEX FREQUENCY PLANE

In computing the dynamic response of linear systems we have essentially solved sets of linear differential equations by a transformation method.   The differential equations are transformed by means of the Laplace transform from the time domain—that is, from functions involving t as the independent variable—to algebraic equations in which s is the independent variable.

Let us look at an interesting characteristic of this variable s. s is first introduced in the definition of the Laplace transformation of $f(t)$.

$$\mathcal{L}\{f(t)\} = F(s) = \int_0^\infty \epsilon^{-st} f(t)\, dt \qquad (4.164)$$

It can be shown that the exponent $(-st)$ in this expression must be dimensionless.*   Thus, since t is time expressed in seconds, s must have the dimensions of inverse time, expressed in $(\text{seconds})^{-1}$.   Instead of using the word *inverse time* for s a new word, *frequency*, has been used to designate s.   Therefore, $F(s)$ is the frequency function corresponding to the time function $f(t)$, the exact correspondence being defined by Eq. 4.164.   It has been seen that we can represent $F(s)$ graphically by plotting its poles and zeros, and since these poles and zeros may be complex, a complex plane—the s plane—must be used.   Therefore, the s plane can very logically be called the *complex frequency plane*, and the poles and zeros of $F(s)$ can be called *critical frequencies* of $F(s)$, since these values of s do represent *critical* values for $F(s)$, namely, the values for which $F(s)$ is either zero or infinite.

Now, the word *frequency* has been used by mathematicians and engineers for many decades to describe one of the salient properties of a very special class of time functions—those which are periodic.   In this traditional use of the term the *frequency* of a periodic time function is taken to be the inverse of the period of the function.   We have occasion in later chapters of this book to study the response of linear systems to periodic (sinusoidal) driving functions, and at that time it will be seen that the sinusoidal time functions transform into s func-

---

* $\epsilon^x = 1 + x + x^2/2! + x^3/3! + \cdots$ Since each of the terms in this series must have the same dimensions, x must be dimensionless.

tions which have poles along the imaginary axis of the s plane. Since sinusoidal time functions are very easily generated by real physical machinery, the imaginary axis of the s plane is sometimes known as the *real frequency* axis. (Actually, it is possible to generate, in real physical equipment, all the time functions with which we are concerned here—damped sinusoids, steps, ramps, first order exponentials, etc.—so that all points in the s plane, not just the imaginary axis, can be associated with time functions generated by real physical systems.)

4.7 SUMMARY

The analytical techniques which are essential to the study of linear control systems have been developed in these first four chapters. The concept of the transfer function, derived from the transformed differential equations, lies at the focal point of this analysis. The major portion of the analysis is based upon the convenient, and by this time familiar, relationship

$$X_0(s) = [G(s)] \times [X_1(s)] \qquad (4.165)$$

Control system analysis is concerned with determining the relationship between the physical properties of the system and its dynamic behavior, $x_0(t)$. The pole-zero-residue type of analysis developed here has emerged over the past two decades as the most convenient method for determining this relationship in engineering problems. Several examples using practical physical systems have been considered in this chapter to illustrate the manner in which this analysis technique is applied in practice. The next three chapters are devoted to applying these techniques to the analysis of feedback control systems. This amounts, essentially, to determining the transfer function of an entire feedback system from the transfer functions of the individual components in the system. No new analytical concepts are used in the next three chapters except for Routh's stability rule and the root locus method, both of which are simple techniques for handling the stability problem in feedback systems.

In Chapters 8 and 9 the real frequency response or sinusoidal method for linear system analysis is introduced and applied to feedback systems. This method is seen to be just a special form of the pole-zero-residue technique already developed, but it is a particularly useful method in practice.

It is again pointed out that this book is intended to be an *introduction* to automatic control system analysis. Although all the analytical tools necessary for the determination of linear system response with transient input signals have already been presented, the reader is reminded that several important areas of analysis are not to be covered in this book. Two of these areas, nonlinear analysis and statistical analysis, are introduced briefly in Chapter 10, but further study of these and other areas is required if the reader is to pursue a career in control system engineering.

REFERENCES

1. Truxal, *Control System Synthesis*, McGraw-Hill, 1955.
2. Blackburn, Reethof, and Shearer, *Fluid Power Control*, Wiley, 1960.
3. Gibson, and Tuteur, *Control System Components*, McGraw-Hill, 1958.
4. Gardner and Barnes, *Transients in Linear Systems*, Wiley, 1942.
5. Mulligan, "The Effect of Pole and Zero Locations on the Transient Response of Linear Dynamic Systems," *Proc. IRE*, Vol. 37, May 1949.

5 Automatic Feedback Control

5.1 THE CONTROL ENGINEERING PROBLEM

An automatic control system may employ components which operate on electrical, mechanical, chemical, thermodynamic, aerodynamic,
nuclear, or optical principles. Systems such as voltage regulators,
servomechanisms, automatic petroleum refineries, temperature regu-
lated furnaces, guided missiles, atomic reactors, and photo-electric
sorting machines are all well known examples of control systems in
modern industry.

Regardless of the particular physical form which a control system
may have, the function for which it is designed—the function of *control*—can be described by the block diagram in Fig. 5.1. If the system

Fig. 5.1. Illustrating the function of a control
system.

is a furnace temperature control, for example, the input would be the
desired temperature of the furnace; the output, or controlled variable,
would be the actual temperature of the furnace; and the disturbances
might be unpredictable draughts or other variable factors affecting the
heat transfer properties of the furnace. Notice that the energy con-
sumed in heating the furnace or in operating the controls is not considered to be an *input* to the system. It is certainly both an important
part of the operation of the system and a physical quantity which goes
into the system, but from the standpoint of the control function it is
incidental. Therefore, it is not included in Fig. 5.1.

Several distinguishing features are found in most control systems aside from the input-output, or cause-effect, relationship which usually exists. The first of these is power amplification. Usually the output quantity is at a much higher power level than the input quantity. In the furnace control system, for example, the input might be an electrical signal which delivers only a small fraction of a watt to the system, while the system might have to consume many kilowatts in order to keep the output (temperature) at the desired level. Therefore, a source of energy must be associated with the system.

Often in a control system the controlled mechanism is located at a distance from the input point. In the furnace control system the desired temperature might be set on a dial located half a mile from the furnace. Whenever two or more parts of the system are separated, *communication*, or a signal transmission path, must exist in the system. Because of the ease with which electrical signals can be transmitted over long distances most control systems employ some electrical equipment. Air, and to a lesser extent, hydraulic lines are also used for signal transmission.

Most control systems must operate in the presence of disturbances, as indicated in Fig. 5.1. In our furnace example a disturbance might consist of a large quantity of cold material suddenly dumped into the furnace, or an unexpected drop in the gas line pressure (assuming a gas fired furnace). Disturbances which are known or predictable can usually be compensated for in the design of the system; only unpredictable disturbances are here designated as such. One measure of performance of a control system is the reflection in the output quantity of the application of a disturbance.

Some writers distinguish *regulator* type control systems from *follower* type systems. The essential difference between these two classes of control systems is this: Usually the input to a *regulator* system is set at a fixed value for long periods of time, while the input of a *follower* system fluctuates with time. A furnace controller designed to maintain a constant output temperature would be a regulator, while a guided missile, receiving guidance instructions to direct it toward a moving target, is an example of a follower system.

The control engineering problem is to specify, design, or synthesize the mechanisms required to realize a given relationship between the input signal and the output variable. This *given relationship* is usually a set of performance specifications which define, in the usual engineering fashion, the limitations under which the system must operate. Some typical performance specifications are discussed in Section 5.4.

5.2 FEEDBACK AND NONFEEDBACK CONTROL SYSTEMS

The block diagram in Fig. 5.1 simply indicates that the purpose of the control system is to maintain a certain functional relationship between an input signal and an output variable. It says nothing about the internal details of the system. Most control systems can be classified as either feedback systems or nonfeedback systems, depending upon the internal details of the block in Fig. 5.1—that is, depending upon the way in which they are designed to accomplish the control task. In order to make this dichotomy clear, let us consider three simple control problems, showing in each case the way in which the system would operate as a nonfeedback (or *open-loop*) system and also as a feedback (or *closed-loop*) system.

Example 1. *Concrete mixer.* Assume that the rotational speed of the tub on a concrete mixer is to be controlled by means of a rheostat connected in the field circuit of the electric motor which drives the tub. Assume that the speed should be maintained constant at 30 rpm. The rheostat could be calibrated by setting it at various points and measuring the tub speed corresponding to each point on the rheostat dial. A special mark would be placed at the 30 rpm point to indicate that this is the desired speed. The block diagram in Fig. 5.2 represents the system as described. The input is θ_R, the rheostat dial setting, and the output is ω_T, the tub speed. This is an example of a nonfeedback, or open-loop, system as it is shown here. The significance of these terms will soon be apparent.

Now, assume that this calibrated rheostat control system is placed in service so that the quality of the finished concrete depends largely upon the speed of the tub during mixing. Unfortunately, many factors in addition to the rheostat setting influence the speed of the tub. Variations in the line voltage, lubrication of gears and bearings, ambient temperature, machine orientation, the gross weight of all the sand, gravel, water, and cement in the tub are some of these factors. These factors are practically unpredictable in a construction job environment, and they cause the rheostat calibration to be in error by an unpredictable amount. The net effect of this unreliable calibration is that the control system fails in its assigned task of keeping the speed constant, and this produces poor quality concrete.

An improvement in this control system can be made if the following viewpoint is adopted. Instead of attempting to calibrate the rheostat, leave it entirely unmarked and find its proper setting by making observations on the

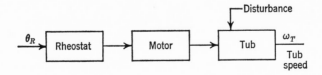

Fig. 5.2. Concrete mixer controlled by rheostat (nonfeedback).

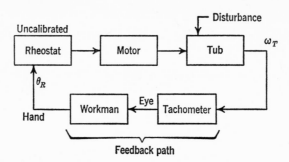

Fig. 5.3. Concrete mixer controlled by workman observing tachometer (feedback).

actual tub speed while the machine is in service. This might be accomplished by installing an accurate tachometer on the tub and stationing a workman at the machine to keep his eye on the tachometer and his hand on the rheostat. In this way he can make compensating adjustments of the rheostat whenever the tub speed deviates from its prescribed 30 rpm because of line voltage variation or other unpredictable disturbances. This refinement on the control system is described by the block diagram in Fig. 5.3. Notice that a *closed loop* of sequentially interdependent agents is now at work in the system. The hand of the workman on the rheostat influences the speed of the tub, and the speed of the tub in turn will influence the hand on the rheostat, if the workman is alert. Now the rheostat need not be calibrated at all; the workman simply has to know in which direction to move it to increase or decrease the tub speed. Of course, the range over which the rheostat may be varied must be large enough to accomodate all the disturbances which will enter the system, or the performance specifications cannot possibly be met.

When the *closed loop* mode of control is incorporated the accuracy of the system is made dependent upon the calibration of the tachometer (and upon the skill and alertness of the workman) rather than upon the calibration of the rheostat. The tachometer can easily be constructed to give highly accurate and dependable speed data in the presence of any probable disturbance, so, although the system still depends upon a calibration, the calibration is unaffected by those factors which caused trouble in the *open loop* system. The term *feedback* is often used to describe the closed loop system because the tachometer-workman combination is a connecting link which observes the output of the system ω_T and provides corrective action at the input end.

The system as it is shown in Fig. 5.3 is a *manual* feedback system, in that it employs a human operator as a vital element in the control loop. It is easy to visualize the way in which the task of the workman in this system could be accomplished by a simple voltage comparison circuit and power amplifier. If the workman were to be so replaced the system would become an *automatic* feedback control system.

Example 2. Home heating system. Consider the open-loop household furnace control system shown diagrammatically in Fig. 5.4. Here the cyclic timer is a device which turns the fuel valve on for T_{on} minutes, then turns it

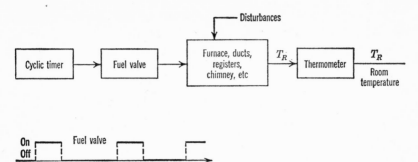

Fig. 5.4.   Home heating system, open loop.

off for T_{off} minutes, repeating this cycle continuously.   The system must be calibrated by determining T_{on} and T_{off} so that the room temperature is maintained at a comfortable level, say 72°F.   Assume that such a calibration is made on an *average* winter day and that it is found that an *on* time of 6 minutes, followed by an *off* time of 15 minutes, cyclically repeated, maintains the room temperature at or near the desired 72°F.   This calibration will be satisfactory only for the type of weather conditions which prevail on the day the calibration is made.   It does not take into account the fluctuation of weather conditions over very wide ranges of temperature, humidity, and wind velocity during the winter months.   Therefore, any calibration of the cyclic timer device in this system will be out of date in a very short time.   This is another example of an open loop system whose calibration is easily upset by unpredictable disturbances (fluctuating weather conditions).

As in the cement mixer example, the performance of the heating system may be vastly improved by the institution of a feedback link from the room temperature indicating device to the fuel valve, as shown in Fig. 5.5.   Here the thermometer has been replaced by a thermostat.   This is a device which measures not only the room temperature but also the difference between the

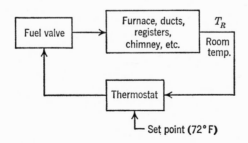

Fig. 5.5.   Home heating system, closed loop.

room temperature and the desired temperature (set point), and which opens
the fuel valve whenever the room is too cold or closes it when the room is
too hot.

The advantages of the closed loop system here over the open loop system
are obvious. In the open loop system the fuel valve timing cycle is constant,
and the weather disturbances cause uncomfortable fluctuations in the room
temperature. The furnace is insensitive to these fluctuations. When the
feedback system is employed the weather disturbances cause fluctuations in
the fuel valve *on* and *off* periods, the furnace responds to these fluctuations,
and the room temperature remains at a comfortable level. It must be
assumed that the furnace has sufficient thermal capacity to heat the house
under the weather conditions which will prevail. Notice that here, as in the
concrete mixer problem, dependence upon calibration has not been eliminated
by the installation of a feedback loop. Instead, the calibration has been
shifted to a part of the system (the thermostat) whose calibration is very
dependable and is unaffected by disturbances which enter the system.

Example 3. Positional servomechanism. Consider the mechanism shown
in Fig. 5.6. Assume that the purpose of this system is to point the searchlight in a given direction. In this positional control system the controlled
quantity is the angular position of the searchlight platform θ_s. If the system
were operated in an open-loop fashion the calibration would have to be made
in the following way. In order to move the table through a given angle,
close switch S, leave it closed for T seconds, and reopen it. During the
closure time the motor would normally accelerate the table until the instant
the switch was opened, after which the table would coast to a stop. The total
distance traveled versus the closure time T must be calibrated. It is obvious
as in the two previous examples, that such a calibration would be very unre-

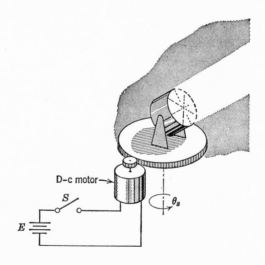

Fig. 5.6. Searchlight control system, open loop.

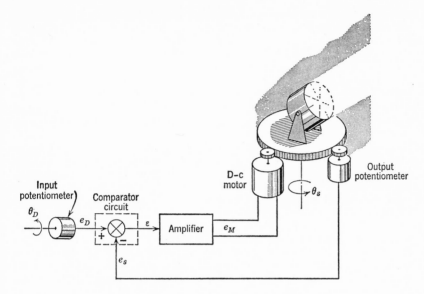

Fig. 5.7. Automatic feedback control on searchlight system.

liable, in this case because of unpredictable torque disturbances on the table—wind loading, table orientation, bearing and gear friction—and fluctuations in the line voltage E.

A manual feedback loop could be used here. An operator would watch the motion of the table and actuate the switch accordingly. Experience has shown, however, that such a man-machine combination has serious drawbacks as a control system because under these circumstances neither the man or the machine is able to make the best use of its inherent characteristics.

A much better automatic system is possible. An automatic feedback loop could be installed by the addition of several simple pieces of equipment, as shown in Fig. 5.7. The motor is now driven by a power amplifier whose output voltage e_M is proportional to its input voltage ε. The voltage ε is in turn derived as follows. A potentiometer is mounted on the searchlight table in such a way that its voltage e_s is directly proportional to the system output θ_s. A second potentiometer, similar to that mounted on the table, is located at a point convenient to the person (or other agent) who is to direct the searchlight. The shaft position of this potentiometer θ_D is proportional to the *desired* searchlight position; hence, θ_D is the input to the control system. e_D is the voltage of the input potentiometer which is fed, along with the output voltage e_s, to a comparator circuit which takes the algebraic difference between the two voltages and produces the *error voltage* ε. Here

$$\varepsilon = e_D - e_s \tag{5.1}$$

This says that the error is the difference between the desired output and the actual output. Of course, e_D and e_s are not themselves the desired and actual outputs but are only proportional to the real desired and actual outputs θ_D

and θ_s. The accuracy of the error voltage is dependent upon the calibration of the input and output potentiometers, but, again, these calibrations can be made independent of the disturbances in the system. Now, if θ_D is set at the desired position, the error-sensing circuit and power amplifier will cause the motor to drive the table until it is located exactly where it should be—that is, until the error is zero. If the input is not held fixed but is moved from time to time in order to make the searchlight sweep or illuminate different points of the sky, the error circuit will tend to cause the output to follow the motion of the input shaft. A more detailed analysis of such motion is made in the following chapters of this book.

A system of this type is called a servomechanism (slave-machine), and because the controlled quantity here is the angular *position* of the searchlight table this is an example of a *positional* servomechanism. The closed loop home-heating system might be called a *temperature* servomechanism, since the controlled variable there is the room temperature. Some writers prefer to call the home-heating system a temperature *regulator*, however, because the input to such a system is usually a fixed set point rather than a time variable quantity. Many writers prefer to restrict the name *servomechanism* to those automatic control systems whose controlled quantity is a mechanical position. This is an arbitrary restriction, since automatic machines are used to control velocity, acceleration, force, voltage, and a variety of other physical quantities.

The three examples given above have served (a) to define the difference between open-loop and closed-loop control systems, (b) to show that the principal reason for using feedback is to eliminate (or at least to minimize) the undesirable effects of the disturbances upon the output, and (c) to demonstrate that this is done by placing the burden of calibration upon a part of the system which can remain calibrated when disturbances enter the system.

If the calibration of an open-loop system is not changed appreciably by disturbances, a feedback loop is unnecessary. An example of such a system is an automatic toaster. Here the heating element is turned on for a fixed period of time. The *on* time can be varied over a certain range to provide darker or lighter toast. The setting which produces a nicely browned, thick slice of whole wheat toast might burn an extremely thin piece of white bread, but usually the differences in the various kinds and slices of bread cause only slight variations in the finished toast. In any case the dark-light setting may be altered to produce an *acceptable* piece of toast. An elaborate feedback scheme designed to produce an *ideal* slice of toast regardless of the size or density of the bread would be considered by most people to be an over-refinement.

Recent advances in the theory of automatic control systems have produced systems which cannot be described as purely open loop or purely closed loop because these systems operate in a combination of both these modes. Thus, strictly speaking, all control systems cannot be divided into these two types. Here the division was made primarily to demonstrate the effectiveness of feedback in control systems. The study of these newer, more complex systems is a logical extension of the material in this volume.

Although feedback can improve the accuracy and reliability of control systems by rendering the output of the system insensitive to disturbances, it also brings certain disadvantages and problems to the system in which it is used. The establishment of a feedback path in which a signal is fed from the output back to the input creates a problem in system stability. Careful measures must be taken in the design of the system to keep the feedback path from actually degrading the performance of the system. It is necessary to develop analytical techniques for determining stability and other dynamic properties of closed-loop systems. Much of the remainder of this book is directed toward this end.

Automatic control technology has been developing over a long period of time, but during the past century, and especially during the past twenty-five years, its development has been very rapid. This technology has been developed by engineers, physicists, and mathematicians who have worked together to solve many engineering problems in connection with automatic control systems and communication systems.

In recent years many people in the biological and social sciences have become increasingly interested in the theory of automatic feedback machines, because the cause and effect behavior which is present in control systems also seems to be embodied in many biological and social systems. It is certainly true that many biological and social systems employ feedback to obtain control. For example, when a person reaches for an object, the position of the hand with respect to the object is registered in the brain through nervous impulses sent from the eyes and from the arm muscles. The brain in turn generates the nervous signals which control the motion of the arm through muscle action, and so the feedback loop is closed.

Broadly speaking, a democratic form of government whose governing agents derive their authority from the consent of the governed is a social system whose very foundation reflects the feedback principle.

However, even though these natural and social systems have exhibited some of the same properties of manmade feedback systems, an exact analysis of them has been impossible. The interrelationships between the components of such systems are extremely numerous and complex and are, therefore, difficult to determine. Many biological control systems are capable of feats which are impossible to achieve in manmade systems employing the most advanced feedback techniques. It must be concluded that some yet undiscovered principles of automatic control may in the future be adapted to the needs of man. Perhaps these principles will be brought to light as scientists learn to understand in greater detail how biological control systems work. At the present time feedback is the most common property of automatic control systems, and for now, at least, we will have to be content to work at understanding it.

5.3 BLOCK DIAGRAMS FOR FEEDBACK CONTROL SYSTEMS

A block diagram conveniently describes the interrelationships which exist between the various parts of a control system. It is desirable to establish a standard form for such a diagram so that the various properties of the system which are important from the standpoint of automatic control will be apparent whether the system elements are electrical, mechanical, chemical, or thermal. If a common nomenclature for control system block diagrams can be agreed upon, engineering work on complex systems will be facilitated. One such standard form has been proposed by a joint committee of the American Institute of Electrical Engineers and the American Standards Association. This form appears in Fig. 5.8, and it, or simplifications of it, are used through the remainder of this book.

Most control systems consist of components or subsystems whose dynamic behavior can be described by an input-output relationship and which are connected in chains and loops, the output of one component being the input of another. Such a system is easily described by a block diagram. If the system is linear a transfer function can be written for each block which has a single input and a single output. Most systems can be represented by diagrams made up of blocks of this type.

A nonlinear component in a control system cannot be described by a transfer function. If the nonlinear element is of a certain class, and if the remainder of the system is linear, with special characteristics, a *describing function*—somewhat similar to a transfer function—may be used in the nonlinear block. A definition of the *describing function* is given in Chapter 10. In some situations the describing function is not applicable; the dynamic analysis of the system must then be performed using the techniques for solving nonlinear differential equations. Many such techniques exist, each one being restricted in its use to a small class of nonlinear equations.

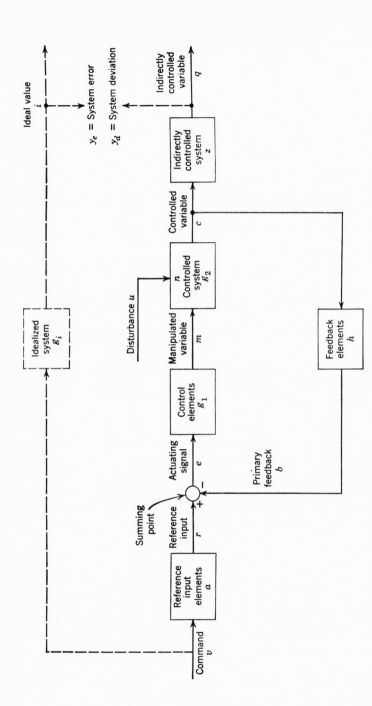

Fig. 5.8. Standard form for feedback system block diagram as proposed by A.I.E.E. and A.S.A. (1951).

179

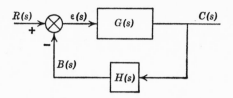

Fig. 5.9. Simplified block diagram of a feedback system.

Much of the discussion in the next four chapters centers around simple feedback systems so that simple block diagrams may be used. Here, and in Chapter 6, the idealized system (Fig. 5.8) is assumed to have a transfer function of unity, and because only linear systems are considered, the blocks in the forward path of the system may be lumped into a single block.   If the disturbances are ignored, a simplified block diagram (Fig. 5.9) may be used.   Here $G(s)$ is the transfer function of the forward path, and $H(s)$ is the transfer function of the feedback path.   From the block diagram in Fig. 5.9 the following three equations may be written.

$$C(s) = G(s)\varepsilon(s)$$

$$B(s) = H(s)C(s)$$

$$\varepsilon(s) = R(s) - B(s) \tag{5.2}$$

Here $C(s)$ is the Laplace transform of the controlled variable (or output) $c(t)$, $B(s)$ is the Laplace transform of the primary feedback $b(t)$, $\varepsilon(s)$ is the Laplace transform of the actuating signal $\varepsilon(t)$, and $R(s)$ is the Laplace transform of the reference input $r(t)$.   A single transfer function for the whole system may be obtained and the diagram reduced to a single block by combining the three equations in Eq. 5.2 in order to eliminate $B(s)$ and $\varepsilon(s)$.

$$W(s) = \frac{C(s)}{R(s)} = \frac{G(s)}{1 + G(s)H(s)} \tag{5.3}$$

$W(s)$ is called the system transfer function.   Equation 5.3 is fundamental to the study of control systems, because it relates the overall system characteristics (transfer function) to the characteristics of the forward and feedback path elements.   The relationship between the individual components of the system and the overall system performance is important in linear feedback control system design.   In the

Fig. 5.10. System transfer function, W(s), obtained from Fig. 5.9.

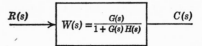

$R(s) \rightarrow \boxed{W(s) = \dfrac{G(s)}{1 + G(s)H(s)}} \rightarrow C(s)$

next few chapters analytical techniques useful in determining this relationship are developed.

Equation 5.3 may be written in more detail if $G(s)$ and $H(s)$ are replaced by these expressions:

$$G(s) = \frac{N_1(s)}{D_1(s)} \qquad H(s) = \frac{N_2(s)}{D_2(s)} \tag{5.4}$$

The Ns and Ds are polynomials in s. This substitution is made here because (as we have seen in Chapters 3 and 4) transfer functions are always written as the ratio of two polynomials. Equation 5.3 then becomes

$$W(s) = \frac{C(s)}{R(s)} = \frac{N_1(s)D_2(s)}{N_1(s)N_2(s) + D_1(s)D_2(s)} \tag{5.5}$$

A special case of the single loop feedback system shown in Fig. 5.9 occurs if $H(s)$ is unity—that is, if $D_2(s) = N_2(s)$. This is called a unity feedback system; the block diagram may be drawn as shown in Fig. 5.11. Now the actuating signal is the system error, since for our present purposes we have considered the transfer function of the ideal system to be unity. The system transfer function reduces to

$$W(s) = \frac{G(s)}{1 + G(s)} = \frac{N_1(s)}{N_1(s) + D_1(s)} \tag{5.6}$$

for the unity feedback case. It is sometimes useful to derive the transfer function relating the system error to the input; for the unity feedback system this transfer function is

$$\frac{\varepsilon(s)}{R(s)} = \frac{1}{1 + G(s)} = \frac{D_1(s)}{N_1(s) + D_1(s)} \tag{5.7}$$

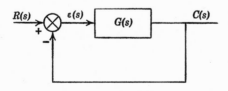

Fig. 5.11. Unity feedback system.

5.4 CONTROL SYSTEM PERFORMANCE

The quality of a control system may be judged by many standards. One of the first tasks of the control systems engineer in the design of a control system is to establish the performance criteria which will satisfy the design specifications for the system. The performance criterion which always exists is the accuracy of the system, since the purpose of a control system is to cause the output quantity to follow a pattern described by the input signal.

Accuracy may be defined in several ways. The *static accuracy* of the system is the system error occurring when all time derivatives of that error are zero—that is, when the system is at rest. In a perfect system the static error is zero, but because of various imperfections which cannot be eliminated from the system components this is never quite achieved in a real system. Therefore, certain tolerances on the static accuracy must be established.

Several different expressions of *dynamic accuracy* are used in modern system design. All of these are based upon the error as a function of time. When such an expression is formulated the input and disturbances which produce the error must be specified. If a unit step input is specified, for example, the performance criteria might be the maximum instantaneous value of the error following the application of the step. Another criterion might be the time required for the error to decrease to a specified value. If the error is oscillatory a specification might be placed upon the maximum overshoot of the error or upon the frequency of the oscillations.

In recent years several integral forms of the *system error* have been developed and used as measures of system accuracy. Three of these are (a) the time integral—from time 0 to time ∞—of the system error, (b) the time integral of the absolute value of the error, and (c) the time integral of the square of the system error. These integral forms are useful because each provides a single quantity which represents the accuracy of the system, this quantity being a function of the variable parameters which the designer is free to adjust.

If the input signal is a random function of time, the mean square value of the system error is often used as a measure of system accuracy. This is discussed briefly in Chapter 10.

Error response to applied disturbances is also used as a measure of accuracy. In a servomechanism, for example, a load torque applied to the output shaft will cause an error. The smaller the error for a given torque the better the system.

In addition to accuracy other important factors must be considered in control system design.   An increase in accuracy is usually accompanied by the expenditure of money or an increase in weight or size, and all systems have limitations on these three commodities.   In all engineering problems it is necessary to know the cost of performance (accuracy) in terms of size, weight, and money and then to decide whether the design is feasible under the specifications for the system.

Sometimes the performance of a system is measured in terms of nonphysical quantities.   For example, a vital measure of performance of an automatically controlled petroleum refinery is the dollar profit on the operation which is realized by the owners.

Another nonphysical measure of performance is the *reliability* of the system.   All systems are subject to breakdown due to failure of the components.   In many systems a breakdown is an extremely serious matter, so that a concerted effort must be made in the design stage to minimize the probability of a breakdown in a given period of time.

In this book we are concerned only with simple forms of accuracy requirements in control systems, such as the overshoot or number of oscillations of the error or the output in response to step inputs and disturbances.   More complex forms of accuracy specifications and the nonphysical figures of merit are left for study beyond this volume.

5.5   CONTROL SYSTEM COMPONENTS

Control system design consists very broadly of two steps.   The first is to determine the manner in which the blocks in the block diagram may best be arranged and to determine the function of each block. The second step is to specify the hardware necessary to perform the functions of the individual blocks.   The designer must consider these two phases to be interdependent processes if he is to produce an effective design.   If, in specifying the arrangement and function of the blocks, the system designer fails to consider the capabilities of the components which will be used in the actual system, he will produce a suboptimum system.

For example, a system analysis might show that the product of amplifier gain and gear reduction ratio should be 100.   The designer must decide how much of the product is to be in amplifier gain and how much in gear ratio.   An amplifier gain of 5000 would require a gear ratio of 0.02, while a gain of 15000 would require a ratio of 0.0067. Because of speed requirements, friction levels, size, weight, and cost considerations the gear ratio must be chosen judiciously; similarly, noise levels and other practical considerations necessitate care in the selection of the amplifier gain.   Clearly, the system designer must understand some of the basic problems of the component designer if he is to produce an effective, workable design.

Unfortunately, the limited size of this volume makes a detailed treatment of the constructional features of control system hardware impossible here. Only the salient physical features of networks, motors, gear trains, hydraulic valves and gyroscopes have been presented to indicate the way in which transfer functions for these devices are derived from their physical characteristics. Several good books devoted exclusively to the description of the constructional features of control system hardware are readily available.

REFERENCES

1. *Automatic Control*, Simon and Schuster, 1955.
2. Truxal, *Control System Synthesis*, McGraw-Hill, 1955.
3. Graybeal, "Block Diagram Network Transformation," *Electrical Engineering*, Vol. 70, November 1951.
4. Mason, "Feedback Theory—Further Properties of Signal Flow Graphs," *Proc. IRE*, Vol. 44, July 1956.
5. Schultz and Rideout, "Control System Performance Measures: Past, Present, and Future," *IRE Trans. on Automatic Control*, Vol. AC-6, No. 1, February 1961.
6. Gibson and Tuteur, *Control System Components*, McGraw-Hill, 1958.
7. Ahrendt, *Servomechanism Practice*, McGraw-Hill, 1954.
8. Pitman, *Inertial Guidance*, Wiley, 1962.

6 Stability Analysis in the Complex Frequency Plane

6.1 THE STABILITY PROBLEM IN FEEDBACK SYSTEMS

In this chapter we begin the study of one of the problems which feedback brings to virtually all systems to which it is introduced, namely, the stability problem. A careful analysis of stability must be made during the design of a feedback system, and the physical properties of the system components must be chosen accordingly to prevent the system from becoming unstable once it is placed in service, since an unstable system is not only useless but may also be dangerous.

A system is stable if, in response to an impulse input applied when the system is at rest, the output approaches zero as time increases. Two such stable impulse responses are drawn in Fig. 6.1. In an unstable linear system the impulse response would have one of the forms shown in Fig. 6.2. Of these forms, a and b are divergent instabilities and unquestionably qualify as unstable responses, while c and d are marginal cases, since $c(t)$ does not grow indefinitely. Some authors would not class these latter as being unstable. It will soon be clear that a and b occur when poles of the transfer function exist in the right-half s plane, and c and d occur only if poles exist on the $j\omega$ axis of

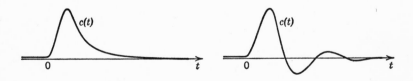

Fig. 6.1.   Impulse responses of stable linear systems.

185

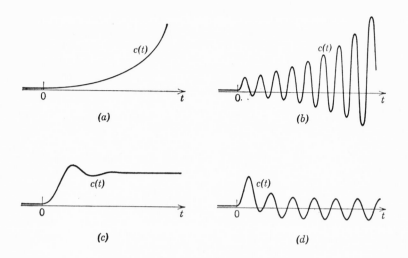

Fig. 6.2.   Impulse responses of unstable linear systems.

the s plane.   (c occurs for a single pole at the origin.) c and d may therefore be termed either unstable or marginally stable.

Now, it is apparent from Fig. 6.2 that if $c(t)$ is any physical quantity such as position, velocity, force, voltage, temperature, etc., that quantity in an unstable system (a or b) will reach very large magnitudes as time goes by.   In fact, these responses would soon reach magnitudes which are physically impossible.   In other words, no real physical system can respond in an *ever-increasing* manner as indicated here. The response of an actual system would soon reach a level beyond which it could not travel, and it would either remain at that level or oscillate back and forth between two limiting levels.   The unstable motions of real systems therefore fall into the realm of nonlinear mechanics.   The exact analysis of nonlinear systems is beyond the scope of this book, although some discussion of this important subject is presented in Chapter 10.

Our linear stability analysis is not sufficiently comprehensive to allow us to compute the exact response of real (nonlinear) systems which are unstable; however, this detracts little from the usefulness of linear stability analysis.   The importance of linear stability analysis is in predicting whether unstable motions will occur and in showing how to avoid such motions, rather than in computing the exact form of such motions when they do occur.   Thus, the stability analysis developed in this chapter is applicable to real systems which are linear (or approximately so) for small changes in the physical variables. Fortunately, many important systems are of this class. However, some important systems are not, and the reader must be aware that the material in this chapter is consequently limited in its application to engineering problems.

   Unstable motions which lead to divergent responses such as those in Fig. 6.2a and b are caused by unfortunate timing between the driving force at the output member and the resulting signal which comes around the feedback loop and develops, through power amplifiers, the driving force itself.   In case a the feedback signal reinforces the driving force, causing it to increase continuously in one direction. The resultant motion at $c(t)$ causes further increase in the actuating force. In case b the feedback loop causes a reversal in the driving force, but since the reversal comes too late and is too strong to be a stabilizing influence, it drives the output faster and farther from the equilibrium point.   In this chapter are developed the analytical procedures which predict whether such unfortunate buildups in driving force will occur in a given control system.

6.2 DETERMINATION OF STABILITY

   It is essential to be able to predict whether a system will be stable or unstable from a knowledge of the physical properties of the system components.   Furthermore, it is necessary to know how the stability situation changes when alterations are made upon the various components.   One approach to this problem is to derive transfer functions for each of the system components, in this way relating the physical properties to the poles, zeros, and constant multipliers, and then to derive a transfer function for the overall system.   It is a simple matter to determine the response to an impulse input from the system transfer function.   In fact, if the system transfer function is known in factored form the stability can be determined by inspection, since the system will be unstable if any poles of this transfer function are on the $j\omega$ axis or in the right-half s plane.   Thus, the determination of stability for linear control systems simply amounts to determining the locations of the poles of the system transfer function.

   Consider the single loop feedback system in Fig. 6.3.   In Chapter 5 the transfer function for this system was defined as

$$W(s) = \frac{C(s)}{R(s)} = \frac{N_1(s)D_2(s)}{N_1(s)N_2(s) + D_1(s)D_2(s)} \qquad (6.1)$$

where the Ns and Ds are the numerators and denominators of the

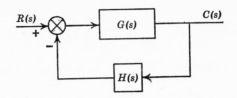

Fig. 6.3. Standard form for single loop feedback system.

forward path and feedback path transfer functions

$$G(s) = \frac{N_1(s)}{D_1(s)} \qquad H(s) = \frac{N_2(s)}{D_2(s)} \qquad (6.2)$$

It is obvious from Eq. 6.1 that the zeros of $W(s)$ are the values of s for which

$$N_1(s) = 0 \qquad \text{and} \qquad D_2(s) = 0 \qquad (6.3)$$

That is to say, $W(s)$ has zeros at the zeros of $G(s)$ ($N_1 = 0$) and at the poles of $H(s)$ ($D_2 = 0$). If both $G(s)$ and $H(s)$ are known in factored form, the zeros of the system transfer function can be determined by inspection.

The poles of $W(s)$ cannot be located as easily as the zeros. From Eq. 6.1 we can see that the poles of $W(s)$ occur at the values of s for which this equation is satisfied:

$$N_1(s)N_2(s) + D_1(s)D_2(s) = 0 \qquad (6.4)$$

This is called the characteristic equation for the system. Even if $G(s)$ and $H(s)$ are known in factored form, the roots of this equation must be determined by factoring. The determination of stability is now reduced to the factoring of a polynomial, the left side of Eq. 6.4. The polynomial has real coefficients which are algebraic combinations of physical parameters, all having real magnitudes.

Such polynomials may be factored in several ways. The least satisfactory of these is performed with paper and pencil, a tedious process if the polynomial is of the fourth degree or higher, although some techniques exist which reduce the labor required to find the roots. The programming of a high speed digital computer to find the roots is the most satisfactory method of factoring polynomials. Such machines are capable of factoring polynomials up to the order of 50 in a few seconds time with an accuracy far beyond that required for most control systems work. Between these two extremes lie the two methods described in this chapter. The first of these, called *Routh's rule*, is described in the next few paragraphs.   Routh's rule determines how many of the roots of the polynomial lie in the right half s plane, but it is not actually a factoring method.   The second method, called *root locus*, is a graphical procedure which not only factors the polynomial but shows how the root locations change when one of the coefficients in the polynomial is varied.   Section 6.3 is used to develop the root locus method.

Routh's stability rule

A sum of two polynomials, such as the denominator of the expression in Eq. 6.1, can always be written in expanded form as follows:

$$N_1(s)N_2(s) + D_1(s)D_2(s) = a_n s^n + a_{n-1} s^{n-1} + \cdots + a_1 s + a_0$$

$$(6.5)$$

The roots of the equation

$$a_n s^n + a_{n-1} s^{n-1} + \cdots + a_1 s + a_0 = 0 \qquad (6.6)$$

are the same as the roots of

$$N_1(s)N_2(s) + D_1(s)D_2(s) = 0 \qquad (6.7)$$

and these roots are the poles of $W(s)$ in Eq. 6.1.   The exact locations of the roots of Eq. 6.6 can be found only by factoring the left-hand side. However, Routh's stability rule will tell, from the coefficients a_n, a_{n-1}, . . . a_1, a_0, how many of these roots lie on the $j\omega$ axis or in the right-half s plane.   This intelligence is of utmost importance, of course, for all the roots must lie in the left half plane if the system is to be stable.

It is easier to apply Routh's test to a polynomial than it is to factor the polynomial.   Because of this, Routh's rule is often applied to the polynomial as the first step in the stability analysis to get a quick yes or no answer to the stability question and to determine over what range a parameter may vary without causing system instability. This test can be followed by a complete factoring technique which tells the designer what must be done to stabilize the system, or if it is already stable, what the dynamic response will be.

Routh's rule is applied in the following manner.

(a) Arrange the polynomial in the form shown in Eq. 6.6.   All the coefficients, a_n, a_{n-1}, . . . a_1, a_0 must be nonzero and of the same algebraic sign if all roots are to lie in the left-half s plane.

(b) If all the coefficients are nonzero and of the same sign, the following array is written.

$$
\begin{array}{cccccc}
a_n & a_{n-2} & a_{n-4} & \cdots & a_1 \\
a_{n-1} & a_{n-3} & a_{n-5} & \cdots & a_0 \\
b_1 & b_2 & b_3 & \cdots & \\
c_1 & c_2 & c_3 & \cdot\cdot & \\
d_1 & d_2 & d_3 & \cdot & \\
\cdot & \cdot & \cdot & & \\
\cdot & \cdot & & & \\
\cdot & & & &
\end{array}
$$

(6.8)

where the bs, cs, ds, etc. are formed according to the pattern indicated here:

$$
b_1 = \frac{(a_{n-1})(a_{n-2}) - (a_n)(a_{n-3})}{(a_{n-1})}
$$

$$
b_2 = \frac{(a_{n-1})(a_{n-4}) - (a_n)(a_{n-5})}{(a_{n-1})}
$$

$$
c_1 = \frac{(b_1)(a_{n-3}) - (a_{n-1})(b_2)}{(b_1)}
$$

$$
c_2 = \frac{(b_1)(a_{n-5}) - (a_{n-1})(b_3)}{(b_1)}
$$

$$
d_1 = \frac{(c_1)(b_2) - (b_1)(c_2)}{(c_1)}
$$

(6.9)

The array terminates when all the remaining terms in the first column of the array are computed to be zero. When the Routh's array is computed as indicated above, the terms in the first column are inspected. If the algebraic signs of all the terms in the first column of the array are alike, all the roots of the polynomial lie in the left half of the s plane, and the system is stable. If the signs of all these terms are not alike, the system is unstable, and there are as many roots in the right-half s plane as there are changes in algebraic sign in the sequence a_n, a_{n-1}, b_1, c_1, d_1, ...

Consider two illustrative examples. Test the following polynomial by Routh's rule.

$$
s^5 + 13s^4 + 72s^3 + 224s^2 + 359s + 195 = 0 \qquad (6.10)
$$

All the coefficients are positive, so the array must be formed to determine stability.   The array for this polynomial is

$$
\begin{array}{lll}
1 & 72 & 359 \\
13 & 224 & 195 \\
54.77 & 344 & \\
142.3 & 195 & \\
269 & & \\
195 & &
\end{array}
$$

All the signs of the terms in the first column are positive, so all the roots of Eq. 6.10 lie in the left-half s plane.   If Eq. 6.10 were factored, the roots would be found in these locations:

$$
s = -1, \qquad s = -3, \qquad s = -5, \qquad s = -2 \pm j3
$$

The reader can check this quickly by synthetic division, direct substitution, or other methods of algebra.

As a second example let us apply Routh's rule to the following polynomial:

$$
s^4 + 6s^3 + 11s^2 + 6s + 30 = 0 \tag{6.11}
$$

Again the coefficients are all positive, so the array must be formed to determine how many roots of Eq. 6.11 lie in the right-half s plane. The array is

$$
\begin{array}{lll}
1 & 11 & 30 \\
6 & 6 & \\
10 & 30 & \\
-12 & & \\
30 & &
\end{array}
$$

When the signs in the first column are considered in sequence; 1, 6, 10, -12, 30 two changes occur in algebraic sign; consequently, two roots of Eq. 6.11 lie in the right-half s plane.   If this polynomial is the denominator of the transfer function of a linear system the system will be unstable.

Sometimes the terms in the Routh array become quite large, making the computation of subsequent terms awkward.   If the terms of a row are large it is possible to divide all the terms in that row by any positive number without altering the result of the stability determination.   If the numbers in subsequent rows become large, this division process can be repeated as often as necessary.

Two special cases which complicate the computation of the array may arise in an array formed from polynomials having roots on the

$j\omega$ axis or in the right half plane.   In one case all the coefficients in a row turn out to be zero.   This occurs if there are two roots of equal magnitude, each of the same order, lying in the s plane radially opposite each other.   The second special case occurs when the first term in a row is zero and the other terms in that row are nonzero.   In this case it is not possible to complete the array because the first term in the next row is infinite.   If the troublesome zero is replaced by a very small number the array can be completed and the number of sign changes in the first column will be the number of roots having real parts equal to or greater than zero.

It is useful for reference purposes to work out Routh's stability criterion for a fourth order polynomial.   If the polynomial has this form

$$As^4 + Bs^3 + Cs^2 + Ds + E = 0 \qquad (6.12)$$

where $A, B, \ldots, E$ are all greater than zero, it will be found, upon forming Routh's array, that the only condition which must be met in order that all terms in the first column of the array will have the same sign is this:

$$D(BC - AD) > B^2E \qquad (6.13)$$

Equation 6.13 may also be applied to a third order polynomial by setting $A = 0$.   For polynomials of fifth or higher order conditions similar to this one can be defined from Routh's array; for those polynomials of higher order more than one condition must be met.

6.3   ROOT LOCUS METHOD

The root locus method for factoring the denominator of $W(s)$ in Eq. 6.1 was developed in 1948 by W. R. Evans.   Since that time it has become a widely used technique in control system analysis and design. The reason for its popularity is that it shows graphically how the locations of the poles of $W(s)$ change as one of the physical parameters of the system is changed.   It is then possible in many situations for the designer to determine the proper values for the physical parameters on the basis of the desired dynamic response of the closed-loop system. Furthermore, it shows in a very direct manner whether or not the desired dynamic performance can be achieved simply by adjusting the parameter values of a given system.   If the required performance cannot be so achieved, the root locus method often indicates the manner in which the system should be redesigned to meet the performance specifications.

As a start, let us assume that the feedback system under study is a unity feedback system—that is, $H(s) = 1$ in Fig. 6.3. (The nonunity feedback case is considered in Section 6.5.) With unity feedback the system transfer function is

$$\frac{C(s)}{R(s)} = W(s) = \frac{N(s)}{N(s) + D(s)} \qquad (6.14)$$

where

$$\frac{N(s)}{D(s)} = G(s) \qquad (6.15)$$

$G(s)$ is the transfer function of the forward path, as shown in Fig. 6.3. It is apparent from Eq. 6.14 that the zeros of $W(s)$ lie at the zeros of $G(s)$. This fact is sometimes stated in the following way: The closed-loop zeros are the same as the open-loop zeros. The poles of $W(s)$ lie at the values of s which satisfy the characteristic equation

$$N(s) + D(s) = 0 \qquad (6.16)$$

To find the poles of $W(s)$, proceed as follows. Rearrange Eq. 6.16 so that it becomes

$$\frac{N(s)}{D(s)} = -1 = G(s) \qquad (6.17)$$

The poles of $W(s)$ are the values of s for which $G(s) = -1$. Now, s is a complex variable; consequently, $G(s)$ is a function of a complex variable and may be represented by a magnitude and an angle as a complex number in polar form:

$$G(s) = |G(s)| \ @ \ \underline{/G(s)} \qquad (6.18)$$

If $G(s)$ is to equal -1, the magnitude of $G(s)$ must be unity, and the angle of $G(s)$ must be $\pm 180°$, $\pm 540°$, $\pm 900°$, etc. In other words, to be a pole of $W(s)$, a particular value of s must pass two qualifying tests. It must make

$$|G(s)| = 1 \qquad (6.19)$$

and

$$\underline{/G(s)} = \pm 180°, \text{ or } \pm 540°, \text{ or } \pm 900°, \text{ etc.} \qquad (6.20)$$

when substituted into $G(s)$.

We can find the poles of $W(s)$ by a process of elimination—first by finding all the values of s which satisfy one of these two equations, and then by finding, within that set, those values of s which satisfy the other of the two equations. It is more convenient to find all the values of s which satisfy the angle requirement (Eq. 6.20) first, and then to determine which of these also satisfy the magnitude requirement (Eq. 6.19).

$G(s)$ may be expressed in factored form as follows:

$$G(s) = \frac{K(s + Z_1)(s + Z_2) \cdots (s + Z_m)}{(s + P_1)(s + P_2)(s + P_3) \cdots (s + P_n)} \qquad (6.21)$$

where $-Z_1, -Z_2, \ldots, -Z_m$ and $-P_1, -P_2, -P_3, \ldots, -P_n$ are the zeros and poles of $G(s)$, and K is a positive constant. Each of the $(s + Z)$ and $(s + P)$ factors has a magnitude and angle when a particular value of s is substituted into Eq. 6.21. Hence both the magnitude and angle of $G(s)$ may be expressed in terms of the magnitudes and angles of the $(s + Z)$ and $(s + P)$ factors. These expressions are:

$$|G(s)| = \frac{K|s + Z_1| \, |s + Z_2| \cdots |s + Z_m|}{|s + P_1| \, |s + P_2| \, |s + P_3| \cdots |s + P_n|} \qquad (6.22)$$

$$\underline{/G(s)} = \underline{/s + Z_1} + \underline{/s + Z_2} + \cdots + \underline{/s + Z_m} - \underline{/s + P_1}$$
$$- \underline{/s + P_2} - \underline{/s + P_3} - \cdots - \underline{/s + P_n} \qquad (6.23)$$

Let us consider a specific example which illustrates a simple method of evaluating Eqs. 6.22 and 6.23 by graphical means on the s plane. This evaluation enables us to determine whether Eqs. 6.19 and 6.20 are satisfied for any given value of s. Consider the unity feedback system whose forward path transfer function is

$$G(s) = \frac{K(s + 2)}{s(s + 1)(s + 4)(s + 10)} \qquad (6.24)$$

The constant K is considered to be adjustable, and it will be seen shortly that the locations of the poles of $W(s)$ depend upon the magnitude of K. In applying the angle requirement, Eq. 6.23, to this function we find that

$$\underline{/G(s)} = \underline{/s + 2} - \underline{/s} - \underline{/s + 1} - \underline{/s + 4} - \underline{/s + 10} \qquad (6.25)$$

We must now find all the values of s which cause $\underline{/G(s)}$ to be $\pm 180°$, $\pm 540°$, $\pm 900°$, etc. Let us first choose an arbitrary point on the s plane; say $s = -10 + j5$, and compute $\underline{/G(s)}$ at that point. This first step will illustrate how the $\underline{/G(s)}$ computation is made; it will also demonstrate the futility of an unorganized search for solution points. For $s = -10 + j5$ the terms in Eq. 6.24 have the following values:

$$s + 2 = -8 + j5$$
$$s = -10 + j5$$
$$s + 1 = -9 + j5$$
$$s + 4 = -6 + j5$$
$$s + 10 = +j5 \tag{6.26}$$

The angles associated with each of these terms are computed as follows:

$$\underline{/s + 2} = \tan^{-1}(5/-8) = 148°$$
$$\underline{/s} = \tan^{-1}(5/-10) = 153.4°$$
$$\underline{/s + 1} = \tan^{-1}(5/-9) = 150.9°$$
$$\underline{/s + 4} = \tan^{-1}(5/-6) = 140.2°$$
$$\underline{/s + 10} = \tan^{-1}(5/0) = 90° \tag{6.27}$$

When these angles are summed according to Eq. 6.25, the total $\underline{/G(s)}$ is

$$\underline{/G(s)} = (148°) - (153.4° + 150.9° + 140.2° + 90°)$$
$$= -386.5° \quad (6.28)$$

Notice that this angle could also be considered to be $-26.5°$ or $+333.5°$. In either event $s = -10 + j5$ does not satisfy the angle requirement, so that we now know that this point is not a pole of the system transfer function $W(s)$.

The calculation of the angles performed in Eq. 6.27 can be made very simply by graphical measurements in the s plane. If the poles and zeros of $G(s)$ are plotted on the s plane and vectors are drawn to the trial value of s from each of the poles and zeros, the angle of each of the $(s + Z)$ and $(s + P)$ terms appears directly on the plot, as shown in

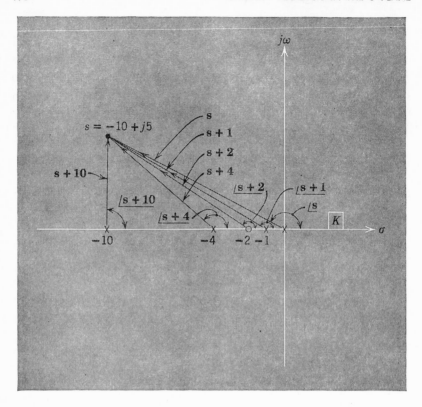

Fig. 6.4. $\underline{/G(s)}$ calculation by vector method for $s = -10 + j5$; $G(s) = \dfrac{K(s + 2)}{s(s + 1)(s + 4)(s + 10)}$

Fig. 6.4.   The algebraic sum of these angles, Eq. 6.28, can be made graphically by measuring each of the angles with a protractor, adding all the angles from the "pole vectors," and subtracting this sum from the angle of the "zero vector."   A Spirule* can be used to advantage in this task, since it can measure an angle and mechanically add or subtract it from an accumulated sum.

It would be too time consuming to test all points on the s plane, one by one, to determine which of them satisfy the angle requirement of Eq. 6.20.   A more systematic search procedure is to test the points which lie along the real axis of the s plane.   First look at point a in Fig. 6.5.   If vectors are drawn from the poles and zeros of $G(s)$ to point a it is clear that the angle of each vector is 0 degrees, so that the sum indicated in Eq. 6.25 will also be 0.   Point a does not satisfy the

* See footnote, page 92.

$\underline{/G(s)} = \pm 180°$ requirement, and therefore it cannot be a root of the characteristic equation (Eq. 6.16). Furthermore, it is clear that any point lying on the real axis to the right of the origin will produce the same result as point a produced in calculating $\underline{/G(s)}$, so all of these points may be eliminated as possible poles of the system transfer function.

Next, consider all points lying between $s = 0$ and $s = -1$, as represented by point b. If the vectors are drawn from the poles and zeros to point b it is seen that the vectors coming from the left of b all have angles equal to 0, but that the one vector coming from the right has an angle of 180°. Equation 6.25 evaluated for point b is then

$$\underline{/G(s)} = 0° - 180° - 0° - 0° - 0° = -180° \qquad (6.29)$$

Point b satisfies the angle requirement, so it (and all points lying between $s = 0$ and $s = -1$) becomes a possible solution to the characteristic equation. In Fig. 6.6 the real axis between $s = 0$ and $s = -1$ is darkened to indicate that all of these points satisfy the angle requirement, $G(s) = \pm 180°$.

Point c may be tested next. Vectors are drawn from the poles and zeros to point c, and again it is observed that those vectors coming from the left do not contribute any net angle to the sum. The two vectors coming from the right have an angular sum of 360°, since each has an angle of 180°. Therefore, point c does not satisfy the angle requirement of $G(s)$.

Going to point d, we find that two vectors come from the left and therefore contribute no angle to the sum; however, of the three vectors

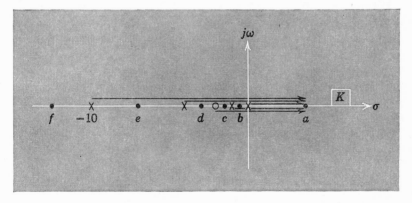

Fig. 6.5.   Testing the points along the real axis for $\underline{/G(s)} = \pm 180°$, $\pm 540°$, etc.

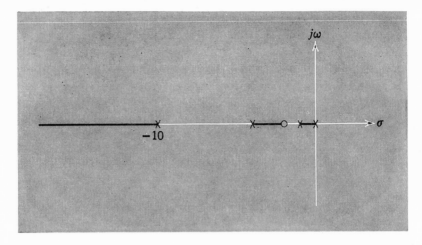

Fig. 6.6. Indicating the points on the real axis which satisfy $\underline{/G(s)} = \pm 180°$.

coming from the right, two come from poles giving a total of $-360°$, and one comes from the zero giving a contribution of $+180°$ to the sum. Therefore, point d and all points on the axis between $s = -2$ and $s = -4$ satisfy the $\underline{/G(s)} = \pm 180°$ requirement. In Fig. 6.6 this section of the axis is also darkened to indicate that a solution point of the characteristic equation could lie there. If points e and f are tested in this way it will be found that e does not satisfy the angle requirement but that f does, so that the three darkened sections of the real axis in Fig. 6.6 include all the points on the axis which satisfy the angle requirement.

It can now be observed that, along the real axis, all points which lie to the left of an odd number of poles and zeros of $G(s)$ satisfy the $\underline{/G(s)} = \pm 180°$ requirement. Point b lies to the left of *one* pole, d lies to the left of *three* singularities (two poles and one zero), and f lies to the left of *five* singularities of $G(s)$.

The next portion of our search is conducted along the imaginary ($j\omega$) axis of the s plane. In Fig. 6.7 vectors are drawn from each of the poles and zeros of $G(s)$ to a test point along the $j\omega$ axis. The $\underline{/G(s)}$ for such a point is

$$\underline{/G(s)} = \tan^{-1}\left(\frac{\omega}{2}\right) - 90° - \tan^{-1}\left(\frac{\omega}{1}\right) - \tan^{-1}\left(\frac{\omega}{4}\right)$$

$$- \tan^{-1}\left(\frac{\omega}{10}\right) \quad (6.30)$$

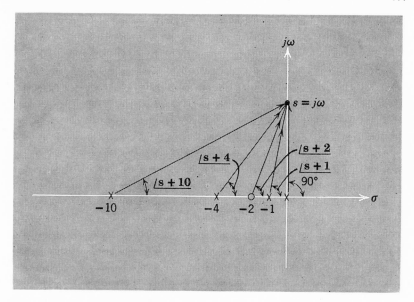

Fig. 6.7. Finding the points on the $j\omega$ axis which satisfy $\underline{/G(s)} = \pm 180°$.

Each of these individual contributions to the total angle may be plotted separately, as in Fig. 6.8. From this plot it is apparent that the total $\underline{/G(s)}$ starts out at $-90°$ for $\omega = 0$ and decreases monotonically toward $-270°$ for $\omega \gg 10$. Therefore, at one point along the $j\omega$ axis the total angle will be $-180°$. This point can be determined from Fig. 6.8 by summing graphically the four individual contributions at several points and then interpolating as required to find the exact

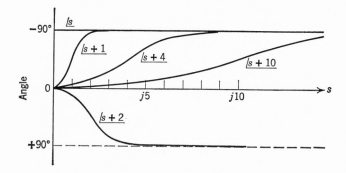

Fig. 6.8. Individual angular contributions to $\underline{/G(s)}$ of the vectors, as a function of s, for points along the $j\omega$ axis.

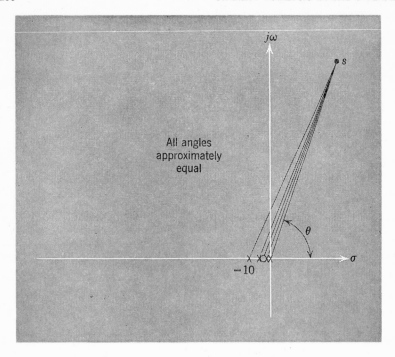

Fig. 6.9. Testing a point in the "remote region" of the s plane for $\underline{/G(s)} = \pm 180°$.

point at which the sum is $-180°$. In this example that point is approximately $s = j5.2$. Of course, a point occurs on the negative imaginary axis at which all vectors will sum to $+180°$, and because of the symmetry of the pole-zero pattern with respect to the σ axis this point occurs at $s = -j5.2$. These are the only two points along the $j\omega$ axis which satisfy the angle requirement.

Consider next the remote regions of the s plane. All vectors drawn from the poles and zeros to points in the remote regions of the s plane have approximately the same angle, as illustrated in Fig. 6.9. If θ is the approximate angle made by all the vectors, some points in the remote regions will satisfy the $\underline{/G(s)} = \pm 180°, \pm 540°$, etc. requirement if a θ can be found so that

θ [Number of zeros] $- \theta$ [Number of poles]
$$= \pm 180°, \pm 540°, \text{etc.} \ldots$$

or

θ [Number of zeros $-$ Number of poles]
$$= \pm 180°, \pm 540°, \text{etc.} \ldots \quad (6.31)$$

In this example one zero and four poles occur, so Eq. 6.31 can be solved for θ:

$$\theta = \frac{\pm 180°}{1 - 4} = \pm 60°$$

$$\theta = \frac{\pm 540°}{1 - 4} = \pm 180°$$

$$\theta = \frac{\pm 900°}{1 - 4} = \pm 300° \tag{6.32}$$

$\pm 300°$ is equivalent, geometrically, to $\pm 60°$, so it is not necessary to solve Eq. 6.31 for any total angle values beyond $\pm 540°$. In this example, then, points which satisfy the $\underline{/G(s)} = \pm 180°$, $\pm 540°$, etc. requirement occur in three remote regions of the s plane. These three regions lie at $\pm 60°$ and $180°$ from the group of poles and zeros of $G(s)$.

As the final step in the search for all points satisfying the angle requirement of $G(s)$ let us explore the areas in the s plane lying between the poles and zeros and the "remote regions." This exploration is made in a more systematic fashion later in this section, but for the present a qualitative discussion will serve our purpose.

Starting at a point in one of the remote regions which satisfies the angle requirement, find a point adjacent to the starting point which also satisfies the angle requirement. A consideration of the way in which the total angle of $G(s)$ changes with small changes in the test point location will indicate that this can be done. The total angle changes smoothly from $(180° + \epsilon)$ to $(180° - \epsilon)$ (ϵ is a small angle) as we shift the test point around in a small region about a solution point. Since we can always find a point nearby which is also a solution point, we can work our way toward the origin of the s plane by finding a series of points which satisfy the angle requirement of $\underline{/G(s)}$. These points form a smooth curve, and for this particular example the curve will turn out to be that shown in Fig. 6.10. Later it will be shown analytically that the curves in Fig. 6.10 include *all* possible solution points to Eq. 6.20, but for the present the measurement of $\underline{/G(s)}$ at a few points lying off the curve will demonstrate that we do not find solution points lying off the curve. The exact location of the curve can be determined by finding solution points by a trial-and-error process; the Spirule is a time-saver in making these trial-and-error measurements.

The solution curves in Fig. 6.10 are called *root loci*, since they are composed of all points which can possibly be roots of the characteristic

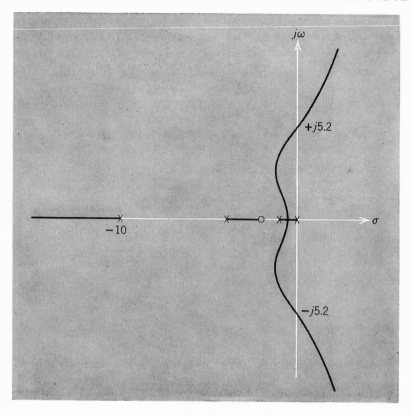

Fig. 6.10. All points satisfying $\underline{/G(s)} = \pm 180°, \pm 540°$.

equation. Those points which actually *are* roots of the characteristic
equation must be determined by finding all points on the root loci which
satisfy Eq. 6.19, namely,

$$|G(s)| = 1 \qquad (6.33)$$

The absolute value of $G(s)$ is given in Eq. 6.22, and if Eq. 6.33 is to be
satisfied in this example, we have

$$\frac{K|s+2|}{|s|\,|s+1|\,|s+4|\,|s+10|} = 1 \qquad (6.34)$$

The loop gain K determines which of the points on the root loci are
the roots of the characteristic equation. If K is allowed to change in

magnitude, the roots of the characteristic equation will also change. It is therefore desirable to study the way in which the roots move along the loci as K is varied. This study can be carried out analytically by considering the system transfer function for this example.

The system transfer function is

$$W(s) = \frac{G(s)}{1 + G(s)} = \frac{K(s + 2)}{K(s + 2) + s(s + 1)(s + 4)(s + 10)} \quad (6.35)$$

$$= \frac{K(s + 2)}{s^4 + 15s^3 + 54s^2 + (40 + K)s + 2K}$$

Our first observation concerning the poles of $W(s)$ is that four occur because the denominator of $W(s)$ is of the fourth order. For $K = 0$ the poles of $W(s)$ will be $s = 0$, $s = -1$, $s = -4$, and $s = -10$, the same as the poles of $G(s)$. As K is increased slightly from 0, the poles of $W(s)$ change position slightly; they must move along the root loci. The pole of $W(s)$ which lies at $s = 0$ when $K = 0$, for example, will be shifted to the left as K is increased, and the pole of $W(s)$ which started at $s = -1$ for $K = 0$ will shift to the right as K is increased. Similarly, the pole of $W(s)$ which was at $s = -4$ for $K = 0$ will move slightly to the right as K is increased slightly, and the pole of $W(s)$ which starts at $s = -10$ for $K = 0$ will move toward the left with an increase in K. As K is increased more and more the poles of $W(s)$ continue their movement along the loci. To determine the magnitude for K which is required to place a pole of $W(s)$ at any given point on the loci, apply Eq. 6.34, rearranged as follows:

$$K = \frac{|s|\, |s + 1|\, |s + 4|\, |s + 10|}{|s + 2|} \quad (6.36)$$

For example, let us compute the value of K required to place a pole of $W(s)$ on the $j\omega$ axis at $s = j5.2$. Substitute $s = j5.2$ into Eq. 6.36.

$$K = \frac{|j5.2|\, |1 + j5.2|\, |4 + j5.2|\, |10 + j5.2|}{|2 + j5.2|}$$

$$= \frac{5.2(\sqrt{1 + (5.2)^2})(\sqrt{16 + (5.2)^2})(\sqrt{100 + (5.2)^2})}{\sqrt{4 + (5.2)^2}}$$

$$= 364.5 \quad (6.37)$$

The evaluation of $|s|$, $|s + 1|$, etc. may also be done graphically, as

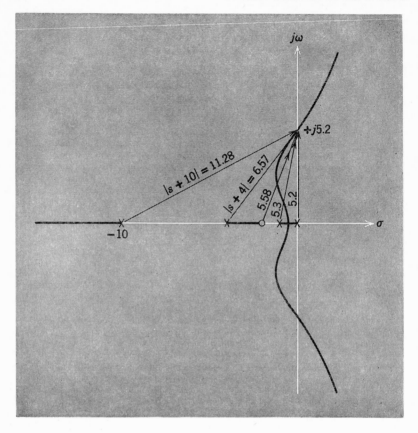

Fig. 6.11. Evaluation of K required to place a pole of W(s) at s = j5.2.

indicated in Fig. 6.11, and the Spirule may be employed to evaluate K in Eq. 6.37. Four poles of $W(s)$ occur in this system, so two other solution points of the characteristic equation must exist for $K = 364.5$. One of these lies on the root locus between $s = -4$ and $s = -2$, and the other lies on the locus to the left of $s = -10$. These can be found simply by testing several points on the loci in these two regions until two points are found which satisfy Eq. 6.36 for $K = 364.5$. Later a more direct method for finding these two points will be demonstrated. This will show that the other two poles of $W(s)$ lie at $s = -12.91$ and $s = -2.09$. As K is increased beyond 364.5, the solution points on the loci must move in such a way that Eq. 6.36 is satisfied. The solution points at $s = \pm j5.2$ for $K = 364.5$ must move outward along the root loci as K is increased, the solution point at $s = -12.91$ will move toward the left, and the point at -2.09 will move toward the right. As K is increased toward infinity the solution points (or poles of $W(s)$) on the complex loci move toward infinity on those loci, the solution point on the real axis to the left of $s = -10$ will move toward infinity along its locus, and the solution point between $s = -4$ and $s = -2$ will move closer to $s = -2$. It is evident from Eq. 6.36 that K will approach infinity where all five vectors become very long (poles of $W(s)$ on the three remote loci) *and* where **s + 2** becomes very short (poles of $W(s)$ near $s = -2$).

Figure 6.12 shows the pole-zero configuration of $W(s)$ for four different values of K. $W(s)$ has one finite zero at $s = -2$. This is obvious from Eq. 6.35. In Fig. 6.12a K is a very small positive number, so that the poles of $W(s)$ are close to the position they would assume if K were 0—that is, close to the poles of $G(s)$. It is easy to see from this pole-zero plot that the step response of this system will be monotonically increasing and the time constant of the principal exponential term will be quite long, since a pole of $W(s)$ occurs very close to the

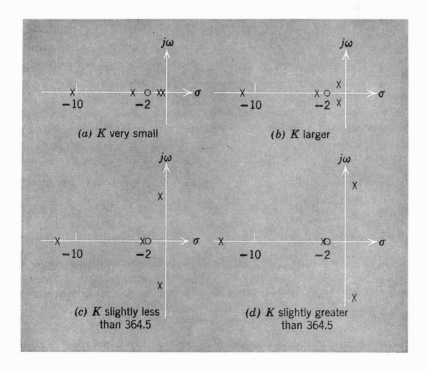

Fig. 6.12.   Pole-zero configuration of W(s) for various values of K.

origin.   In Fig. 6.12*b* K has been increased so that the poles of $W(s)$ have moved along the root loci in the directions demanded by Eq. 6.36. Now the step response of the system will be somewhat faster than that in *a*, and some overshoot due to the damped sinusoidal term will occur.   In Fig. 6.12*c* K is larger than in *b*, and the poles have moved farther along the root loci.   Now a step response will be very oscillatory because of the lightly damped complex poles.   In Fig. 6.12*d* the gain has been increased beyond 364.5 so that the two complex poles of $W(s)$ have moved along the root loci into the right-half *s* plane.   Now a step response will exhibit an unstable (negatively damped) oscillation.   Therefore, the gain would have to be kept below 364.5 to insure stability, and for most systems it would be set at the value which would give a pole-zero configuration like that in *b*, since the step response of *b* would be sufficiently fast but not excessively oscillatory.

It should be noted here that the critical value of K for stability, namely $K = 364.5$, could be determined by applying Routh's rule to the denominator of Eq. 6.35.   This is a good check on the root locus calculation.

It is now possible to make a more general statement about the relationship between K and the poles and zeros of $W(s)$ and those of $G(s)$. Using the general expression for $G(s)$ given in Eq. 6.21, we may write $W(s)$ as

$$W(s) = \frac{K(s + Z_1)(s + Z_2) \cdots (s + Z_m)}{K(s + Z_1)(s + Z_2) \cdots (s + Z_m) + (s + P_1)(s + P_2) \atop \cdots (s + P_n)}$$

$$(6.38)$$

It should be observed here that $G(s)$, like any transfer function, has an equal number of poles and zeros, even though some of the zeros may be at infinity.   (In the above example three zeros of $G(s)$ occur at infinity.)   Therefore, we can say that the same number of $(s + Z)$ terms as $(s + P)$ terms occur in Eq. 6.38.   Now, from Eq. 6.38 we can draw three conclusions:

(a) The zeros of $W(s)$ are at $s = -Z_1$, $s = -Z_2$, $s = -Z_3$, etc. They are the same as the zeros of $G(s)$, and there are as many zeros of $G(s)$ as poles of $G(s)$, although some of these may be at infinity.

(b) For $K = 0$ the left-hand part of the denominator of $W(s)$ disappears, so that the poles of $W(s)$ are at $s = -P_1, s = -P_2, s = -P_3$, etc.   The poles of $W(s)$ are the same as the poles of $G(s)$.

(c) For $K \to \infty$ the right-hand part of the denominator of $W(s)$ becomes insignificant compared to the left-hand part, so the poles of

$W(s)$ approach $s = -Z_1$, $s = -Z_2$, $s = -Z_3$, etc. The poles of $W(s)$ approach the zeros of $G(s)$ [which are also the zeros of $W(s)$]; again, some of these zeros might be at infinity.

These general conclusions can be applied to the root locus plot for a particular system in the following way. If the "open-loop" transfer function, $G(s)$, has n poles and m *finite* zeros, assuming that $n > m$, then $G(s)$ must have $(n - m)$ zeros at infinity. [$G(s)$ behaves as $K/s^{(n-m)}$ as $s \to \infty$.] Therefore, as K is increased from zero toward infinity the poles of $W(s)$ must move along the root loci *toward the zeros* of $G(s)$. Since there are m finite zeros of $G(s)$, m poles of $W(s)$ will move along loci toward the finite zeros as K is increased. In other words, m branches of the root locus connect poles of $G(s)$ to the finite zeros of $G(s)$. But since $(n - m)$ zeros of $G(s)$ occur at infinity, $(n - m)$ branches of the root locus will lead out toward infinity in the s plane, and $(n - m)$ poles of $W(s)$ will move along these branches toward the $(n - m)$ zeros at infinity. This is another way of showing that $(n - m)$ asymptotes must occur for the remote region root loci.

It is now possible to derive a general expression for the asymptotes of the remote region loci. $G(s)$ can be written as follows:

$$G(s) = \frac{K(s + Z_1)(s + Z_2) \cdots (s + Z_m)}{(s + P_1)(s + P_2) \cdots (s + P_n)} \tag{6.39}$$

This equation can be expanded into

$$G(s) = \frac{K(s^m + a_1 s^{m-1} + \cdots + a_m)}{(s^n + b_1 s^{n-1} + \cdots + b_n)} \tag{6.40}$$

At this point an important relationship between Eqs. 6.39 and 6.40 should be noted. This relationship is expressed by the following identities:

$$a_1 = Z_1 + Z_2 + \cdots + Z_m$$

$$a_m = Z_1 Z_2 \cdots Z_m$$

$$b_1 = P_1 + P_2 + \cdots + P_n$$

$$b_n = P_1 P_2 \cdots P_n \tag{6.41}$$

The coefficient of the second term in an expanded polynomial is equal to the sum of the constant terms in each of the factors of the polynomial, and the constant term in the expanded form is equal to the product of the constant terms in each of the factors. Hence we can say "$-a_1$ is the sum of the zeros of $G(s)$, and $-b_1$ is the sum of the poles of $G(s)$." If the numerator of $G(s)$ is divided into the denominator, $G(s)$ may be written as follows:

$$G(s) = \frac{K}{s^{n-m} + (b_1 - a_1)s^{n-m-1} + \cdots} \qquad (6.42)$$

Now the root loci occur for $G(s) = -1$; so for those values of s which lie on the root loci, Eq. 6.42 may be written as

$$s^{n-m} + (b_1 - a_1)s^{n-m-1} + \cdots = -K \qquad (6.43)$$

The asymptotes are found by considering s to be very large, making Eq. 6.43 essentially a polynomial of degree $(n - m)$ whose roots have the sum $-(b_1 - a_1)$, since $(b_1 - a_1)$ is the coefficient of the s^{n-m-1} term in Eq. 6.43. The asymptotes are approximately the loci of these roots for large values of s. The intersection point of the asymptotes in the region where s is small is found by extrapolating the straight lines for large s in toward the origin. Since $(n - m)$ roots exist for Eq. 6.43, and since the sum of these roots, for large s, is $-(b_1 - a_1)$, the extrapolation of the asymptotes will show that they must intersect at the point $s = -(b_1 - a_1)/(n - m)$, making angles of $\pm 180°/(n - m)$, $\pm 540°/(n - m)$, etc. with the real axis. The point of intersection, $-(b_1 - a_1)/(n - m)$, is the sum of the poles minus the sum of the finite zeros of $G(s)$ divided by the number of poles minus the number of finite zeros of $G(s)$. Three asymptotes occur in the above example, since there are four poles and one finite zero of $G(s)$. The asymptotes pass through the point $s = -(0 + 1 + 4 + 10 - 2)/3 = -4.33$, making angles of $\pm 60°$ and $180°$ with the real axis.

The algebraic relationships defined by Eq. 6.41 may be put to use in plotting root loci. In the example above the system transfer function is given in Eq. 6.35 as

$$W(s) = \frac{K(s + 2)}{s^4 + 15s^3 + 54s^2 + (40 + K)s + 2K} \qquad (6.44)$$

This could also be written as

$$W(s) = \frac{K(s + 2)}{(s + Q_1)(s + Q_2)(s + Q_3)(s + Q_4)} \qquad (6.45)$$

where $-Q_1$, $-Q_2$, $-Q_3$, and $-Q_4$ are the poles of $W(s)$. These are the points lying on the root loci which satisfy the condition $|G(s)| = 1$.

Comparing Eqs. 6.44 and 6.45, we may conclude that

$$Q_1 + Q_2 + Q_3 + Q_4 = 15$$

$$Q_1 Q_2 Q_3 Q_4 = 2K \qquad (6.46)$$

These relationships are often useful in finding Q_1, Q_2, Q_3 and Q_4, once a value for K is specified. In the example above, when $K = 364.5$, two of the poles of $W(s)$ appear at $s = \pm j5.2$. The remaining two poles may then be found by substitution into Eq. 6.46:

$$Q_1 + Q_2 + j5.2 - j5.2 = 15$$

$$Q_1 Q_2 (+j5.2)(-j5.2) = 2(364.5) \qquad (6.47)$$

These reduce to

$$Q_1 + Q_2 = 15$$

$$Q_1 Q_2 = 26.96 \qquad (6.48)$$

The two equations are solved simultaneously to give the two remaining pole locations.

This sum and product relationship may be used in another way to uncover information about the root locus plot through simple observation of the way in which the sum and product of the system poles change with changes in K. In this example the sum of the roots remains constant as K is increased; consequently, as the two complex roots move toward the right (for large K) the real pole beyond $s = -10$ must move toward the left in order to keep the sum of the poles constant at -15. (For large K the real pole near $s = -2$ moves very little as K is increased.) Similarly, since the product of the poles is proportional to K, the product of the absolute values of the poles of $W(s)$ must increase as K is increased. Here the poles move toward infinity along the asymptotic loci as K is increased.

Two additional properties of root locus plots can be illustrated by another example. Consider the unity feedback system shown in Fig. 6.13. The poles and zeros of the system transfer function are to be

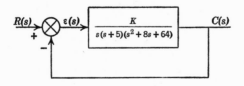

Fig. 6.13. System for second example.

located as functions of K, the loop gain. The system transfer function is

$$W(s) = \frac{K}{s(s + 5)(s^2 + 8s + 64) + K} \qquad (6.49)$$

which can be expanded to

$$W(s) = \frac{K}{s^4 + 13s^3 + 104s^2 + 320s + K} \qquad (6.50)$$

$W(s)$ has no finite zeros, but four poles occur whose locations depend upon K. The root locus method is employed to determine how the poles of $W(s)$ vary as K is changed.

The poles of $W(s)$ are defined as the values of s for which the denominator of $W(s)$ is zero—in other words, the values of s for which

$$\frac{K}{s(s + 5)(s^2 + 8s + 64)} = \frac{K}{s(s + 5)(s + 4 + j\sqrt{48})(s + 4 - j\sqrt{48})}$$
$$= -1 \quad (6.51)$$

Equation 6.51 may be expressed as the angle and magnitude requirements

$$\underline{/0°} - \underline{/s} - \underline{/s + 5} - \underline{/s + 4 + j\sqrt{48}} - \underline{/s + 4 - j\sqrt{48}}$$
$$= \pm n\,180° \quad (6.52)$$

where $n = 1, 3, 5, 7, \ldots$, and

$$\frac{K}{|s|\,|s + 5|\,|s + 4 + j\sqrt{48}|\,|s + 4 - j\sqrt{48}|} = 1 \qquad (6.53)$$

The root locus plot locates all points in the s plane which satisfy Eq. 6.52, and it is constructed first. The poles of $C(s)/\varepsilon(s)$ are placed in the s plane, as in Fig. 6.14. The portion of the real axis lying to the left of the pole at the origin and to the right of the pole at $s = -5$ is a section of the root locus, since all points on this line segment satisfy the angle requirement specified by Eq. 6.52. No other points on the real axis will satisfy the angle requirement. It is apparent from the expression for $W(s)$ in Eq. 6.49 that the poles of $W(s)$ for $K = 0$ are the same as the poles of $C(s)/\varepsilon(s)$. Therefore, a branch of the root locus starts at each of the poles of $C(s)/\varepsilon(s)$ for $K = 0$. The branch starting at $s = 0$ lies to the left of $s = 0$, and the branch starting at $s = -5$ lies to the right of $s = -5$. The two branches come together

at some intermediate point, where they then leave the axis and move
out toward infinity in the s plane, terminating at two of the zeros of
$C(s)/\varepsilon(s)$, which are at infinity. The two branches which start at the
complex poles $-4 \pm j \sqrt{48}$ also move out toward infinity.

As an aid in drawing the root locus, construct the asymptotes, of
which there are four, since there are four poles and no finite zeros of
$C(s)/\varepsilon(s)$. The angles which these four asymptotes make with the

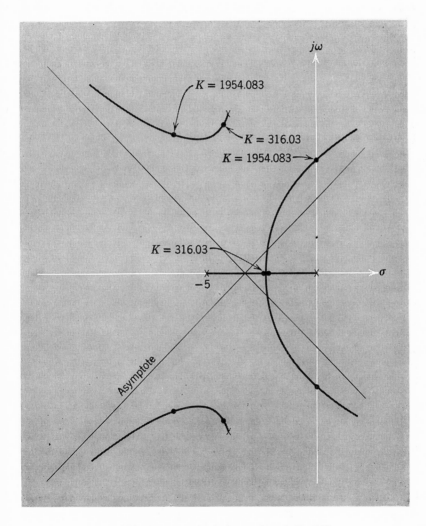

Fig. 6.14.   Root locus plot for system shown in Fig. 6.13.

real axis are given by Eq. 6.32 as

$$\theta_{asy} = \frac{\pm 180°}{4-0}, \frac{\pm 540°}{4-0}, \frac{\pm 900°}{4-0}, \text{etc.}$$

$$= \pm 45°, \pm 135°, \pm 225°, \text{etc.} \tag{6.54}$$

Since $\pm 225°$ is geometrically the same as $\pm 135°$, it is not necessary to carry the series in Eq. 6.54 beyond the first two terms; these two terms give the four angles of the four asymptotes.

The point of intersection of the asymptotes is computed (see page 208).

$$\frac{\sum \left(\text{pole values of } \frac{C(s)}{\varepsilon(s)} \right) - \sum \left(\text{finite zero values of } \frac{C(s)}{\varepsilon(s)} \right)}{\left(\text{number of poles of } \frac{C(s)}{\varepsilon(s)} \right) - \left(\text{number of finite zeros of } \frac{C(s)}{\varepsilon(s)} \right)}$$

$$\tag{6.55}$$

In this example the point of intersection is

$$\frac{[0 + (-5) + (-4 + j\sqrt{48}) + (-4 - j\sqrt{48})] - [0]}{4 - 0} = -3.25$$

$$\tag{6.56}$$

The asymptotes are drawn in Fig. 6.14. A few trial-and-error tests along the imaginary axis will show that the angle requirement of Eq. 6.52 is satisfied at only two points, $\pm j4.96$. A few more trials will show that the branches of the root locus which pass through the $\pm j4.96$ points are the branches which started at $s = 0$ and $s = -5$, and that these branches move out toward the $\pm 45°$ asymptotes, as shown in Fig. 6.14.

The point at which the two branches meet on the real axis and then break away can be determined analytically as follows. Call the point at which the breakaway occurs $s = -x$, and consider q to be a point on the complex part of the locus just a slight distance ϵ above the breakaway point, as shown in Fig. 6.15. Since point q lies on the root locus, it must satisfy the angle requirement given by Eq. 6.52. Figure 6.15 indicates that the angles of the vectors drawn from each of the poles to point q must sum to 180°, as follows:

$$\theta_1 + \theta_2 + \theta_3 + \theta_4 = 180° \tag{6.57}$$

Each of these angles can be expressed in terms of α, $\zeta\omega_n$, ω_0, and x as

$$\theta_1 = 180° - \tan^{-1}\frac{\epsilon}{x}$$

$$\theta_2 = \tan^{-1}\frac{\epsilon}{\alpha - x}$$

$$\theta_3 = 360° - \tan^{-1}\frac{\omega_0 - \epsilon}{\zeta\omega_n - x}$$

$$\theta_4 = \tan^{-1}\frac{\omega_0 + \epsilon}{\zeta\omega_n - x} \tag{6.58}$$

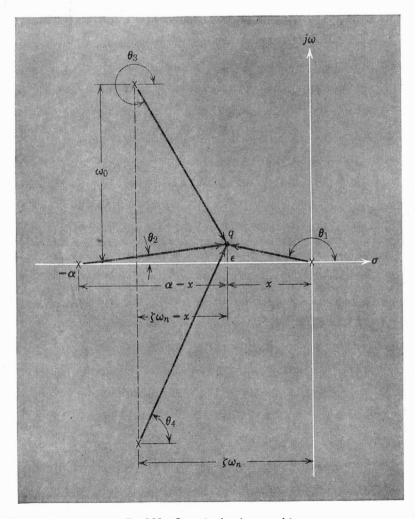

Fig. 6.15. Computing breakaway point.

When these expressions are substituted into Eq. 6.57 the angle requirement may be written as

$$\tan^{-1}\frac{\epsilon}{\alpha - x} - \tan^{-1}\frac{\epsilon}{x} = \tan^{-1}\frac{\omega_0 - \epsilon}{\zeta\omega_n - x} - \tan^{-1}\frac{\omega_0 + \epsilon}{\zeta\omega_n - x} \qquad (6.59)$$

The right-hand side of this equation is of the form $\tan^{-1}(A - B) - \tan^{-1}(A + B)$. This may be expressed by trigonometric manipulation as

$$\tan^{-1}\frac{\epsilon}{\alpha - x} - \tan^{-1}\frac{\epsilon}{x} = \tan^{-1}\frac{2\epsilon(x - \zeta\omega_n)}{(x - \zeta\omega_n)^2 + \omega_0^2 - \epsilon^2} \qquad (6.60)$$

If ϵ is considered to be very small, the tangent of each of these three angles is very nearly equal to the angle itself, and the ϵ^2 term can be neglected. Equation 6.60 can be written as

$$\frac{\epsilon}{\alpha - x} - \frac{\epsilon}{x} = \frac{2\epsilon(x - \zeta\omega_n)}{(x - \zeta\omega_n)^2 + \omega_0^2} \qquad (6.61)$$

ϵ can be eliminated by dividing each of these terms by ϵ, so that x is given implicitly as a function of $\zeta\omega_n$, ω_0, and α:

$$\frac{1}{\alpha - x} - \frac{1}{x} = \frac{2(x - \zeta\omega_n)}{(x - \zeta\omega_n)^2 + \omega_0^2} \qquad (6.62)$$

In this example $\alpha = 5$, $\zeta\omega_n = 4$, and $\omega_0^2 = 48$. Equation 6.62 is most easily solved by trial and error. The solution is known from the root locus plot to be somewhere between 2 and 3, and a few trials will produce the solution, which turns out to be $x = 2.292$.

It is a simple matter to compute the angle at which the root locus leaves the complex poles. A point q on the root locus, but very close to one of the complex poles is considered in Fig. 6.16. Since point q is on the locus, all vectors drawn to q from the poles must have angles which sum to 180°.

$$\theta_1 + \theta_2 + \theta_3 + \theta_4 = 180° \qquad (6.63)$$

Since q is very close to the complex pole, θ_3 is the angle at which the root locus leaves the pole. Furthermore, in this case θ_1, θ_2, and θ_4 are approximately the same as they would be if q were placed right at the complex pole. Therefore, θ_1, θ_2, and θ_4 are easily computed from the positions of the poles of $C(s)/\varepsilon(s)$. In this example we have

$$\theta_1 = 120°$$
$$\theta_2 = 81.79° \qquad (6.64)$$
$$\theta_4 = 90°$$

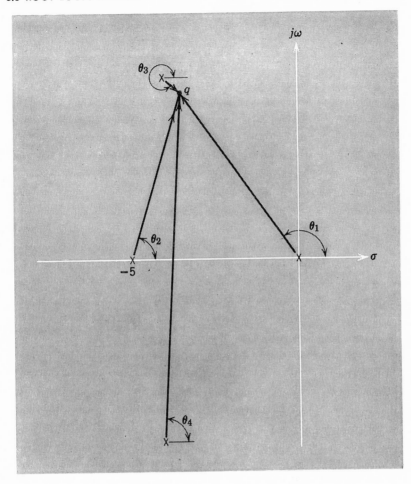

Fig. 6.16.   Computing the angle at which the locus leaves the complex pole.

so that θ_3 can be found from Eq. 6.63.   It is

$$\theta_3 = 180° - 120° - 81.79° - 90° = -111.79° \qquad (6.65)$$

With the asymptotes sketched on the s plane, the breakaway point at $s = -2.292$ determined, the angle of departure of the locus from the complex poles computed as $-111.79°$, and the points of intersection with the imaginary axis $\pm j4.96$ known, the complete root locus can be sketched accurately, as in Fig. 6.14, by finding several additional points which satisfy the angle requirement and connecting these with a smooth curve.

To establish the relationship between the locations of the poles of $W(s)$ and the loop gain, compute K at several points along the locus. We know that as K is increased from zero, the poles of $W(s)$ move from the poles of $C(s)/\varepsilon(s)$ out along the root loci toward the zeros of $C(s)/\varepsilon(s)$, which in this case are all at infinity. Thus, if K is very small, two real poles of $W(s)$ will occur, one lying just to the left of the pole at the origin and one lying just to the right of the pole at $s = -5$. A pair of complex poles will also be found lying on the loci near the complex poles at $s = -4 \pm j\sqrt{48}$. As K is increased, the complex poles simply move farther out to the left along the loci, while the two real poles move toward each other until they meet at the breakaway point $s = -2.292$. The value for K required to place both real poles at the breakaway point can easily be computed as the product of the absolute values of the four vectors drawn to the breakaway point from the poles of $C(s)/\varepsilon(s)$. This value, $K = 316.03$, is noted on the root locus plot, Fig. 6.14. As K is increased further, one pole of $W(s)$ moves away from the breakaway point up its complex branch while the other moves down along its branch. The threshold of instability is reached at the point where the loci pass into the right-half s plane, in this example at $s = \pm j4.96$. The critical value for K at this point can be computed by the vector method, or by applying Routh's rule to the denominator of Eq. 6.50. In this example $K = 1954.08$ will put the two poles of $W(s)$ on the $j\omega$ axis, and any higher value of K will cause the system to be unstable. The location of the two remote complex poles for $K = 1954.08$ is easily found, since the sum of the four pole values is -13 and the sum of the two poles on the imaginary axis is 0. The real parts of the two remote poles, then, must be -6.5; they are spotted on the loci at the points where the real parts are -6.5, as indicated in Fig. 6.14.

Before applying the root locus method in more examples, let us summarize the important features of the method as a guide in plotting the root loci for a unity, negative feedback system. The order of procedure for plotting the loci, once $G(s)$ is expressed in factored form with the loop gain K left as a variable, is as follows:

(1) The poles and zeros of $G(s)$ are plotted to scale on the s plane. It is assumed here that the number of finite poles equals or exceeds the number of finite zeros in $G(s)$.

(2) The asymptotes are sketched by computing the point of intersection as

$$\frac{\Sigma(\text{Pole values of } G(s)) - \Sigma(\text{Zero values of } G(s))}{n - m} \tag{6.66}$$

where n and m are the number of finite poles and zeros of $G(s)$, and the *pole values* and *zero values* refer to the finite poles and zeros only. The angles which the asymptotes make with the real axis are $\dfrac{\pm 180°}{n-m}$, $\dfrac{\pm 540°}{n-m}$, $\dfrac{\pm 900°}{n-m}$, etc.

(3) The root loci are drawn by showing each branch emanating from a pole of $G(s)$ and terminating on a zero of $G(s)$ as K varies from zero to infinity. The branches on the real axis lie to the left of an odd number of singularities, as the singularities are numbered beginning with the rightmost pole or zero.

(4) The angle at which the locus leaves a complex pole is easily computed by the method shown in Fig. 6.16.

(5) A branch of the loci lying between two poles of $G(s)$ will break away from the real axis at some point and form two complex branches, each of which will terminate on a zero of $G(s)$, possibly at infinity. The point of breakaway is computed by using the method illustrated in Fig. 6.15. Another method for finding the breakaway point is explained below, in connection with Fig. 6.25.

(6) For a given value of K a pole of $W(s)$ is found on each branch of the root loci. The exact locations of the poles of $W(s)$ are the points on the loci which satisfy the gain requirement

$$K = \frac{\Pi|\mathbf{P}|}{\Pi|\mathbf{Z}|} \tag{6.67}$$

where $|\mathbf{P}|$ is the absolute value of the vector drawn from a pole of $G(s)$ to the solution point on the locus, and $|\mathbf{Z}|$ is the absolute value of the vector drawn from a zero to the point. $\Pi|\mathbf{P}|$ is the product of all the vector lengths drawn from poles, and $\Pi|\mathbf{Z}|$ is the product of all vector lengths drawn from finite zeros. The value for K at which a pole of $W(s)$ lies on the imaginary axis corresponds to the critical value which is computed from the Routh test.

Two useful relationships which are often used to find the exact locations of the poles of $W(s)$ for a given value of K are:

(a) The sum of the pole values of $W(s)$ is the negative of the coefficient of the second term in the polynomial $1 + G(s)$.

(b) The product of the absolute values of the poles of $W(s)$ is equal to the constant term in the polynomial $1 + G(s)$.

These two relationships are illustrated in Eqs. 6.44, 6.45, 6.46.

6.4 SETTING LOOP GAIN FOR DESIRED DYNAMIC PERFORMANCE

In a unity feedback system the *open-loop* transfer function $G(s)$ can always be written in factored form with unity as the coefficient of the s term in each factor.

$$G(s) = \frac{K(s + Z_1)(s + Z_2) \cdots (s + Z_m)}{(s + P_1)(s + P_2)(s + P_3) \cdots (s + P_n)} \qquad (6.68)$$

For example, a transfer function expressed as

$$G(s) = \frac{6(2s + 1)(s + 1)}{s(4s + 12)(\frac{1}{3}s + 1)} \qquad (6.69)$$

can be written equivalently as

$$G(s) = \frac{9(s + \frac{1}{2})(s + 1)}{s(s + 3)^2} \qquad (6.70)$$

In this book the coefficient K of a transfer function written in the form defined by Eq. 6.68 is called the *loop gain* in a unity feedback system. It is important to note that K is not usually equal to a particular physical parameter which might logically be thought of as the *gain* around the loop. The steady state *gain* of $G(s)$, when defined as the steady state output of the block represented by $G(s)$ in response to a unit step input, is not K but $(KZ_1Z_2 \cdots Z_m)/(P_1P_2P_3 \cdots P_n)$. In servomechanism systems it is often convenient to refer to a *torque gain* or a *voltage gain* of a particular block. Sometimes these terms are mistakenly called the *loop gain.* K in Eq. 6.68 is defined as *loop gain* here because in the root locus method K is the constant which is related directly to the positions of the system poles.

The techniques for relating the poles and zeros of a transfer function to the dynamic response of the system represented by the transfer function were developed in Chapter 4. Briefly, this technique is that of expanding a function of s in partial fractions so that it becomes a sum of very simple functions of s; the inverse transform of each can then be determined by inspection. The residues of the function of s form the coefficients of the terms in the partial fraction expansion, and the residues are related to the pole and zero locations in a definite way. The dynamic response of a system can then be specified in terms of the pole and zero locations in its transfer function.

The root locus method is the most direct way of finding the locations of the poles and zeros of a system transfer function in terms of the parameters of the system. In this section four examples are considered; in each example the root locus method is used to determine that value of loop gain which places the poles and zeros of $W(s)$ on the s plane so that they will satisfy a given dynamic performance specification.

Second order servomechanism

A very simple servomechanism is sketched in Fig. 6.17. The input to this system is to be the position of the shaft on the input potentiometer, and the output is to be the position of the load shaft, which is sensed directly by the output potentiometer. The input potentiometer is excited with E_1 volts and has an active winding over γ_1 radians of the shaft motion. Similarly, E_0 and γ_0 describe the output potentiometer. The voltage summing circuit provides an error voltage e, which is the difference between e_1 and e_0; e is therefore a function of the error, or misalignment, between the input shaft position R and the output shaft position C. The exact relationship between e and the physical error, or misalignment, is easily derived from the following relationships:

$$e_1 = R\left(\frac{E_1}{\gamma_1}\right)$$

$$e_0 = C\left(\frac{E_0}{\gamma_0}\right)$$

$$e = e_1 - e_0 \tag{6.71}$$

The amplifier boosts the level of e and supplies enough power to drive the servomotor. Amplifier gain K_A is assumed to be a numeric (no time lag), and is

$$K_A = \frac{e_M}{e} \tag{6.72}$$

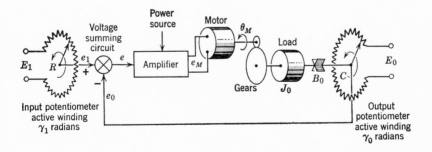

Fig. 6.17. Second order servomechanism.

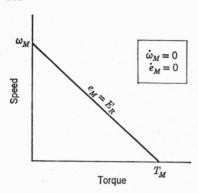

Fig. 6.18. Speed-torque curve for bare servomotor in Fig. 6.17.

A steady state speed-torque curve for the bare motor is drawn in Fig. 6.18. Although it is shown as a straight line here, most servomotors have speed-torque characteristics which are slightly curved, and the straight line drawn between the no-load speed point and the stall-torque point is an approximation made in order that the system may be treated as a linear one. From the speed-torque curves the torque constant for the motor is defined as

$$K_M = \frac{T_M}{E_R} \tag{6.73}$$

The equivalent viscous friction coefficient is

$$f_M = \frac{T_M}{\omega_M} \tag{6.74}$$

If the moment of inertia of the motor is J_M and the gear ratio between the motor shaft and output shaft is n, that is,

$$\theta_M = nC \tag{6.75}$$

the transfer function relating the output to the motor voltage is

$$\frac{C(s)}{E_M(s)} = \frac{nK_M}{(J_0 + n^2 J_M)s^2 + (B_0 + n^2 f_M)s} \tag{6.76}$$

J_0 is the moment of inertia of the output shaft, and B_0 is the viscous friction coefficient for the output shaft.

The moments of inertia of the gears are not included in Eq. 6.76, and all friction other than the viscous variety has also been neglected.

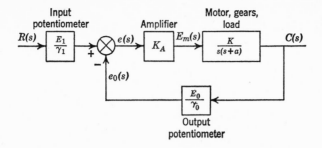

Fig. 6.19.   Block diagram for second order servomechanism.

Equation 6.76 can be simplified to

$$\frac{C(s)}{E_M(s)} = \frac{K}{s(s + a)} \tag{6.77}$$

where $\qquad K = \dfrac{nK_M}{J_0 + n^2 J_M} \qquad$ and $\qquad a = \dfrac{B_0 + n^2 f_M}{J_0 + n^2 J_M} \tag{6.78}$

Now the system, which is described physically by the schematic diagram in Fig. 6.17, may be described analytically by a block diagram having a transfer function in each of the blocks. Such a diagram is drawn in Fig. 6.19, where each block represents a particular physical element. As it is shown here, the system is not a unity feedback system, unless, of course, E_0/γ_0 happens to be unity. However, the block diagram can be rearranged into a simpler, unity feedback form without a change in its analytical meaning. This is done in Fig. 6.20,

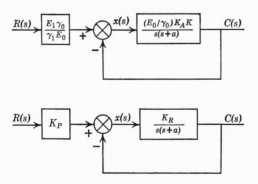

Fig. 6.20.   Simplified block diagram for the second order servomechanism.

where the rearrangement, while preserving the analytical relationship between $C(s)$ and $R(s)$, has destroyed the identity of each block with a particular physical element. If the following definitions are made

$$\frac{E_0}{\gamma_0} K_A K = K_R$$

$$\frac{E_1 \gamma_0}{\gamma_1 E_0} = K_P \qquad (6.79)$$

the system transfer function can be written as

$$W(s) = \frac{C(s)}{R(s)} = \frac{K_P K_R}{s(s + a) + K_R} \qquad (6.80)$$

Let us assume that all the physical parameters except the amplifier gain are fixed and that we wish to determine the way in which the dynamic response of the system to a step input changes as K_A is varied. K_A is not contained in K_P or in a but is directly proportional to K_R, as shown by Eq. 6.79. The locations of the poles of $W(s)$ will therefore change as K_A is varied. The root locus method is the most direct way of illustrating the manner in which the poles of $W(s)$ move around in the s plane as K_A is changed. The poles of $W(s)$ occur at the values for s for which

$$s(s + a) + K_R = 0 \qquad (6.81)$$

This equation may be rearranged to the standard root locus form

$$\frac{K_R}{s(s + a)} = -1 \qquad (6.82)$$

where $K_R/[s(s + a)]$ is recognized as the transfer function of the forward path of the unity feedback loop in Fig. 6.20. A root locus plot for this system is begun with the plotting of the poles and zeros of $K_R/[s(s + a)]$ on the s plane. No finite zeros occur, and the only two poles are at $s = 0$ and $s = -a$. These are plotted in Fig. 6.21. The only points on the real axis which satisfy the angle requirement

$$\bigg/ \frac{K_R}{s(s + a)} = 0° - \underline{/s} - \underline{/s + a} = \pm 180° \qquad (6.83)$$

are located between the two poles, or, as the rule states, "to the left of an odd number of singularities." The off-axis loci are found with

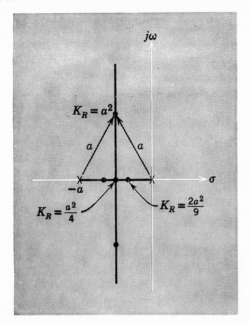

Fig. 6.21. Root locus plot for second order servomechanism.

the aid of the asymptotes, which in this case intersect the axis at

$$\frac{\Sigma \text{ pole values} - \Sigma \text{ zero values}}{n - m} = \frac{(0 - a) - (0)}{2 - 0} = -\frac{a}{2} \quad (6.84)$$

n is the number of poles, and m is the number of finite zeros. The angles of intersection of the asymptotes are

$$\frac{\pm 180°}{n - m} = \pm 90° \quad (6.85)$$

The loci happen to coincide with the asymptotes in this case because of the symmetry of the asymptotes with respect to the two poles.

It is now possible to trace the path made by the poles of $W(s)$ as K_R is varied from zero to infinity. The magnitude requirement

$$\left| \frac{K_R}{s(s + a)} \right| = 1 \quad (6.86)$$

which may also be written as

$$K_R = |s| \, |s + a| \tag{6.87}$$

shows that for $K_R = 0$, $s = 0$ and $s = -a$ satisfy Eq. 6.87 and are therefore the poles of $W(s)$. This is also apparent from Eq. 6.80.

If K_R is increased from zero to a small value, say $2a^2/9$, the two poles of $W(s)$ will lie at $s = -a/3$ and $s = -2a/3$, since these are the two values for s which satisfy Eq. 6.87 for $K_R = 2a^2/9$. These two points are marked with dots in Fig. 6.21. For $K_R = a^2/4$ both poles of $W(s)$ lie at $s = -a/2$, as shown on the root locus plot. As K_R is increased beyond $a^2/4$, the poles of $W(s)$ must move off the axis along the loci to points at which the magnitude requirement is satisfied. For $K_R = a^2$, for example, the poles of $W(s)$ lie at $s = -a/2 \pm j\, a\, \sqrt{3}/2$, because at these points $|s| = a$ and $|s + a| = a$ satisfy Eq. 6.87. As K_R is increased beyond a^2, the system poles move outward along the loci.

Since $W(s)$ has just two poles, it is apparent from the transfer function for $W(s)$ in Eq. 6.80 that this servomechanism is a second order system. It is possible to write $W(s)$ in terms of a damping ratio and an undamped natural frequency, and since $W(s)$ has no finite zeros, the second order transient response curves in Fig. 3.35 may be used to represent the dynamic response of this system to a step input. We have

$$W(s) = \frac{K_P K_R}{s^2 + as + K_R} = \frac{K_P \omega_n{}^2}{s^2 + 2\zeta\omega_n s + \omega_n{}^2} \tag{6.88}$$

where $\qquad \omega_n{}^2 = K_R \qquad$ and $\qquad \zeta = \dfrac{a}{2\sqrt{K_R}} \tag{6.89}$

Notice that for critical damping, $\zeta = 1$, K_R must be $a^2/4$. This checks with the root locus plot which shows a pair of poles at $s = -a/2$ for $K_R = a^2/4$.

Assume that the physical parameters for the servomechanism are known to be the following:

Motor parameters (from speed torque curve)

$$T_M = 10.0 \text{ in.-oz}$$

$$\omega_M = 8000 \text{ rpm}$$

$$E_R = 100 \text{ v}$$

Other parameters

$$J_M = 4 \text{ g-cm}^2$$
$$n = 10$$
$$J_0 = 1 \text{ lb-cm}^2$$
$$B_0 = 0.5 \text{ in.-oz/rad/sec}$$
$$E_0 = 6 \text{ v}$$
$$\gamma_0 = 360°$$
$$E_1 = 6 \text{ v}$$
$$\gamma_1 = 180°$$
$$K_A = \text{adjustable}$$

Let us find the amplifier gain K_A which will give the system an output response to a step input with approximately 5 percent overshoot. From the second order curves in Fig. 3.35 it is found that a damping ratio of about 0.7 will give 5 percent overshoot. A damping ratio of 0.707 requires that the poles lie on the loci and on lines drawn through the origin, making angles of $\pm 45°$ with the negative real axis. (See Fig. 4.28.) In this example $K_R = a^2/2$ will place the system poles at the required locations. It is now necessary to find a numerical value for a from the physical parameters of the system. To do this, adopt a consistent set of units and express the physical parameters in that set. With grams as the unit of mass, dynes as the unit of force, centimeters for length, seconds for time, and radians for angular measurement, the above described physical parameters are:

$$T_M = 705{,}000 \text{ dyne-cm}$$
$$\omega_M = 837 \text{ rad/sec}$$
$$E_R = 100 \text{ v}$$
$$J_M = 4 \text{ g-cm}^2$$
$$n = 10$$
$$J_0 = 454 \text{ g-cm}^2$$
$$B_0 = 35{,}400 \text{ dyne-cm/rad/sec}$$
$$E_0 = 6 \text{ v}$$
$$\gamma_0 = 2\pi \text{ rad}$$
$$E_1 = 6 \text{ v}$$
$$\gamma_1 = \pi \text{ rad}$$

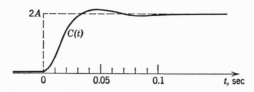

Fig. 6.22.   Output response of second order servomechanism to step input of A radians.

From these values and Eqs. 6.73, 6.74, and 6.78 we have:

$$K_M = 7{,}050 \text{ dyne-cm/v}$$

$$f_M = 842 \text{ dyne-cm/rad/sec}$$

$$K = 82.5 \text{ 1/v-sec}^2$$

$$a = 140 \text{ 1/sec}$$

$K_R = 9800$ is the necessary loop gain for this system, and the amplifier gain is obtained from Eq. 6.79 as

$$K_A = \frac{K_R \gamma_0}{K E_0} = 124 \text{ v/v} \tag{6.90}$$

If a step input of A radians is applied to the input potentiometer shaft, the resulting output shaft motion will have the same form as the curve in Fig. 3.35 for $\zeta = 0.7$. Since the output shaft must move twice as far as the input shaft in order to balance the voltage of the input potentiometer, the steady-state value for the output will be $K_P A$, or $2A$. $C(t)$ is plotted in Fig. 6.22, where the time scale is determined for $\omega_n = 99$ from Fig. 3.35.

Third order servomechanism

As a second example, assume that in the servomechanism just described the amplifier is replaced by an amplifier which has a time lag of $1/b$ seconds and a steady state gain of K_1/b. A block diagram for the modified servomechanism is drawn in Fig. 6.23, where the transfer function of the new amplifier is given. The block diagram can be simplified to a unity feedback diagram by a manipulation of the blocks, as shown in Fig. 6.24. If the time constant of the amplifier is 5 msec, $b = 200$, and the system transfer function may be written as follows:

$$W(s) = \frac{2K_R}{s(s + 140)(s + 200) + K_R} = \frac{2K_R}{s^3 + 340s^2 + 28000s + K_R} \tag{6.91}$$

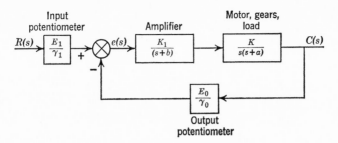

Fig. 6.23. Block diagram for a third order servomechanism.

To determine how the transient response of this servomechanism will vary with changes in K_1, find the poles of $W(s)$, using a root locus plot.   In this system the poles lie at the points at which the following equation is satisfied:

$$\frac{K_R}{s(s + 140)(s + 200)} = -1 \qquad (6.92)$$

Begin the root locus plot by plotting the poles of Eq. 6.92 on the s plane and finding the real axis loci, as shown in Fig. 6.25.   Compute the angles and point of intersection of the asymptotes as follows:

$$\text{Angles:} \quad \frac{\pm 180°}{3 - 0} = \pm 60°$$

$$\frac{\pm 540°}{3 - 0} = \pm 180°$$

$$\text{Point of intersection:} \quad \frac{(0 - 140 - 200) - (0)}{3 - 0} = -113.33 \qquad (6.93)$$

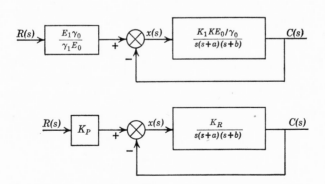

Fig. 6.24. Simplified block diagram for third order servomechanism.

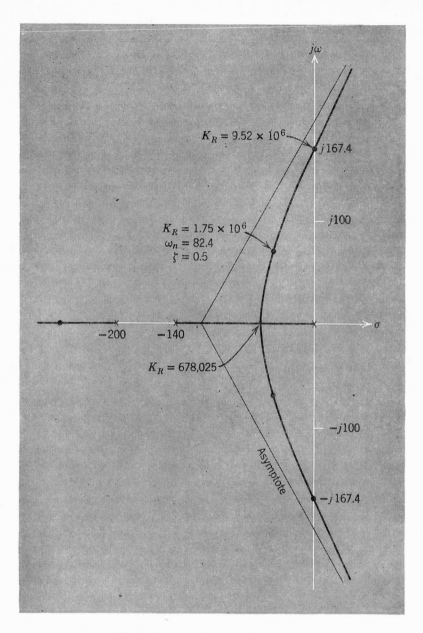

Fig. 6.25. Root locus plot for third order servomechanism.

Once the asymptotes are sketched on the s plane it becomes apparent that the root locus has a branch point somewhere between $s = 0$ and $s = -140$, and that the branches from this point approach the asymptotes.

The breakaway point may be found by the method described in Section 6.3, or it may be found by reasoning as follows: As K_R is increased from 0, two of the poles of $W(s)$ start from 0 and -140 and move along the axis toward one another, meeting at the breakaway point. When the two poles are at the breakaway point the value of K_R is higher than it is when the poles are at any other locations on the axis. Since the value for K_R required to place a pole of $W(s)$ at $s = -\sigma \, (0 < \sigma < 140)$ is

$$K_R = \frac{(\sigma)(140 - \sigma)(200 - \sigma)}{1} \tag{6.94}$$

a plot of K_R versus σ will show K_R to be at a maximum when σ is the coordinate of the breakaway point. In this system the breakaway point occurs at $\sigma = 54.079$ and $K_R = 678,025$.

The points at which the root loci cross the imaginary axis are also easily determined by trial-and-error measurements. A starting point may be found quickly by reasoning as follows: At the point $s = j140$ the total angle of the transfer function in Eq. 6.92 will be less than the 180° required for point s on the locus. (The angle of a vector drawn from the origin to $s = j140$ is 90°, that of a vector drawn from the pole at $s = -140$ is exactly 45°, and the angle of the vector drawn from the pole at $s = -200$ is less than 45°.) The total angle of the transfer function is more than the required 180° at the point $s = j200$. Therefore, a first estimate of the crossover point might be $s = j170$, halfway between $s = j140$ and $s = j200$. In this system the crossover point is actually at $s = j167.4$.

A second way to find the crossover point is to apply Routh's rule to the denominator of $W(s)$ in Eq. 6.91 in order to find the critical value for K_R. This value is $K_R = 9.52 \times 10^6$. From the coefficients in the denominator of $W(s)$ we know that the sum of the poles of $W(s)$ is -340 and that the product of the absolute value of the poles is K_R. At the critical value of gain, $K_R = 9.52 \times 10^6$, two poles of $W(s)$ are on the imaginary axis, and since the sum of these two is zero, the pole on the real axis must be at $s = -340$. Then, from the product relationship,

$$\left|+j\omega_c\right| \left|-j\omega_c\right| \left|-340\right| = 9.52 \times 10^6 \tag{6.95}$$

$\pm j\omega_c$ are the crossover points. This equation is solved for ω_c.

$$\omega_c = \sqrt{\frac{9.52 \times 10^6}{340}} = 167.4 \qquad (6.96)$$

Once the real axis loci, asymptotes, breakaway and crossover points are plotted, the entire root locus plot can be completed by finding, through a process of trial-and-error estimation, several additional points which satisfy the angle requirement. These points are then connected in a smooth curve. The complete locus is shown in Fig. 6.25.

Now let us determine the proper amplifier gain for this system. Ordinarily it is desirable to use as high a gain as possible because this minimizes the static error due to friction and other miscellaneous torque disturbances on the output shaft. On the other hand, as the gain is increased toward the point of instability, the transient response becomes oscillatory. It is therefore necessary to establish a specification for the transient response and to find the maximum value of gain which fulfills that specification. Assume that the specification for the transient response is that the overshoot of $c(t)$ in response to a step in $r(t)$ must be 16 percent or less of the final value of $c(t)$. We must now decide where the poles of $W(s)$ ought to lie in order to satisfy this requirement for the percentage overshoot of $c(t)$ and also what K_R must be in order to put the poles in the desired location. This may be done in the following manner.

It is seen from the root locus plot that for $K_R < 678{,}025$ all the poles of $W(s)$ will lie on the real axis. No finite zeros occur in $W(s)$, so $C(s)$ will have the form

$$C(s) = \frac{2AK_R}{s(s + Q_1)(s + Q_2)(s + Q_3)} \qquad (6.97)$$

where A is the magnitude of the step input, and Q_1, Q_2, and Q_3 are all real numbers. The inverse transform of $C(s)$ yields the transient response

$$c(t) = K_0 + K_4\epsilon^{-Q_1 t} + K_2\epsilon^{-Q_2 t} + K_3\epsilon^{-Q_3 t} \qquad (6.98)$$

K_0, K_4, K_2, and K_3 are the residues of $C(s)$ at the four poles and may be evaluated by the methods discussed in Chapter 4. It may easily be shown that this response never overshoots—that is, $c(t) \leq K_0$ for all values of t. Therefore, it will be possible to operate this system within the stated specification when $K_R > 678{,}025$—that is, when two poles of $W(s)$ are on the complex portion of the locus. With two complex poles the output will overshoot by an amount depending upon the positions of the poles.

Consider the system when K_R is set so that the damping ratio of the complex poles is 0.5. It may be determined from the root locus plot that when $K_R = 1.747 \times 10^6$, poles of $W(s)$ will occur at $s = -257.647$ and $s = -41.176 \pm j71.320$. In Chapter 4 it was shown that the step response of a third order system having two complex poles is very nearly the same as the step response of a second order system, provided the single real pole is "far" from the imaginary axis. (In this system, when $K_R = 1.747 \times 10^6$, the real pole is approximately 6.3 times as far from the imaginary axis and over 3 times as far from the origin as are the complex poles.) If the input is a step function, the residue at the real pole will be considerably smaller than the residues at the other poles of $C(s)$, and the time constant of the component in $c(t)$ associated with the real pole will also be relatively small. $c(t)$, then, will be very close to the response of a second order system whose damping ratio is 0.5; Fig. 3.35 shows this to be a response having approximately 16 percent overshoot, which is the specification for this system. We know that the proper value for loop gain for this system will be close to $K_R = 1.747 \times 10^6$.

Actually, the gain can be set a trifle higher than this value without exceeding 16 percent overshoot. Since the component in $c(t)$ associated with the pole at $s = -257.647$ is negative in sign, $c(t)$ will always be slightly less than the second order response. If K_R is increased to, say, 1.8×10^6, the damping ratio of the complex poles will be slightly less than 0.5, the real pole will be slightly farther from the origin than $s = -257.647$, and the response to a step input will overshoot by an amount slightly less than that of a second order system whose damping ratio is a little less than 0.5. The overshoot, in other words, will be 16 percent.

A K_R of 1.8×10^6 corresponds to an amplifier gain of $K_1/b = 114.1$ v/v. Notice than in the previous example, where the amplifier was assumed to have no time lag, a gain of 124 v/v produced an overshoot of only 5 percent. In this system the time lag of the amplifier puts a pole at $s = -200$, which in turn causes the root locus to curve into the right half plane, limiting the amplifier gain which can be used.

In practice the amplifier is ordinarily designed with an adjustable gain, since the value for gain which is determined by linear analysis is based on data which is usually not exact. The speed-torque characteristics of small servomotors, for example, will vary with small fluctuations in the manufacturing process. In this system the amplifier would probably be built so that its gain could be varied up to 150.

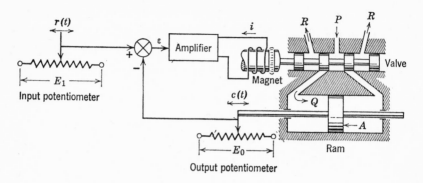

Fig. 6.26.   Electro-hydraulic servomechanism.

After the servomechanism is assembled, the exact value for amplifier gain would be determined by experiment.   Because the linear analysis is only an approximate representation of the physical system it need not always be as precise as that shown in this example.

Electro-hydraulic servomechanism

As a third example of design procedure used to set loop gain at the desired value, consider the problem of finding the proper amplifier gain in the electro-hydraulic servomechanism shown in Fig. 6.26.   In this system the error signal is again derived by taking the difference between the voltages from the input and output potentiometers.   The error signal drives an amplifier which produces in the magnet coil a current proportional to the error voltage.   The magnet-valve-ram operation is described in detail in Chapter 4.   From this physical description of the system components a block diagram is drawn (see Fig. 6.27), and a transfer function for each of the blocks is derived.   In

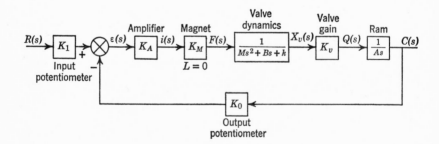

Fig. 6.27.   Block diagram for electro-hydraulic servomechanism.

this system the inductance of the magnet has been ignored, so that the transfer function representing the amplifier is a simple gain constant having no time lag. If the magnet and valve characteristics are assumed to be linear, the transfer functions for the blocks representing these components will be like those represented in Fig. 6.27. These can be combined to form a unity feedback diagram, as shown in Fig.

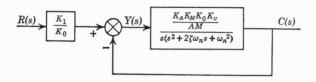

Fig. 6.28.   Figure 6.27 redrawn as a unity feedback diagram.

6.28.   The damping ratio and undamped natural frequency of the valve are defined in the usual fashion:

$$\zeta = \frac{B}{2\sqrt{kM}} \qquad \omega_n = \sqrt{k/M} \qquad (6.99)$$

Now, assume that all the parameters except the amplifier gain are known and that the amplifier gain is to be set as high as possible without causing overshoot in $c(t)$ in response to a step input $r(t)$. The values of the known parameters are:

$$K_1 = 1 \text{ v/cm}$$

$$K_0 = 0.2 \text{ v/cm}$$

$$K_M = 27,400 \text{ dynes/ma}$$

$$M = 69 \text{ grams}$$

$$k = 17.25 \times 10^6 \text{ dynes/cm}$$

$$B = 20,700 \text{ dynes/cm/sec}$$

$$K_v = 2760 \text{ cm}^3/\text{sec/cm}$$

$$A = 5 \text{ cm}^2$$

$$\zeta = 0.3$$

$$\omega_n = 500 \text{ rad/sec}$$

From these parameters the loop transfer function can be written as

$$\frac{C(s)}{Y(s)} = \frac{K_R}{s[s^2 + 2(.3)(500)s + (500)^2]} \tag{6.100}$$

where
$$K_R = K_A(43,900) \tag{6.101}$$

The system transfer function is

$$W(s) = \frac{5K_R}{s(s^2 + 300s + 250,000) + K_R}$$

$$= \frac{5K_R}{s^3 + 300s^2 + 250,000s + K_R} \tag{6.102}$$

The poles of $W(s)$ are found by the root locus method. First, the poles of $C(s)/Y(s)$ are located on the s plane, and the real axis loci is drawn to the left of the pole at the origin, as shown in Fig. 6.29. Next, the asymptotes are computed:

$$\text{Asymptote angle:} \quad \pm \frac{180°}{3 - 0} = \pm 60°$$

$$\pm \frac{540°}{3 - 0} = \pm 180° \tag{6.103}$$

$$\text{Point of intersection:} \quad \frac{(-150 + j477) + (-150 - j477) + 0}{3 - 0}$$

$$= -100 \tag{6.104}$$

The asymptotes are sketched on the root locus plot. The angle at which the root loci depart from the complex poles is easily computed.

$$\text{Angle of departure} = 180° - 90° - 107.46° = -17.46° \tag{6.105}$$

Next, the point at which the loci cross into the right half plane may be determined by finding the points along the imaginary axis which satisfy the angle requirement

$$\bigg/ \frac{C(s)}{Y(s)} = 180° \tag{6.106}$$

The points $s = \pm j500$ satisfy this requirement. If one or two additional points on the loci are found by trial-and-error measurements the loci may be sketched with a fair degree of accuracy, as shown here. Now the root locus plot shows all the possible pole configurations for $W(s)$ as a function of the loop gain K_R. All that remains to be done is to select the pole configuration which satisfies the design specification and then to find the value of K_R which will give that configuration.

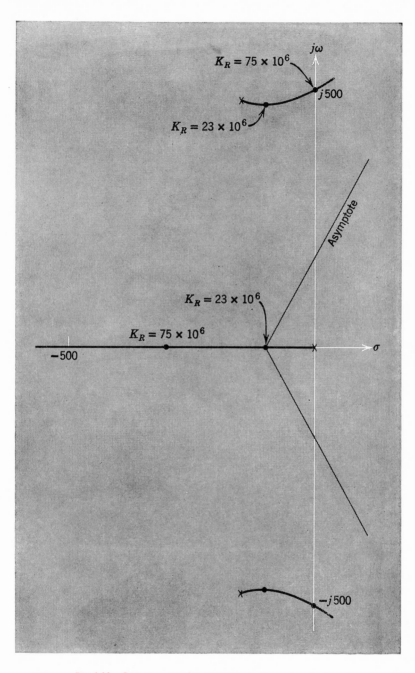

Fig. 6.29.   Root locus plot for electro-hydraulic servomechanism.

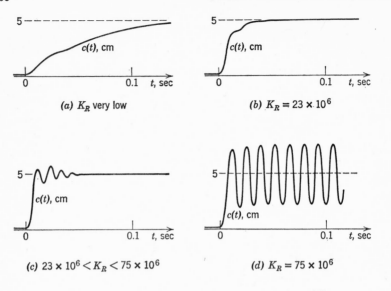

Fig. 6.30.   Response to a 1-cm step input for various values of K_R.

In Chapter 4 the dynamic response of the third order system as a function of the pole locations was explored quite thoroughly.   Recalling these relationships, let us reason in the following way.   For very low values of K_R the system transfer function will have poles close to the poles of $C(s)/Y(s)$.   Therefore, the response to a step input will be dominated by the first order term corresponding to the pole of $W(s)$ near the origin.   (The residues at the complex poles will be very small, and the time constant of the underdamped component in $c(t)$ will be small, also.)   Figure 6.30a shows a sketch of this response.   As K_R is increased from low values, the real pole moves along the axis toward the left, and the complex poles move along their loci toward the right. At some value for K_R all three poles will lie along the same vertical line—that is, the real parts of all the poles will be equal.   It is easy to see that this will occur when the real part is -100; this follows from Eq. 6.102, in which it is seen that the sum of the three poles of $W(s)$ is always -300.   A computation for K_R shows that $K_R = 23 \times 10^6$ will place the three poles directly in line.   It was shown in Chapter 4 that when the three poles are in line the step response will not overshoot but will have the form indicated in Fig. 6.30b.   The slope of the $c(t)$ curve becomes zero, but never negative, during this response; hence $c(t)$ does not overshoot.

When $K_R > 23 \times 10^6$ the real pole will lie farther from the imaginary axis than do the complex poles. The residues and time constant associated with the complex poles will be larger than they were previously, and the step response will therefore be more oscillatory than it was. Figure 6.30c is an example showing that some overshoot occurs. Finally, if the gain is raised to 75×10^6, the critical value for stability, the complex poles will lie on the imaginary axis, and the step response will have an undamped sinusoidal component with a frequency of 500 rad/sec. Figure 6.30d shows this case.

It is apparent from the above analysis that $K_R = 23 \times 10^6$ is the solution to the problem, since any higher value of gain will cause the step response to overshoot. When Eq. 6.101 is used to relate this to the actual amplifier gain, it is seen that the amplifier gain should be $K_A = 525$ ma/v in order to satisfy the design requirement.

It should be noted here that because of the difference in K_1 and K_0 the steady-state gain of this servomechanism is not unity but $K_1/K_0 = 5$. Because of the integrator (ram) inside the loop the steady state value of $y(t)$ will be zero; consequently, the steady-state gain of the servomechanism is independent of the amplifier, valve, and ram parameters. In the paragraphs which follow, the control system of a nonintegrating process is analyzed, and it will be seen that the steady-state gain of that system is dependent upon the parameters of the mechanisms within the loop.

Nonintegrating process

Consider the air temperature regulating system shown in Fig. 6.31. Here the purpose of the system is to control the temperature of the air

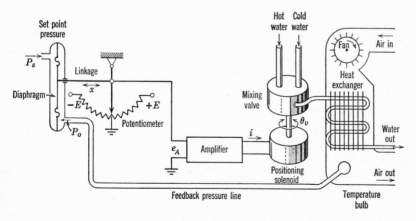

Fig. 6.31. Air temperature control system.

flowing through the duct in accordance with the set point pressure at the left of the diagram. Pressure P_0 is generated by the temperature of the air in the duct; if it is different from the set point pressure a force will occur on the spring-restrained diaphragm, causing it to deflect and to move the wiper of the potentiometer. The voltage at the input of the amplifier is therefore proportional to the difference in the two pressures. This voltage will also be proportional to the temperature error in the system if the temperature bulb is properly calibrated. A current proportional to e_A is produced in the winding of the positioning solenoid, so that the position of the mixing valve θ_v is also proportional to the temperature error in the system.

In summary, the system operates as follows. Suppose that the air temperature in the duct is exactly at its proper level so that e_A is zero and the mixing valve shaft is centered. The set point pressure is then suddenly increased, calling for a higher temperature in the air. The diaphragm will be deflected to the right by this increase in pressure, and a positive voltage will be developed at the input of the amplifier. The solenoid and valve are designed so that a positive voltage at the amplifier will cause the valve to move toward the *hot* position, increasing the temperature of the water in the heat exchanger. As the temperature of the air moving across the heat exchanger increases, the temperature bulb will cause the feedback pressure P_0 to increase until it reaches the set point pressure, at which time the system will again be in equilibrium at the new temperature level.

With this information at hand it is now a simple matter to predict the manner in which the system reacts to other disturbances, such as a change in the temperature of the input air, the accumulation of oil or dust on the heat exchanger fins, or a change in the temperature of the hot water into the mixing valve. We know that this qualitative analysis of the operation of the air temperature control system is at best inexact, primarily because of the time lags associated with each of the components in the system. For example, the diaphragm cannot respond instantaneously to changes in pressures P_s or P_0; the current in the solenoid winding cannot change instantaneously, and the shaft of the mixing valve will not respond immediately to fluctuations in the solenoid current. Time lags are associated with the heat exchanger and temperature bulb responses as well. These time lags in a feedback system may very well cause instability; consequently, a quantitative analysis must be made to determine whether the system will really be capable of maintaining the condition of equilibrium predicted by the qualitative analysis.

This quantitative stability analysis is made in the usual fashion,

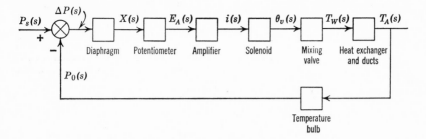

Fig. 6.32. Block diagram for air temperature control system.

starting with a block diagram for the system (Fig. 6.32). It is now necessary to obtain a transfer function for each of the blocks so that a root locus plot can be drawn. It is assumed here that each component of the system is operated over its linear range, although this assumption is not a reasonable one in some temperature control systems.* The transfer function for each block can be determined experimentally by making suitable dynamic measurements on the equipment, or it can be derived analytically from the physical parameters of the components. Let us assume that each of the transfer functions is determined as follows:

A step change in the temperature of the air surrounding the temperature bulb causes the pressure P_0 to rise abruptly, reaching its new level within a fraction of a second. Although there is a small time lag here, it can be neglected, and the transfer function for the bulb is taken to be

$$\frac{P_0(s)}{T_A(s)} = K_B \qquad (6.107)$$

A test made on the diaphragm-potentiometer-amplifier portion of the system shows that the solenoid current, in response to a step change in pressure, is of the form shown in Fig. 6.33a. This response is very nearly the same as a first order response having a time constant of 1 sec, except that the slope of the curve is zero at $t = 0$. Therefore, the transfer function may be approximated by a second order lag, where a second time constant of $\frac{1}{10}$ sec is approximately that which is required to fit the curve:

$$\frac{i(s)}{\Delta P(s)} = \frac{K_1}{(s + 1)(s + 10)} \qquad (6.108)$$

* If one of the system components is nonlinear, a transfer function cannot be defined for that component, and a different type of analysis must be used.

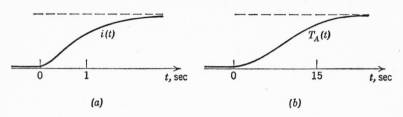

Fig. 6.33. Dynamic tests to determine component transfer functions.

Because of the inductance of the solenoid, it would be difficult to measure the transfer function relating solenoid current to the water temperature out of the mixing valve by applying a step of current to the valve.   However, other forms of time-varying currents, such as a ramp, may be generated and the response in water temperature noted. Assume that such a test is conducted and the transfer function is determined to be

$$\frac{T_w(s)}{i(s)} = \frac{K_2(s + 0.3)}{(s + 0.25)(s + 0.5)} \qquad (6.109)$$

Finally, the dynamic characteristics of the heat exchanger and ducts are determined by measuring the fluctuations in the air temperature of the duct which are produced by variations of a known character in the water temperature. Say, for example, that a step change in water temperature T_w is applied and the response shown in Fig. 6.33b is observed.   This response is characteristic of a transfer function:

$$\frac{T_A(s)}{T_w(s)} = \frac{K_H}{(s + 0.07)(s + 0.6)} \qquad (6.110)$$

Now that the transfer functions are defined, a simplified block diagram can be drawn (see Fig. 6.34a), and this can be further reduced to a unity feedback diagram (Fig. 6.34b).   Assume that the measurements which were made on the components to determine their transfer functions showed that the constants involved in this system have the following values:

$$K_B = .08 \text{ psi/}^\circ\text{F}$$

$$K_2 = 25^\circ\text{F/(amp)(sec)}$$

$$K_H = .033 \quad 1/\text{sec}^2$$

$$K_1 = K_1 \quad \text{amp/(psi)(sec}^2) \qquad (6.111)$$

We must now determine the proper value for K_1 in order to insure an acceptable transient response for the whole system. The transient response should be as fast as possible, but it should not exhibit an excessive overshoot. For the sake of illustration, let us consider the maximum overshoot permissible to be 5 percent.

A root locus plot for this system is drawn in Fig. 6.35. Since this is a sixth order system having one zero, five branches of the root locus extend out toward infinity in the s plane. The asymptotes for these branches meet at $s = -2.424$, making angles of $\pm 36°$, $\pm 108°$, and $\pm 180°$ with the real axis. If the loop gain is defined as

$$K_R = K_1 K_2 K_B K_H \qquad (6.112)$$

the positions of the system poles corresponding to various values of K_R will be as noted on the root locus sketch. When K_R is set at about 0.236, a pair of complex poles having a damping ratio of 0.7 and an undamped natural frequency of about 0.2 rad/sec occur in the system transfer function. If no other poles or zeros occurred in the system transfer function the step response would have about 5 percent overshoot. However, when $K_R = 0.236$, four other poles occur at $s = -0.326$, $-0.9 + j0.17$, $-0.9 - j0.17$, and -10.00004, and a zero occurs at $s = -0.3$ in the system transfer function. It is necessary to assess the effect of these poles and zeros upon the transient response.

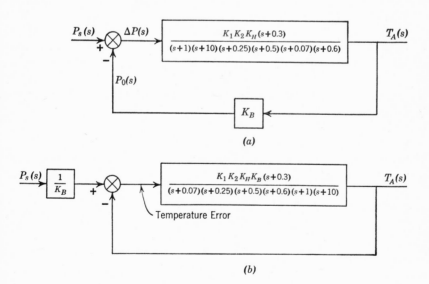

Fig. 6.34. Block diagrams for air temperature control system.

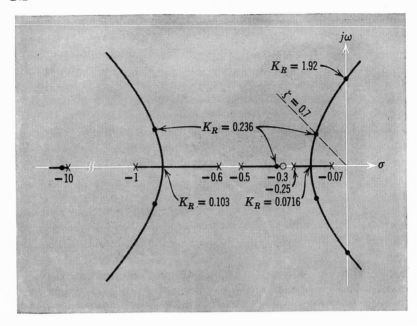

Fig. 6.35.   Root locus plot for air temperature control system.

With a step input applied there will be a pole of $T_A(s)$ at the origin. The residue at the pole located at $s = -10.00004$ will be very small, and because of its remote location it will have little influence on the relative values of the other residues.   Hence this remote pole may be neglected and the system transfer function taken to be fifth order with a zero.   Next, the dipole in the region near $s = -0.3$ can also be neglected since we are interested only in an estimate of the percentage overshoot.   This reduces the approximate system to fourth order, with two somewhat remote poles at $s = -0.9 \pm j0.17$.   The principal poles are those at $s = -0.14 \pm j0.14$.   At the instant of peak overshoot the terms in $T_A(t)$ corresponding to the complex poles at $s = -0.9 \pm j0.17$ will have decayed to an insignificant magnitude, so that the only influence which these poles can have on the percentage overshoot is through their effect on the residues at the principal poles. Because of their somewhat remote location these poles will have very little influence on the relative magnitudes of the residues at the principal poles as compared to the residue at the origin; however, they have an appreciable effect on the angle of the residue at the principal complex poles.   This effect amounts to about 20 degrees.   Therefore, in comparing the transient response of this system to that of a simple second order system, we will find that the peak overshoot in this system will occur about 2.5 seconds later than it does in the simple second order system. (20 degrees corresponds to 2.5 seconds for $\omega_0 = 0.14$ rad/sec.) The time constant of the envelope of the damped sinusoidal term is about 7 seconds, so we see that the overshoot will be about 3.5 percent in this system as compared to 5 percent in the simple second order system. Therefore, K_R could be set slightly higher than 0.236 in this system to achieve 5 percent overshoot.

From Eq. 6.111 and 6.112 the amplifier gain corresponding to $K_R = 0.236$ is found to be $K_1 = 3.54$ amp/(psi)(sec)^2. This number is related to the actual physical gain characteristic of the diaphragm-potentiometer-amplifier assembly by Eq. 6.108. The calibration for this part of the system would be such that a change in pressure of 1 psi in the diaphragm chamber would produce a change of 0.354 amp in the solenoid coil. In practice this calibration would be adjustable over a broad range—say, from 0 to 2 amp/psi—so that after the controller is put into actual service the gain could be set at the point which gives the best system performance.

The final operating gain is usually slightly different from that determined by a root locus analysis, either because the transfer function for the controlled elements are not always precisely known, or because the original design criterion (5 percent overshoot in this example) proves in practice to be an unsatisfactory criterion.

Consider the system transfer function for this temperature regulator:

$$W(s) = \frac{T_A(s)}{P_s(s)} = \frac{K_1 K_2 K_H(s + 0.3)}{\begin{array}{c}(s + 0.07)(s + 0.25)(s + 0.5)(s + 0.6)(s + 1) \\ (s + 10) + K_1 K_2 K_B K_H(s + 0.3)\end{array}} \quad (6.113)$$

The steady-state gain for this system is

$$\frac{0.3(K_1 K_2 K_H)}{0.3 K_1 K_2 K_B K_H + 0.0525} \quad (6.114)$$

and the steady-state error, in response to a step input of P psi, would be

$$P\left[\frac{1}{K_B} - \frac{0.3 K_1 K_2 K_H}{0.3 K_1 K_2 K_B K_H + 0.0525}\right]$$

$$= P\left\{\frac{0.0525}{K_B(0.3 K_1 K_2 K_B K_H + 0.0525)}\right\} \quad (6.115)$$

Notice that this error is not zero, as in the case of those servomechanism systems having an integrating element in the forward part of the control loop. In those systems a steady-state error could not exist;

such an error would cause the output to move at a constant rate because of the integrating element between the error signal and the output, and the output could be at rest only when the error is zero. In this system, however, no integrating element is present between the error pressure ΔP and the output T_A, and a steady-state ratio of $(5.71)K_1K_2K_H$ exists between the two. Hence, there must be a steady-state error in order that there may be a steady-state output! In many instances the steady-state gain between error and output can be made high enough so that the error is very small. In this system, however, if the set point pressure is increased above its usual set point, for example, by 2 psi, a pressure difference corresponding to 25°F, the steady-state output temperature will rise by only 14.3°. This is a steady-state error of 10.7°, or a pressure difference of 0.86 psi across the diaphragm. If K_1 is increased in an attempt to reduce this steady-state error, the system will become less stable, as shown by the root locus plot in Fig. 6.35. An integrating device inserted somewhere in the loop between the error signal and the output would improve the accuracy of this system by an appreciable amount. Very often a lag network having a long time constant will serve as a "pseudo-integrator." In this system such a network would be connected at the input to the amplifier.

This section has illustrated the way in which the loop gain of a feedback control system influences the dynamic response of the system. The root locus method has been shown to be a convenient way of determining the locations of the poles and zeros of the system transfer function as a function of the loop gain and the poles and zeros of the loop transfer function. Using the analytical methods developed in Chapter 4 it is possible to relate the dynamic response specification of a system to the pole-zero configuration of the system transfer function. The root locus method is therefore a convenience in finding that value of loop gain which will satisfy given dynamic performance specifications for the system.

In many instances, however, the performance specifications can not be met simply by adjusting the loop gain of the system. A simple example of this occurs in a third order servomechanism in which the static torque gain between the error signal and the output shaft is required to be at a given level, a level which can be attained only by increasing the loop gain beyond the stability point of the system! Clearly, such a situation demands that some changes must be made in the design of the system. Several measures which may be effected to satisfy performance specifications in such cases are discussed in Chapter 7.

6.5 NONUNITY FEEDBACK SYSTEMS

The general form for a single feedback loop control system is drawn in Fig. 6.36. In the preceding sections attention has been concentrated on the "unity feedback" system—the system in which $H(s)$ is unity (or a constant). It is a simple matter to extend the root locus method to include the general case in which the feedback elements have a transfer function other than a simple constant.

Let us set

$$G(s) = \frac{N_1(s)}{D_1(s)} \quad \text{and} \quad H(s) = \frac{N_2(s)}{D_2(s)} \qquad (6.116)$$

where the $N(s)$ and $D(s)$ terms are polynomials.

The system transfer function is

$$W(s) = \frac{C(s)}{R(s)} = \frac{G(s)}{1 + G(s)H(s)} = \frac{N_1(s)D_2(s)}{N_1(s)N_2(s) + D_1(s)D_2(s)} \qquad (6.117)$$

The zeros of $W(s)$ occur where

$$N_1(s)D_2(s) = 0 \qquad (6.118)$$

It may then be said that $W(s)$ has zeros where $G(s)$ has zeros and where $H(s)$ has poles. The poles of $W(s)$ occur where

$$N_1(s)N_2(s) + D_1(s)D_2(s) = 0 \qquad (6.119)$$

Equation 6.119 may be factored by the root locus method by rearranging it as follows:

$$\frac{N_1(s)N_2(s)}{D_1(s)D_2(s)} = G(s)H(s) = -1 \qquad (6.120)$$

It is now obvious that the poles of $W(s)$ can be found by applying the root locus method to Eq. 6.120, where $G(s)H(s)$ is treated as $G(s)$ was treated in the unity feedback case. Two examples will serve to illustrate the application of the root locus method to nonunity feedback systems.

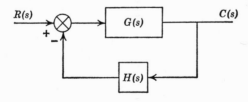

Fig. 6.36. Single loop control system.

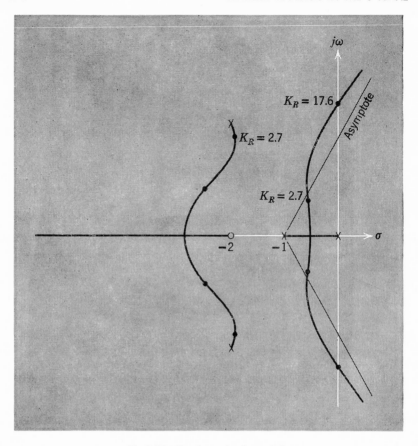

Fig. 6.37. Root locus plot, Example 1.

Example 1. Let the forward and feedback transfer functions be

$$G(s) = \frac{K_R}{s(s^2 + 4s + 8)}$$

$$H(s) = \frac{(s + 2)}{(s + 1)} \qquad (6.121)$$

The system transfer function is then

$$W(s) = \frac{K_R(s + 1)}{K_R(s + 2) + s(s + 1)(s^2 + 4s + 8)} \qquad (6.122)$$

The one zero of $W(s)$ at $s = -1$ is due to the pole in $H(s)$. The four poles of $W(s)$ will be found where

$$\frac{K_R(s + 2)}{s(s + 1)(s^2 + 4s + 8)} = -1 \qquad (6.123)$$

A root locus plot for Eq. 6.123 is drawn in Fig. 6.37. When $K_R = 2.7$, for example, the system poles will be found at the following locations in the s plane:

$$s = -0.558 \pm j0.688 \quad \text{and} \quad s = -1.941 \pm j1.762$$

The system transfer function will have the pole-zero plot shown in Fig. 6.38.

Example 2. If $H(s)$ has a zero at the point where $G(s)$ has a pole, the zero of $H(s)$ will cancel the pole of $G(s)$ when the root locus plot is drawn. Nevertheless, a pole in $W(s)$ will occur at that point. Consider the system in which

$$G(s) = \frac{K_R}{s(s^2 + 4s + 8)}$$

$$H(s) = \frac{s}{s + 2} \tag{6.124}$$

The system transfer function is found by substituting Eq. 6.124 into Eq. 6.117.

$$W(s) = \frac{K_R(s + 2)}{K_R s + s(s^2 + 4s + 8)(s + 2)} \tag{6.125}$$

Notice that since $H(s)$ has a zero and $G(s)$ has a pole at the origin, an s may be factored out of the denominator of $W(s)$.

$$W(s) = \frac{K_R(s + 2)}{s[K_R + (s + 2)(s^2 + 4s + 8)]} \tag{6.126}$$

The poles of $W(s)$ may be found by factoring the expression

$$G(s)H(s) = \frac{K_R(s)}{(s)(s + 2)(s^2 + 4s + 8)} = -1 \tag{6.127}$$

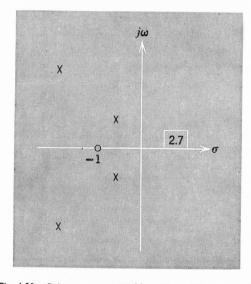

Fig. 6.38. Pole-zero map of $W(s)$ for $K_R = 2.7$, Example 1.

This is most conveniently accomplished by the root locus method.   A pole-zero plot for $G(s)H(s)$ is drawn in Fig. 6.39, and a root locus plot is also sketched. Notice the cancellation of the zero and pole at the origin.   If K_R is set at 5, for example, the root locus plot will show poles of $W(s)$ to be located at $s = -3$ and $s = -1.5 \pm j2.179$.   The pole of $W(s)$ at the origin may be thought of

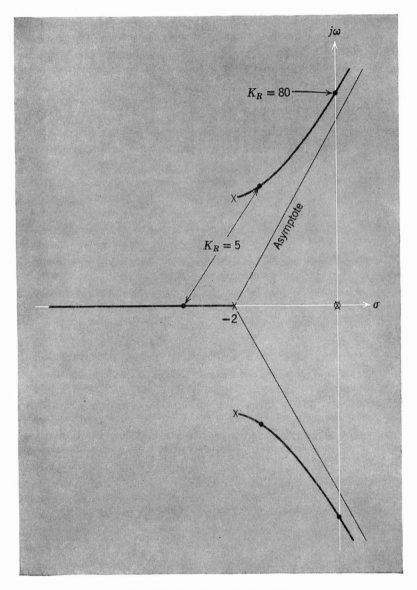

Fig. 6.39.   Root locus plot, Example 2.

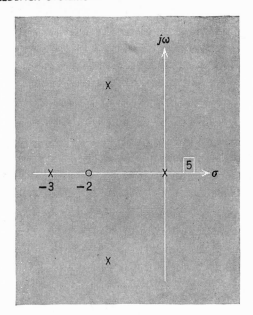

Fig. 6.40. Pole-zero map of W(s), for $K_R = 5$, Example 2.

as being located on the branch of the root locus, of zero length, which connects the zero at the origin to the pole at the origin. A pole-zero plot for $W(s)$ is drawn in Fig. 6.40.

In summary, the pole-zero configuration for the system transfer function defined by Fig. 6.36 and Eqs. 6.116 and 6.117 is determined as follows:

Zeros of $W(s)$ occur

(a) At zeros of $G(s)$
(b) At poles of $H(s)$

Poles of $W(s)$ occur

(a) At the solution of the characteristic equation $G(s)H(s) = -1$ (determinable by a root locus plot)
(b) At points where $H(s)$ has a zero and $G(s)$ has a pole, if any such points exist. (*Example 2* above is such a case.)

6.6 POSITIVE FEEDBACK SYSTEMS

Consider the unity feedback system (Fig. 6.41) in which the feedback is called *positive* or *regenerative* because the quantity $\varepsilon(s)$ is the

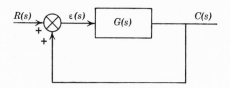

Fig. 6.41.   Positive feedback system.

sum of the input and output.   In contrast, the quantity $\varepsilon(s)$ in a
negative feedback situation is the difference between input and output.
The system transfer function for the positive feedback configuration is
derived in the usual fashion.

$$\frac{C(s)}{R(s)} = W(s) = \frac{G(s)}{1 - G(s)} \tag{6.128}$$

If $G(s)$ is expressed as

$$G(s) = \frac{N(s)}{D(s)} \tag{6.129}$$

the system transfer function is

$$W(s) = \frac{N(s)}{D(s) - N(s)} \tag{6.130}$$

The zeros of $W(s)$ are the same as the zeros of $G(s)$, and the poles of
$W(s)$ are at the roots of the characteristic equation

$$D(s) - N(s) = 0 \tag{6.131}$$

which can be rearranged to

$$\frac{N(s)}{D(s)} = 1 \tag{6.132}$$

Now, Eq. 6.132 is satisfied at values of s for which the following two
conditions hold:

$$\bigg/ \frac{N(s)}{D(s)} = 0°, \ \pm 360°, \ \pm 720°, \ \text{etc.}$$

$$\left| \frac{N(s)}{D(s)} \right| = 1 \tag{6.133}$$

Notice that these two conditions are the same as those for the negative
feedback system except that the angle requirement is 0° rather than
180°.   A root locus plot may be used to find the points on the s plane
which satisfy Eq. 6.133.   This is illustrated by the following example:

Let the loop transfer function for the positive feedback system be

$$G(s) = \frac{K_R(s + 2)}{(s + 1)(s + 5)(s^2 + 4s + 8)} \qquad (6.134)$$

The first step in making the root locus plot is to spot the poles and zeros of $G(s)$ on the s plane (see Fig. 6.42). Next, find the root loci, which

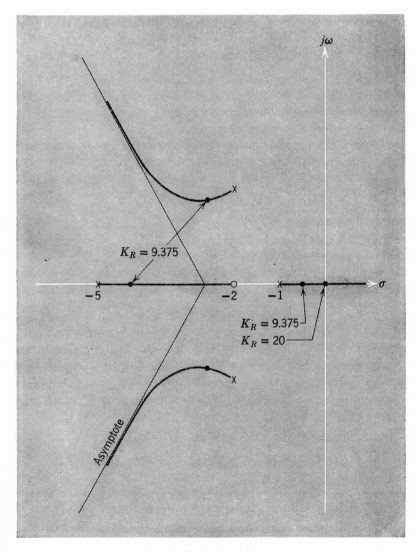

Fig. 6.42. Root locus plot for positive feedback system.

are all the points satisfying the angle requirement. Along the real axis of the s plane these points lie to the *right* of the odd numbered singularities (the number of singularities being counted from the right). In this example two branches lie: (a) to the right of the first singularity at $s = -1$ and (b) to the right of the third singularity at $s = -5$. The asymptotes lie at angles $\pm\theta$ from the real axis where

$$3\theta = 0°$$

$$3\theta = 360°$$

$$3\theta = 720° \qquad (6.135)$$

since there are three more poles than zeros in $G(s)$. Hence the asymptotes lie at angles of $0°$ and $\pm120°$. The point of intersection of the asymptotes is found by the usual technique.

$$\frac{\Sigma(\text{pole values}) - \Sigma(\text{zero values})}{4 - 1} = \frac{-10 + 2}{3} = -\frac{8}{3} \qquad (6.136)$$

The complete root locus is drawn in Fig. 6.42. For a loop gain $K_R = 9.375$, for example, the poles of the system transfer function are situated at $s = -0.5$, $s = -4.29$, and $s = -2.60 \pm j1.77$. The zero of $W(s)$ is at $s = -2$. Notice that the system will become unstable for $K_R > 20$, since the system pole moves into the right half plane at the origin at that value for gain.

Some general observations about positive feedback systems may be made from this example.

(a) In many practical systems positive feedback will not be desirable from the standpoint of stability because the root loci on the real axis lie to the right of the odd numbered singularities. In most servomechanism systems, for example, an integrating element in the loop puts a pole at the origin in $G(s)$. Positive feedback in such systems will cause instability when K_R is just slightly greater than zero.

In this example no pole occurs at the origin in $G(s)$, so the loop gain may be as high as 20 before instability occurs. If negative feedback were used, the critical value of loop gain would be $K_R = 146.71$, more than seven times greater than the positive feedback value.

(b) In this example the system is stable when $K_R < 20$. However, a pole in $W(s)$ is close to the origin, and the higher the loop gain, the closer this pole moves to the origin. As a result, the dynamic response of the system will be very slow.

(c) It should be noted that the feedback may be changed from positive to negative simply by changing the algebraic sign of K_R. This can usually be accomplished in a physical system by reversing two electrical connections in an amplifier or a potentiometer. Changing the sign of K_R will also change the sign of $W(s)$, since K_R appears as the multiplying constant of $W(s)$. This means that the output will move in the opposite direction. If, for example, when K_R is positive the output moves clockwise in response to a positive step input, a change in the algebraic sign of K_R will cause the output to move in a counterclockwise direction in response to a positive step input.

REFERENCES

1. Gardner and Barnes, *Transients in Linear Systems*, Wiley, 1942.
2. Routh, *Dynamics of a System of Rigid Bodies, Part 2*, 7th ed., Macmillan, 1905.
3. Evans, *Control System Dynamics*, McGraw-Hill, 1954.
4. Truxal, *Control System Synthesis*, McGraw-Hill, 1955.
5. Harris, *Introduction to Feedback Systems*, Wiley, 1961.

7 Control Loop Design

7.1 INTRODUCTION

In the preceding chapters we have been concerned with problems of analysis—that is, with determining the dynamic response of a given system from the parameters of that system. In this chapter we study some of the simpler methods for determining that configuration for a system which will satisfy certain performance requirements placed upon the system. Ordinarily the design problem is rather complex because of the variety of constraints which may be imposed upon the design. The more common physical constraints are accuracy, size, weight, and energy consumption; economic constraints include the costs of design and manufacture. Usually the reliability of the system must be considered, and often certain subjective or psychological considerations (such as the comfort of passengers in an automatically controlled airliner) must be taken into account. The relationships of these various constraints to each other must be determined by the designer before he may expect to arrive at a satisfactory configuration for his system.

The design problem is distinct from the analysis problem in the following respect. The analysis problem has only one correct answer; given a system and an input, a unique response will occur. The design problem, on the other hand, may have many different answers, each of which satisfies all the design specifications, or it may have no answer if two or more of the design constraints are mutually unrealizable. It is the first task of the designer to determine whether a solution to a given problem exists; only then can he pursue the solution itself.

Because the general design problem is so complex, the scope of the design specifications considered here are limited to those dealing with system accuracy and dynamic response. We work with relatively simple systems in which it is possible to see directly the manner in which our design decisions affect the dynamic response of the system; it is then possible to arrive at a satisfactory solution through a short series of "cut-and-try" attempts.

In more complex problems, in which one or more constraints are placed upon the system, the effect of a design change upon the whole situation is usually less evident. In these systems the idea of "analytical design" is sometimes used; the design specifications are expressed as an analytical function, called a performance measure or figure of merit. The design parameters and system constraints are related to this figure of merit, and an "optimum" design is arrived at through minimization techniques applied to the figure of merit. Very often the designer uses the knowledge he has gained from the "cut-and-try" approach in the analytical design approach, so the material in this chapter should be regarded as basic to control system design, even though its direct use may be limited to relatively simple systems.

Dynamic response and system accuracy are judged by looking at the system error. A generalized definition for system error was given in Fig. 5.8, and a simplified version of this general definition was used in Chapters 5 and 6. In this chapter we return to the more generalized definition of system error, although we do not use all the details shown in Fig. 5.8.

The system configuration used here appears in Fig. 7.1. Here $W(s)$ is the transfer function of the system. Inside the $W(s)$ block there will probably be one or more feedback loops designed to make $W(s)$ satisfy the performance specifications. The exact way in which the disturbance enters the system is discussed in Section 7.6. $M(s)$ is the transfer function of the "model" or ideal system. It represents the performance specifications for the system, at least as they apply to the

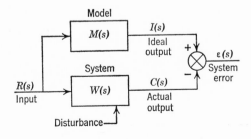

Fig. 7.1. Definition of system error.

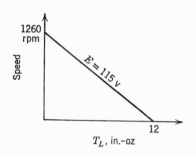

Fig. 7.2 Speed-torque curve for servomotor.

desired dynamic response of the system. If the designer restricts $M(s)$ to unity the system error is simply (input)—(output), but if he chooses $M(s)$ carefully the system error can reflect the performance specifications.

7.2 SERIES COMPENSATION

In Chapter 6 the root locus method described the relationship between the loop gain of a feedback system and the poles and zeros of $W(s)$ and made it possible to "design" the loop gain for the desired pole-zero location, provided the root locus passed through regions which satisfied the requirement for pole-zero location. In this section we consider problems which arise when (a) the gain must be set at a higher value than may be tolerated from the standpoint of pole-zero locations or (b) the root locus does not pass through the desired regions in the s plane. The solution of these problems lies in altering the loop transfer functions by placing additional dynamic elements, such as networks, in strategic places in the loop.

A third order servomechanism is used as an example to illustrate the ideas involved in the compensation problem. A servomotor whose moment of inertia is given as 0.14 oz-in.[2] is rated at 115 v and has a steady-state speed-torque curve as shown in Fig. 7.2. The motor drives a frictionless load of negligible inertia through a gear train, also inertialess, whose ratio is 22.5:1. Both the output and input potentiometers have constants of 1 v/rad. The amplifier has a time lag of 5 msec and an adjustable gain K_A. From this information the block diagram in Fig. 7.3 can be constructed, and the constants shown in

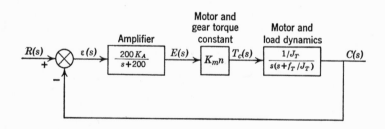

Fig. 7.3. Block diagram for third order servomechanism.

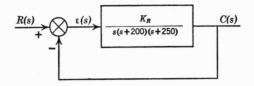

Fig. 7.4.   Simplified block diagram for third order servomechanism.

that diagram will have the following values when expressed in the cgs system of units.

$$n = 22.5$$

$$K_m = 7350 \text{ dyne-cm/v}$$

$$J_M = 25.6 \text{ gm-cm}^2$$

$$f_M = 6430 \text{ dyne-cm/rad/sec}$$

$$J_T = J_M n^2 = 12{,}960 \text{ gm-cm}^2$$

$$f_T = f_M n^2 = 32.58 \times 10^5 \text{ dyne-cm/rad/sec}$$

Here the system error is taken to be $r(t) - c(t)$; the model transfer function is unity.   If the three blocks in Fig. 7.3 are combined and numbers are assigned, the system reduces to the unity feedback diagram shown in Fig. 7.4.   The loop gain K_R is related to the amplifier gain in this way:

$$K_R = 2550 K_A \tag{7.1}$$

It should also be noted that the steady state torque gain of the forward path is

$$K_T = 1.65 \times 10^5 K_A \ \frac{\text{dyne-cm}}{\text{radian error}} \tag{7.2}$$

A root locus plot for this system (Fig. 7.5) shows that K_R must be less than 22.55×10^6 ($K_A < 8850$ v/v) for system stability, and if the damping ratio of the complex pair of system poles is to be 0.4, K_R should be 5.4×10^6 ($K_A = 2120$).   When K_R is set at 5.4×10^6 the response of the system will be almost the same as that of a second order system with 0.4 damping ratio, because the third pole in $W(s)$ will be far enough out in the s plane to be considered "remote."

Let us assume that the design specifications for this system list two requirements:

(a) The transient response to a step input should not overshoot more than 24 percent.

(b) The forward path torque gain must be at least $K_T = 17.5 \times 10^8$ dyne-cm/rad.

This second requirement is called a "droop" requirement. If a load torque is applied to the output shaft when the servomechanism is at rest, a "droop", or error, will occur in the output shaft position. The droop will be inversely proportional to the torque gain of the forward path; consequently, a high torque gain is desirable. It is evident that both these design requirements cannot be met simply by adjusting the amplifier gain. If it is increased to $K_A = 10,600$ in order to satisfy the droop requirement, the system will be unstable, and if it is set at $K_A \cong 2120$ to satisfy the overshoot requirement, the droop will be excessive.

Consider the effect which an additional element, placed in the error channel (Fig. 7.6), can have upon this system. Physically, this series

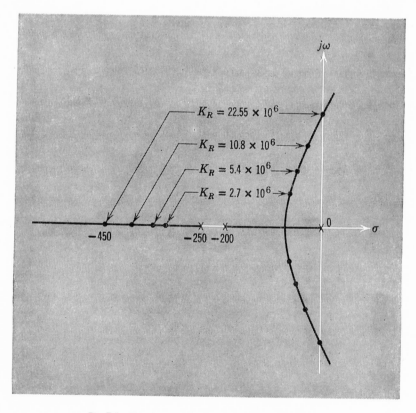

Fig. 7.5.   Root locus plot for third order servomechanism.

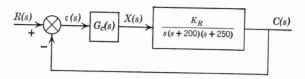

Fig. 7.6.   Third order servomechanism with a series compensating element.

element would probably be an R-C network, since the error signal is present in electrical form.   (It will be shown shortly that by placing the poles and zeros of the network properly the system design specifications can be more than satisfied.)   In choosing the pole and zero locations for $G_c(s)$ we should keep in mind the effect of this choice upon the practical problem of constructing a physical network to satisfy the pole-zero configuration.   Ordinarily, it is wise to keep the number of poles and zeros in the compensator to a minimum, as this tends to simplify the physical configuration of the network.   Also, it is usually simpler to realize (construct) a network whose poles and zeros are all real, although complex poles and zeros may be obtained if they are really needed.   Further discussion of the network synthesis problem occurs later in this section.   For the present let us assume that any choice we wish to make for the poles and zeros of $G_c(s)$ will be physically realizable, provided $G_c(s)$ is kept simple.

When additional poles and zeros are placed in the control loop, both the root locus plot and the torque gain of the forward loop will be altered. $G_c(s)$ must be chosen so that the root locus will pass through the proper regions of the s plane.   These regions are determined by the dynamic response requirements made upon $W(s)$.   The loop gain must be high enough to satisfy the droop requirement when the poles of $W(s)$ are placed in the desired regions.   It is also advisable to make the root locus plot remain within the acceptable areas for a wide range of loop gain values.

As the first trial design for $G_c(s)$ it is advisable to choose a simple configuration in order to keep the analysis as manageable as possible in the early stages.   A first order compensator having a single zero in its transfer function is the simplest form

$$G_c(s) = \frac{s + Z}{s + P} \qquad (7.3)$$

The steady state gain of this compensator is

$$G_c(0) = \frac{Z}{P} \qquad (7.4)$$

so that if this is to be a lead network ($Z < P$) it will be realizable with passive $R\text{-}C$ elements, but if it is to be a lag network ($P < Z$) some amplification will be required in the $G_c(s)$ box. (Actually, the required amplification attributable to the $G_c(s)$ box in this case could be supplied by the amplifier in the main part of the system.) Since the steady-state gain of the compensator is not unity, the torque gain of the loop will be affected by the insertion of the compensator; it will be related to K_R as

$$K_T = \frac{64.7 K_R Z}{P} \quad \frac{\text{dyne-cm}}{\text{rad}} \tag{7.5}$$

At this point we see that a large K_T may be realized if P is made very small. A root locus diagram is drawn for $P = 4$ in Fig. 7.7. Z is set arbitrarily between 200 and 250 in this diagram. A detailed evaluation of this root locus diagram will show that when K_R is set so that

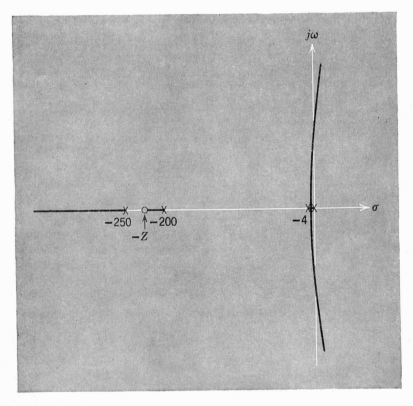

Fig. 7.7. Root locus plot for compensated system, $Z = 225$, $P = 4$.

the damping ratio of the complex poles is about 0.4, the torque gain will be only about $\frac{1}{100}$ the value it must assume in order to satisfy the design specifications. Furthermore, the complex poles would have an ω_n of only about 5 rad/sec, which means that the system would be very slow compared to the uncompensated system. Although no stipulation is made in the design specifications for the speed of response, it may be assumed that a reduction in the response speed by this much (about 25 times) would be too serious to be overlooked by the user. Therefore, we seek a way to encourage the root loci coming from the two poles near the origin to move into the left part of the s plane. Moving Z beyond -250 will not alter the root locus near the origin, nor will it increase K_T. However, if Z is moved in closer to the origin —say, to $s = -25$—the root locus will have the desired shape. Fig. 7.8 shows the result.

It may be predicted in the following way that moving the zero from $s = -225$ to $s = -25$ will have the desired effect on the root loci. The system transfer function is

$$W(s) = \frac{K_R(s + 25)}{s^4 + 454s^3 + 51800s^2 + (200,000 + K_R)s + 25K_R} \quad (7.6)$$

Remember that the sum of the poles of $W(s)$ must be -454, a constant. The zero, when placed at $s = -25$, will draw a branch of the root locus from the pole at $s = -200$ *toward the right*. Therefore, as K_R is increased, the pole value associated with this branch will be decreasing, and since the sum of the poles is constant the other system poles will have to have a net *leftward* drift. Now the remote pole is moving leftward, but because it is remote it cannot move nearly as far with a given change in K_R as can the poles closer to the origin; hence it is the leftward movement of these poles which will contribute most to offset the rightward moving pole. As the system pole nears $s = -25$ its movement as K_R is increased is greatly retarded, so that the movement of the remote pole more than offsets this slight rightward drift, and the complex poles then reverse their leftward trend and move to the right toward the asymptotes.

When K_R is set at 4.56×10^6 the damping ratio of the complex pair will be 0.4, as indicated by the dot on the locus. However, because of the zero in $W(s)$ at $s = -25$, the overshoot in response to a step input will be about 45 percent. Therefore, although the torque constant is 18.48×10^8 d-cm/rad (more than is required), this design is not yet satisfactory, and a further adjustment of P and Z is necessary to reduce the overshoot. Many combinations of P and Z will satisfy the design

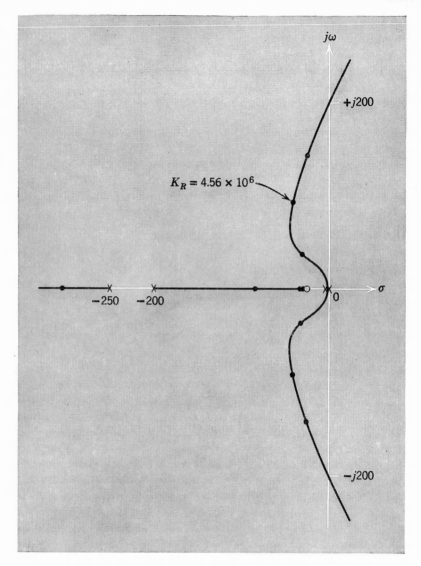

Fig. 7.8. Root locus plot for lag network compensation, $P = 4$, $Z = 25$.

requirements, and it is left as an exercise for the reader to find one of these. He can be guided in his search by the following observations.

K_T may be increased by increasing Z or decreasing P, provided K_R is held fixed. However, P, Z, and K_R are all interdependent, K_R being determined partly by the acceptable regions in the s plane through which the root loci pass. If P is changed from 4 to 2, the root locus plot will not be altered very much, K_R will be virtually unchanged, so the torque constant will be doubled. In fact, as P approaches zero the torque gain approaches infinity. The compensator becomes very much like an integrator, so that a very small steady-state error will cause a very large signal at X (Fig. 7.6). If we attempt to double the torque constant by increasing Z from 25 to 50, however, we will find that the root locus plot will be altered (it will not come as far into the left half plane), and the acceptable value for K_R will be decreased. Consequently, it is doubtful whether any increase in K_T could be realized in this way.

From this analysis we may conclude that a simple lag network will be very effective in increasing the steady state loop gain of this servo-mechanism system for a given percentage overshoot, but that this increase will be realized at a sacrifice in the *speed* of response (compared to that of an uncompensated system). Later we will see that a slightly more complicated network will give a high steady-state gain *and* a fast response.

Now let us go back to the uncompensated system and consider a different design problem. Assume that a torque constant of 35×10^7 dyne-cm/rad is sufficient for this servomechanism, but that a faster speed of response is required. The error signal in the uncompensated system first reaches an instantaneous zero 0.021 sec after the application of the step. Let us assume that this is to be reduced to about 0.01 sec, so that the system design specifications now become:

(a) Maximum overshoot not to exceed 24 percent.
(b) Speed of response to be 0.01 sec (first zero crossing of $\varepsilon(t)$).

It is also assumed that the steady-state torque gain should not be decreased appreciably from 35×10^7 d-cm/rad.

As a first trial, consider a single pole–single zero configuration for $G_c(s)$. The design specifications indicate that the root loci must be made to travel much farther out in the s plane than they do in the uncompensated system. Since we have seen that a lag network will not accomplish this, let us consider the effects of a lead network $(P > Z)$ upon the locus. It is almost immediately apparent that a lead network will have the desired effect; Fig. 7.9 is a root locus plot drawn for $Z = 70$ and $P = 300$. A comparison of this with the uncompensated system (Fig. 7.5) shows that the zero at $s = -70$ has attracted the locus emanating from the origin so that the complex poles in $W(s)$ will lie on the loci emanating from the two poles at $s = -200$ and -250, and these loci, of course, lie far out in the s plane.

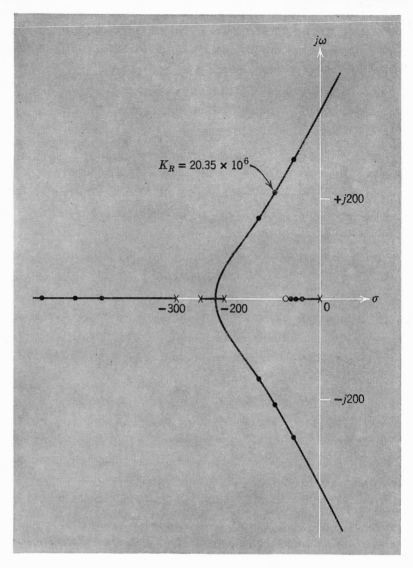

Fig. 7.9. Root locus plot for lead network compensation, $P = 300$, $Z = 70$.

For practical reasons which are explained later it is desirable that P be as small as possible, yet the larger the value of P, the steeper will be the complex loci and the faster the response. $P = 300$ is a compromise which at least serves to illustrate the effect of the lead network upon this system. If the loop gain is adjusted to $K_R = 20.35 \times 10^6$, the damping ratio of the complex poles will be 0.4, as indicated by the dots on the locus. The torque constant will be 30.8×10^7, about 10 percent under the uncompensated case. From Fig. 7.9 it is apparent that the overshoot will be less than the allowable 24 percent, because of a pole of $W(s)$ inside the zero at $s = -70$. The overshoot is, in fact, only 2 percent, but the speed of response is 0.016 sec, slower than the specifications require.

Although this particular combination of K_R, P, and Z will not satisfy the specifications it is clear that they very nearly do so, and that some small adjustments in the parameter values will do the job. For example, K_R may be increased to bring the overshoot up to the allowable 24 percent, and this alone will improve the speed of response by an appreciable amount. Also, if P is increased to 400 or 500 the root locus will shift toward the left, thereby increasing the speed of response. Again, it is left as an exercise for the reader to arrive at a final adjustment for the three compensator parameters.

In a lead network it is desirable to keep the ratio P/Z as small as possible because of noise. A first order network with a zero may be thought of as a device which produces an output signal with two components, one of which depends upon the input signal and the other upon the *derivative* of the input signal. The derivative component is emphasized approximately in the proportion P/Z; hence this emphasis is most prominent in the lead network, and it is undesirable because the noise (which is always present) at the input is usually fluctuating very rapidly compared to the data portion of the signal   The signal-to-noise ratio of a signal is therefore usually made worse by passing the signal through a lead network. For a fixed Z this effect can be minimized by keeping P as small as possible. A rule of thumb which has grown out of servomechanism technology is that P/Z should not exceed 20; obviously there will be many instances in which 20 will be either too low or too high to suit the particular circumstances, but it can be used as an average limit.

Returning to the original uncompensated third order system, let us assume that we wish to improve both the speed of response and the steady state torque gain through the use of a series compensator. From the experience gained in the analysis of the lag and lead compensators we know that a more complex network will be required to reshape the root locus so that it is brought out into the left half plane and at the same time to produce a pole-zero configuration which gives a high static gain. The next step in complexity is a compensator having two poles and two zeros.

$$G_c(s) = \frac{(s + Z_1)(s + Z_2)}{(s + P_1)(s + P_2)} \tag{7.7}$$

With this compensator in the loop the static torque gain is

$$K_T = \frac{64.7 K_R Z_1 Z_2}{P_1 P_2} \tag{7.8}$$

which indicates that one of the poles should be close to the origin in order to satisfy the torque requirement. If P_1 is placed close to the origin, a few rough root locus sketches will indicate that both Z_1 and Z_2 must be placed inside the pole at $s = -200$ if the complex branches of the locus are to emanate from the remote poles and remain far out in the s plane. P_2 should be placed beyond 250 in order to prevent its influencing the complex loci adversely.

Figure 7.10 shows a first trial configuration in which $P_1 = 5$,

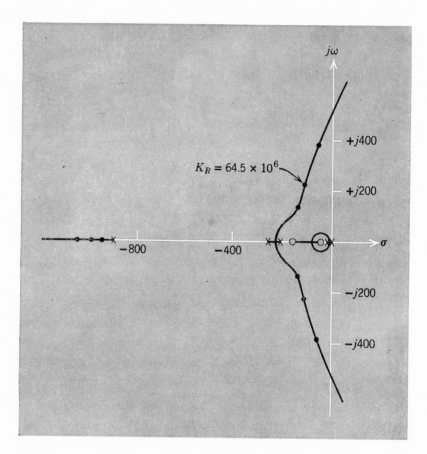

Fig. 7.10. Root locus plot for lag-lead network compensation, $G_c(s) = \dfrac{(s + 30)(s + 150)}{(s + 5)(s + 900)}$.

$P_2 = 900$, $Z_1 = 30$, and $Z_2 = 150$. A network having these particular poles and zeros is called a lag-lead network because of its frequency response properties (see Chapter 8). If K_R is set to 64.5×10^6, the damping ratio of the complex poles of $W(s)$ will be 0.4, and a double dipole will occur on the real axis, as shown in Fig. 7.11. Because the zero at $s = -30$ is *inside* the pole, and because this dipole is much closer to the origin than is the other dipole, we expect that the overshoot will be more than the allowable 24 percent. It is 33 percent, but the torque gain is twelve times higher than in the uncompensated system—418×10^7 dyne-cm/rad. This configuration, because of excessive overshoot, does not quite satisfy the design specifications, but again it is clear that small adjustments in the poles and zeros will result in a satisfactory design. These final adjustments are left as an exercise for the reader.

The table in Fig. 7.11 compares the uncompensated system with the system using the three forms of compensation. Figure 7.12 shows an accurate sketch of the four responses. Note that in all cases some adjustment in the poles, zeros, and K_R is necessary to satisfy the design specifications. By setting K_R so that the damping ratio of the complex poles is 0.4 we establish a base point from which to make the adjustments. On each branch of the root locus in Figs. 7.8, 7.9, and 7.10 3 dots appear. The center dots show the pole locations for K_R set at the indicated values and the other dots are the pole locations for K_R set at *half* and at *twice* the indicated value.

An important consideration to be kept in mind when judging the relative merits of the different forms of compensation described in Fig. 7.11 and the response curves in Fig. 7.12 is that it seems possible to make a vast improvement in system performance simply by inserting a network in the error channel and providing additional amplification in the loop. This improvement is evident in the actual system *only* when the system is in its linear range of operation. The last column in Fig. 7.11 shows the linear range, expressed in degrees error required to produce maximum static torque at the output shaft. In each case the linear range is quite small. When a step input of several degrees rotation is applied to the input potentiometer, the system will almost immediately go into saturation. The motor will accelerate to its maximum velocity and will run until the error becomes zero, at which time a settling transient will occur as the system comes to rest. The response of each of the four systems in Fig. 7.11 to large inputs would differ only in the short starting and settling transients; the maximum speed of the motor is not affected, of course, by the compensating networks. Therefore, series compensation is not the approach to be taken in order

System	$G_c(s)$	$W(s)$	K_R	K_T Dyne-cm/rad	Percentage Overshoot	Linear Range (static) Degrees Error
Uncompensated	1	$\dfrac{5.4 \times 10^6}{(s + 351.5)[s^2 + 2(0.4)(124)s + (124)^2]}$	5.4×10^6	35×10^7	23%	3.1°
Lag compensation	$\dfrac{s+25}{s+4}$	$W(s) = \dfrac{4.56 \times 10^6(s + 25)}{(s + 32.3)(s + 340)[s^2 + 2(0.4)(102)s + (102)^2]}$	4.56×10^6	185×10^7	45%	0.59°
Lead compensation	$\dfrac{s+70}{s+300}$	$\dfrac{20.35 \times 10^6(s + 70)}{(s + 51.4)(s + 513)[s^2 + 2(0.4)(232)s + (232)^2]}$	20.35×10^6	30.8×10^7	2%	3.6°
Lag-lead compensation	$\dfrac{(s+30)(s+150)}{(s+5)(s+900)}$	$\dfrac{64.5 \times 10^6(s + 30)(s + 150)}{(s + 34.1)(s + 135)(s + 997)[s^2 + 2(0.4)(251)s + (251)^2]}$	64.5×10^6	418×10^7	33%	0.26°

Fig. 7.11. Table comparing the different forms of series compensation. K_R set so damping ratio of complex poles is 0.4.

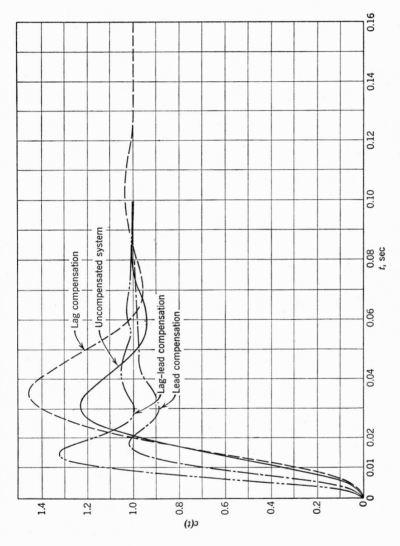

Fig. 7.12. Transient responses of the four systems listed in Fig. 7.11.

269

to improve the large signal (or slewing speed) response characteristics of a system. The advantages to be gained by series compensation are evident only in the linear region—however, many practical situations occur in which the behavior in the linear region is of extreme importance to the system performance.

Another practical problem arising from the use of electric networks in series compensation is the design of the network itself to satisfy the pole-zero locations of the compensator. If the compensator is only of the first order, a simple two or three element R-C network may be used to realize almost any pole-zero configuration which may be desired. However, if the compensator is of the second order or higher, a network must be designed especially for the particular transfer function desired. This is called the network synthesis problem. We cannot develop the theory of network synthesis in the limited space available here, but we can outline some of the practical aspects of this technology.

First, for any given transfer function an infinite number of physical networks will satisfy the pole-zero and gain requirements. Most of these solutions will be impractical because:

(a) The network requires too many elements.

(b) The element values are of impractical magnitudes.

(c) The steady-state attenuation is excessive.

(d) The pole and zero locations are overly sensitive to small errors in the network element values.

It is often a formidable task to find a practical solution. Designers sometimes try to force an easy solution to this problem by using a network configuration directly from a handbook, with appropriate values for the network elements. For example, the network shown in Fig. 7.13 is a standard form network whose transfer function has two poles and two zeros. However, this network cannot be made to satisfy an arbitrary pole-zero configuration simply by the selection of values for

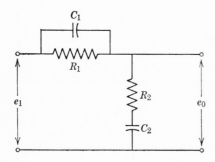

Fig. 7.13. Lag-lead network of standard form.

R_1, R_2, C_1, and C_2. Its range of possible pole-zero configurations happens to be restricted by the relationship $P_1P_2 = Z_1Z_2$. (The reader should prove this as an exercise.) Generally speaking, handbook forms are of limited use because of restrictions like this. It is poor practice to select a network configuration first and then to attempt to adjust the network parameters to fit the compensation problem. Rather, the desired pole-zero configuration for the network should be determined first and the network designed to fit these specifications. Occasionally however, for expediency, the pole-zero configuration may be bent slightly to fit a handbook form; this was the case with the lag-lead network used in Fig. 7.10.

A sometimes useful technique of series compensation is that of pole-zero cancellation between the compensator and the main part of the forward path. The need for compensation arises because the pole-zero configuration of the forward loop is undesirable. Why not, then, build a compensator having zeros at the places where the main transfer function has troublesome poles, poles where there are troublesome zeros, and also any additional poles or zeros which are necessary to satisfy the design requirements? Theoretically, this is a perfect way to compensate the system, since it gives the designer complete control over the pole-zero configuration of the loop transfer function. From a practical standpoint, also, the cancellation technique is sometimes the most direct solution to the compensation problem. However, certain practical aspects of this technique limit its usefulness. These are:

(a) A compensator designed as a cancellation device may be more complex than necessary. A lower order compensator might satisfy the design requirements.

(b) The cancellation compensator may have two or more zeros "inside" its poles, thus creating a bad noise problem in the main part of the loop.

(c) Often the pole and zero locations of the main part of the loop are estimated from physical measurements, and, therefore, they are not known precisely. Also, these poles and zeros may shift with time due to environmental changes. It is not possible to realize exact cancellation in these cases.

(d) Of particular note in (c) is the case in which the main part of the loop is an unstable device—one whose transfer function has a pole in the right half plane. An attempt to cancel this pole with a zero in the compensator will invariably produce a short branch of the root locus in the right half plane because of the impossibility of constructing a compensator with a zero *precisely* over the unstable pole. Consequently, $W(s)$ will have a pole in the right half plane. The problem of controlling an unstable device is discussed further in Section 7.5.

Series compensation is one form of modification of the loop transfer function in order to satisfy system design requirements. It may also be possible to make physical modifications in the main part of the loop, when this is permissable. In the third order servomechanism such a physical modification might be the replacement of the servomotor with one which has greater torque capacity or a higher torque-to-inertia ratio. A mechanical modification in the gear train may reduce friction, change the ratio, or reduce the effective moment of inertia of the gears. A modification at the load shaft, such as the installation of a viscous or inertial damping device, might in some cases be the most practical solution.

7.3 PARALLEL COMPENSATION

Instead of placing the compensator in series with the main loop elements, as shown in Fig. 7.6, it is sometimes better to alter the loop transfer function by placing the compensator in the feedback path, as shown in Fig. 7.14. The influence which $H_c(s)$ has upon the system response may be determined by the root locus principles set forth in

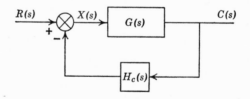

Fig. 7.14. Compensator in feedback path.

Section 6.5 for the nonunity feedback system. The principal point to keep in mind here is that a pole of $H_c(s)$ becomes a zero of $W(s)$, but a zero of $H_c(s)$ does not show up as a zero of $W(s)$. Two simple examples will illustrate this point.

Consider the effect of placing the lead network used in Fig. 7.9 in the feedback path of the third order servomechanism. The root locus plot will be the same as that shown in Fig. 7.9, with the poles of $W(s)$ occurring at the dots if K_R is set at 20.35×10^6. However, the zero in $W(s)$ will be at $s = -300$—the zero was at $s = -70$ in the series compensated system—and this will change the system transient response to a marked degree. Inasmuch as the effect of a zero in $W(s)$ is that of contributing to the output a derivative term whose relative magnitude is inversely proportional to the zero value, it may be seen that the derivative term in $c(t)$ in the parallel compensated case is less than one-fourth what it is in the series compensated case; hence the output will not be as fast.

Figure 7.15 compares the responses for the two systems. In order that the steady-state gain of the system be unity, $H_c(s)$ must have a constant multiplier to make its steady-state gain equal to unity. The total loop gain, K_R, will therefore be distributed between the forward path and the feedback path.

As a second example, consider the lag network compensation scheme having the compensator in the feedback path. When $K_R = 4.56 \times 10^6$, the poles of $W(s)$ will be at the dotted points shown in Fig. 7.8, but the zero will be at $s = -4$, indicating that the derivative term in $c(t)$ will be more than six times as large as that in the series compensated case.

Figure 7.16 compares the transient responses of the series and parallel compensated systems having the same loop gain. The excessive overshoot in the feedback compensated case could be reduced

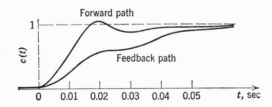

Fig. 7.15. Comparison of transient responses; lead network in forward path, lead network in feedback path.

either by lowering the loop gain, in which case the response would become much slower, or by moving the pole in $H_c(s)$ farther from the origin, which would reduce the derivative component in $c(t)$.

Consider once again the design problem of improving the speed of response of the uncompensated third order servomechanism. Let us review the manner in which this problem was solved by both the series compensation and the feedback compensation methods. In the

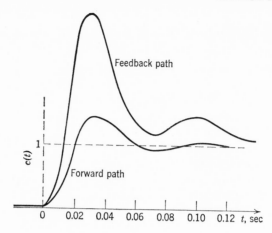

Fig. 7.16.   Comparison of transient responses; lag network in forward path, lag network in feedback path.

series compensation method a lead network was employed in order to reshape the root locus, putting the principal complex poles farther out in the s plane than they had been in the uncompensated case.   The improvement in the speed of response was due to the new location of the principal poles; the ω_n was increased by nearly 100 percent in the example summarized in Fig. 7.11.   A solution of the speed of response problem by feedback compensation was obtained by employing a lag network in the feedback path.   The improvement in response speed was effected in this case by the large derivative component in $c(t)$ due to the proximity of the zero of $W(s)$ to the origin, this zero being generated from the pole of the lag network.

Which of these two compensation schemes could best be used in a design problem depends upon the particular system.   If a noise problem exists in the loop, the lag network in the feedback path might be used in preference to the lead network, since it would offer a better signal-to-noise ratio at the input to the servoamplifier.   On the other hand, if the feedback signal is mechanical in nature, or if it is an a-c signal which cannot be conveniently converted to d-c, a series lead network would be a more practical solution than would feedback compensation by electrical networks.   (The practical difficulties of using networks in a-c servomechanisms are discussed in Chapter 10.)

Another form of parallel compensation which is often useful is an auxiliary feedback loop introduced around a portion of the forward path elements in order to modify the dynamic characteristics of those

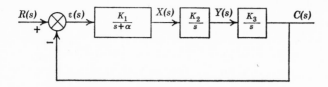

Fig. 7.17.   Feedback system with double integration in the loop.

elements and to make them suitable as forward path elements of the
outer loop.   As a simple example of the way in which an inner loop
closure can improve the performance of a system, consider the double
integration configuration shown in Fig. 7.17.   Control systems which
provide flight path control for air or water-borne vehicles often have
a configuration similar to this.   As it is shown here the system is
unstable because of the double integration in cascade with a first order
lag element.   (A root locus sketch will quickly verify the instability of
the system.)   This system may be stabilized by feeding the Y signal
back to the input of the first integrator and summing it degeneratively
with X, as shown in Fig. 7.18.   Now the transfer function relating
X to Y is a first order lag.

$$\frac{Y(s)}{X(s)} = \frac{K_2}{s + K_2} \tag{7.9}$$

The system will be stable, provided, of course, that

$$K_1 K_3 < (K_2 + \alpha)\alpha \tag{7.10}$$

It is sometimes desirable to have two integrations in the outer control loop; an inner loop closure which eliminates one of the integrations
is therefore not a universally acceptable compensation technique.
This system could be stabilized by a series lead network, preserving
the advantage of the double integration.

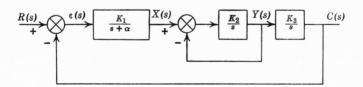

Fig. 7.18.   Inner loop closure to stabilize double integration system.

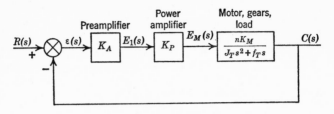

Fig. 7.19. Second order servomechanism.

As a second example of inner loop compensation, consider the damping problem in a simple second order electric servomechanism. Let the block diagram in Fig. 7.19 define the system. The symbols used are conventional for a gear-connected load where

$$J_T = J_L + n^2 J_M$$

$$f_T = f_L + n^2 f_M \tag{7.11}$$

K_M is the bare motor torque constant, and n is the gear ratio. The system transfer function will be

$$W(s) = \frac{n K_P K_A K_M / J_T}{s^2 + \dfrac{f_T}{J_T} s + \dfrac{n K_P K_A K_M}{J_T}} \tag{7.12}$$

Let us assume that in order to satisfy a specification on system droop, we must increase the loop gain to such a high value that the damping ratio is exceedingly low. The system damping ratio could be improved by the addition of a viscous damping device on the output shaft or on the motor shaft, increasing f_T. This would damp the system without decreasing the steady-state torque gain of the loop, but such a solution has several drawbacks—

(a) It is not possible to add a viscous damper without also adding friction and mass to the rotating member.

(b) The damping coefficient of the damper is usually temperature sensitive.

(c) The maximum speed of the motor (in the slewing condition) is reduced in the same proportion as f_T is increased.

(d) The damper absorbs energy which must be supplied by the servomotor. This reduces the energy efficiency of the system.

The effect of the viscous damper upon the system and a clue to a different method of damping the system are best observed in the differential equation relating the power amplifier input voltage to the shaft velocity.

$$e_1 n K_M K_P = J_T \frac{d\omega}{dt} + f_T \omega \qquad (7.13)$$

This is a torque equation; the viscous damping coefficient contributes a torque term proportional to velocity. Now, if the velocity of the shaft is sensed by a tachometer, and the voltage so generated is subtracted from the amplifier voltage, Eq. 7.13 will be changed to

$$(e_1 - K_T \omega) n K_M K_P = J_T \frac{d\omega}{dt} + f_T \omega \qquad (7.14)$$

where K_T is the tachometer constant, volts per radian per second. Equation 7.14 may be rearranged to

$$e_1 n K_M K_P = J_T \frac{d\omega}{dt} + (f_T + K_T n K_M K_P)\omega \qquad (7.15)$$

Comparing Eqs. 7.15 and 7.13, we see that the tachometer feedback has the same effect as the addition of a viscous damper on the output shaft. Both reduce the torque available for accelerating the shaft. The tachometer feedback does this by subtracting from the applied voltage, thereby reducing the power delivered to the shaft, while the damper does it by absorbing power after the power has been delivered to the shaft. Clearly, the tachometer damping scheme is better from an energy efficiency standpoint, and, in fact, it is more satisfactory than the viscous damper in many other respects as well. The maximum slewing speed of the tachometer-damped motor will be the same as that of the undamped motor, since in the slewing condition full rated voltage will appear at the motor terminals. Figure 7.20 shows the tachometer loop in block diagram form.

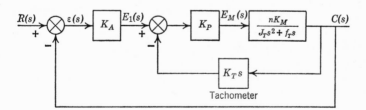

Fig. 7.20. Tachometer damped second order servomechanism.

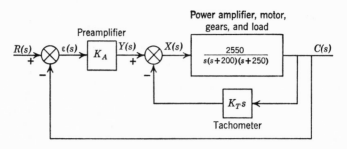

Fig. 7.21.   Third order servomechanism with velocity feedback.

Tachometer feedback can be useful in providing damping for higher order servomechanisms, although the effect of the tachometer feedback is less apparent from the physical standpoint than it is in the second order system because of the time lag between the applied voltage and torque developed at the shaft.   A root locus plot will illustrate the effect.

Let the block diagram in Fig. 7.21 represent the third order system having tachometer feedback.   Assume that the gain of the preamplifier must be at least $K_A = 10,000$ in order to satisfy the droop requirement, and that the dynamic response to a step input should be as fast as possible but should not exceed 24 percent.   When there is no velocity feedback ($K_T = 0$), the system will be unstable, so we must find the proper value of K_T to satisfy the design requirements.

First let us analyze the inner loop by drawing a root locus plot with K_T as the gain parameter.   This is shown in Fig. 7.22; the zero at the origin contributed by the tachometer transfer function cancels the pole at the origin due to the motor, so this is now a simple second order root locus plot.   The closed loop transfer function $C(s)/Y(s)$ will have a pole at the origin and a pair of poles lying on the root locus at points determined by the value of K_T.   We must find the best value for K_T by the trial-and-error process of setting K_T at an arbitrary level and then making a root locus study of the outer loop with $K_A = 10,000$ to see whether the dynamic response specifications are satisfied.

As a first trial let $K_T = 20.1$.   This places two poles of $C(s)/Y(s)$ at $s = -225 \pm j225$.   A root locus plot for the outer loop showing K_A as a gain parameter is drawn in Fig. 7.23. $K_A = 10,000$ places a pair of complex poles of $W(s)$ at approximately $s = -41 \pm j259$ and a real pole at about $s = -368$.   The overshoot in response to a step input will be about 45 percent, which is excessive according to the stated specifications.   An increase in K_T is therefore indicated.

As a second trial, let $K_T = 50$, so that the complex poles of $C(s)/Y(s)$ will lie approximately at $s = -225 \pm j356$. The root locus plot for the outer loop, showing K_A as the gain parameter, is also drawn in Fig. 7.23. With K_A at the required level of 10,000 poles of $W(s)$ will be located at approximately $s = -200$ and $s = -125 \pm j338$. Now, using the third order curves in Fig. 4.60 ($\beta = 1.6$, $\zeta = 0.347$), we may estimate the percentage overshoot in response to a step input to be about 4 percent.

The speed of response of a third order system with β in the neighborhood of 2 is determined by the ω_n of the complex poles. In general, the farther the poles are from the origin the faster the response of the system. In this particular system we may increase the overshoot to the allowable 25 percent by decreasing K_T. This would decrease ω_n but increase the value of the real pole so that the exact effect of decreasing K_T on the speed of response is not completely apparent. However, the speed of response will not be very much faster or slower than it is when $K_T = 50$. One or two more trials with K_T set in the neighborhood of 40 will show more precisely the proper setting for K_T.

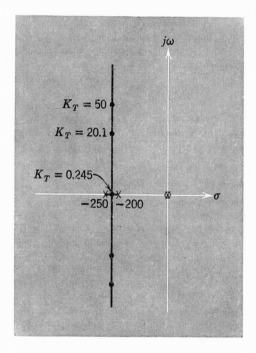

Fig. 7.22.   Root locus plot of inner loop.

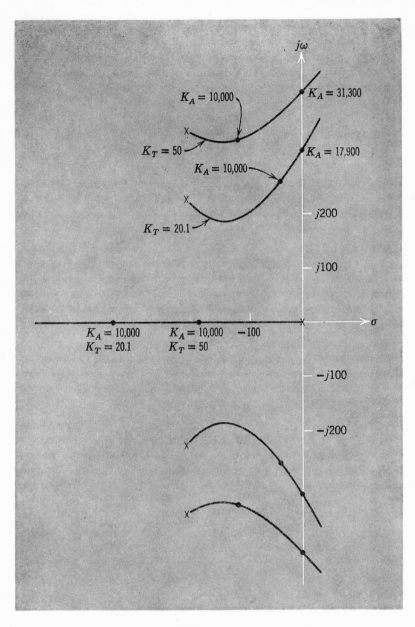

Fig. 7.23. Root locus plots, outer loop, $K_T = 20.1$ and $K_T = 50$.

An alternate way to approach this problem leads directly to the proper setting for K_T without a series of trial-and-error plots. Inasmuch as K_T is the only variable parameter in this system, the block diagram may be rearranged so that K_T appears as an "outer loop" gain constant, and the fixed portions of the system will appear as a series element in the outer loop. This is accomplished by summing the tachometer feedback into the forward path at the input of the amplifier and by dividing K_T by K_A in order to preserve the system transfer function. When the block diagram is drawn so that the positional feedback and the velocity feedback (modified by the $1/K_A$ constant) both sum into the input to the amplifier, either may be called the

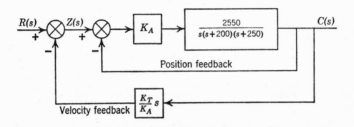

Fig. 7.24. Block diagram drawn to place tachometer in "outer loop."

"outer loop"; therefore, the block diagram may be drawn as in Fig. 7.24.

A root locus plot of the positional loop with $K_A = 10{,}000$ will set the pole locations of $C(s)/Z(s)$. Notice that this root locus plot is the same as that in Fig. 7.5, and that $K_A = 10{,}000$ places two complex poles in the right half plane. The pole locations are $s = -461.4$ and $s = +5.7 \pm j235$. The inner, closed loop transfer function is

$$\frac{C(s)}{Z(s)} = \frac{25.50 \times 10^6}{(s + 461.4)(s^2 - 11.4s + 55267)} \qquad (7.16)$$

A root locus plot for the outer loop may be drawn with K_T as the gain parameter, and all possible choices for the pole configuration for $W(s)$ will be displayed on the single plot. This plot appears in Fig. 7.25. Using the several points spotted on the root locus plot, it is possible to construct a curve showing the way in which the percentage overshoot varies with K_T. The third order curves in Fig. 4.60 are used to obtain the percentage overshoot for each pole configuration

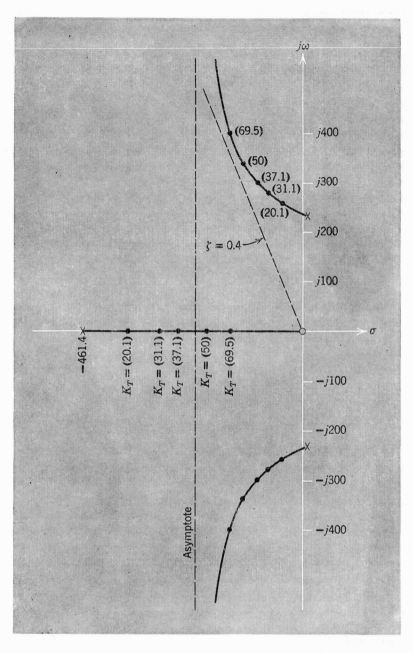

Fig. 7.25. Root locus plot of "outer loop" $K_A = 10,000$, K_T shown as the gain parameter.

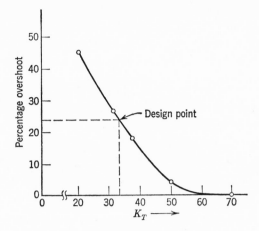

Fig. 7.26. Determination of design value for K_T.

corresponding to the K_T points on the locus. From the curve drawn through the five points plotted in Fig. 7.26 it is apparent that K_T should be set at about 32.2 in order to satisfy the 24 percent overshoot requirement. In a practical design situation K_T would be made adjustable, so that after the system was finally constructed K_T could be set experimentally at the best setting. The analysis serves to determine the *approximate* value of K_T so that equipment of the proper capacity may be built into the system.

7.4   DESIGN IN TERMS OF ERROR COEFFICIENTS

The performance of a control system is often measured in terms of the system error. The system error may be used in many ways to define a performance figure of merit. Ideally, the figure of merit would reflect all the important characteristics of the system error, including its maximum value, the number and frequency of the transient oscillations, the decay time, and its steady-state value. Unfortunately, such an ideal figure of merit can be defined and used in relatively few systems. In those systems in which the error is likely to have large transient fluctuations due to the input signal or unexpected disturbances within the system, no single function of the system error has been found to be useful as a figure of merit for system performance. Some such functions, based upon the transient response to a step input, or upon a random input of known statistical character, have been used to advantage in the design process. (See Chapter 10, Section 10.2.)

In this section two types of performance measures based upon system error are defined. These are the *steady-state error coefficients* and the so-called *generalized error coefficients*. Both these performance measures are of limited usefulness in actual system design, but they do serve to illustrate some important features of feedback systems.

The system error is defined in Fig. 7.1. From this block diagram we have

$$\varepsilon(s) = R(s)[M(s) - W(s)] \tag{7.17}$$

if the disturbance is considered to be zero. Equation 7.17 may be simplified by defining an error transfer function $F(s)$.

$$F(s) = M(s) - W(s) \tag{7.18}$$

The system error may be written as

$$\varepsilon(s) = R(s)F(s) \tag{7.19}$$

Now, if the input is a step function, $R(s) = A/s$, the system error function will be

$$\varepsilon(s) = \frac{A}{s} F(s) \tag{7.20}$$

The final value theorem may be used (if the system is stable) to find the steady-state error

$$\varepsilon(t) \Big|_{t=\infty} = \lim_{s \to 0} AF(s) = \frac{A}{K_s} \tag{7.21}$$

Here A/K_s is the value of the steady-state error, and K_s is defined as the *step error coefficient* for the system. If the steady-state error should be zero, it may be said that the step error coefficient is infinite, and if the function $AF(s)$ should have a pole at the origin, so that $\varepsilon(t)$ would approach a ramp function as t grows large, K_s may be said to be zero. Therefore, K_s has a finite, non-zero value only when the steady-state error is finite and non-zero.

A question which often arises in a system design is this: What should the configuration of $W(s)$ be in order that the steady-state step error be zero? To answer this question, inspect Eq. 7.21. The required condition for zero steady-state error is

$$F(0) = 0 \tag{7.22}$$

This may be related back to the model and system transfer functions so that the requirement made upon those becomes

$$M(0) = W(0) \tag{7.23}$$

If $M(s)$ and $W(s)$ are of the following form:

$$M(s) = \frac{K_M(s + Z_{m1})(s + Z_{m2}) \cdots}{(s + P_{m1})(s + P_{m2}) \cdots}$$

$$W(s) = \frac{K_W(s + Z_{w1})(s + Z_{w2}) \cdots}{(s + P_{w1})(s + P_{w2}) \cdots}$$

(7.24)

the condition for zero steady-state step error becomes

$$\frac{K_M Z_{m1} Z_{m2} \cdots}{P_{m1} P_{m2} \cdots} = \frac{K_W Z_{w1} Z_{w2} \cdots}{P_{w1} P_{w2} \cdots}$$

(7.25)

which may also be written in short form as

$$\frac{K_M \Pi Z_m}{\Pi P_m} = \frac{K_W \Pi Z_w}{\Pi P_w}$$

(7.26)

The steady-state gain of the model must equal the steady-state gain of the system.

If the model has a transfer function of unity, and if $W(s)$ represents a unity feedback system, Eq. 7.23 may be used to show which properties the forward path elements must have in order to provide zero steady-state error. In this case we have

$$W(s) = \frac{G(s)}{1 + G(s)} = \frac{N(s)}{N(s) + D(s)}$$

(7.27)

where $G(s) = N(s)/D(s)$ in the usual form. Equation 7.23 requires that

$$\frac{N(0)}{N(0) + D(0)} = 1$$

(7.28)

which in turn requires that $D(0) = 0$. Hence $D(s)$ must have a factor (s); in other words, $G(s)$ must be the transfer function of an integrating element.

If a nonunity feedback element is employed, zero steady-state step error may be realized even though the forward path does not contain an integrating element. Let $G(s) = N_1(s)/D_1(s)$ and $H(s) = N_2(s)/D_2(s)$. Equation 7.23 will require that

$$\frac{N_1(0)D_2(0)}{N_1(0)N_2(0) + D_1(0)D_2(0)} = 1$$

(7.29)

If $G(s) = 2/(s + 1)$, for example, Eq. 7.29 will be satisfied if $H(s) = 0.5$. In fact, any $H(s)$ whose steady-state gain is 0.5 will satisfy the zero steady-state error requirement, provided that the system is stable.

The second steady-state error coefficient to be defined here is the *ramp error coefficient*. This is a constant which describes the steady-state system error when the input is a pure ramp function—$r(t) = Rt$. With a ramp input the system error is given as

$$\varepsilon(s) = \frac{R}{s^2}[M(s) - W(s)] \tag{7.30}$$

Applying the final value theorem, we have

$$\varepsilon(t)\Big|_{t\to\infty} = \lim_{s\to 0}\frac{R}{s}[F(s)] = \frac{R}{K_r} \tag{7.31}$$

where K_r is the ramp error coefficient. Like the step error coefficient, K_r has a finite, nonzero value only when the steady-state ramp error is finite and non-zero.

If the system is to have a steady-state ramp error of zero, Eq. 7.31 must be zero. Notice that one requirement for this is that $F(s)$ must have a factor (s) in order to cancel the (s) in the denominator of the middle expression. Consider the implications of this requirement for a unity model, unity feedback system. In this system Eq. 7.31 becomes

$$\varepsilon(t)\Big|_{t\to\infty} = \lim_{s\to 0}\frac{R}{s}\left[\frac{D(s)}{N(s) + D(s)}\right] \tag{7.32}$$

where $G(s) = N(s)/D(s)$ as usual. Now, it is clear that $D(s)$ must have a factor $(s)^2$ if the steady-state error is to be zero. One factor (s) is required to cancel the s in the denominator in order to insure that the error be finite, and the second factor (s) is required to make the error zero. The forward path elements must therefore have a *double integration* property if the steady-state ramp error is to be zero. If a nonunity feedback is employed, however, we find that it is not necessary for the forward path elements to have a double integration for zero steady-state ramp error. This is best illustrated in the following way.

The system output, with a ramp input, is

$$C(s) = \frac{R}{s^2} \times \frac{K_W(s + Z_{w1})(s + Z_{w2})\ \cdots}{(s + P_{w1})(s + P_{w2})\ \cdots} \tag{7.33}$$

where all the poles of $W(s)$ are in the left half plane. Equation 7.33 may be expanded into partial fractions in the usual way.

$$C(s) = \frac{K_1}{s^2} + \frac{K_2}{s} + \frac{K_3}{s + P_{w1}} + \frac{K_4}{s + P_{w2}} + \cdots \tag{7.34}$$

$c(t)$ is then the inverse transform of Eq. 7.34.

$$c(t) = K_1 t + K_2 + \text{(Decaying transients)} \qquad (7.35)$$

Now, since the model has been assumed to have a unity transfer function and the input is $r(t) = Rt$, the steady-state ramp error will be

$$\varepsilon(t)\Big|_{t \to \infty} = (R - K_1)t - K_2 \qquad (7.36)$$

Therefore, if the steady-state ramp error is to be zero, two conditions must prevail—these are, from Eq. 7.36:

$$(i)\ K_1 = R$$

$$(ii)\ K_2 = 0 \qquad (7.37)$$

Let us now interpret these two conditions in terms of the restrictions which they impose upon $W(s)$. In the partial fraction expansion of Eq. 7.33 we have

$$K_1 = s^2 C(s)\Big|_{s=0} = \frac{R K_W Z_{w1} Z_{w2} \cdots}{P_{w1} P_{w2} \cdots} \qquad (7.38)$$

If condition (i) is to hold, the right side of Eq. 7.38 must be R, and, consequently, we have the requirement

$$\frac{K_W Z_{w1} Z_{w2} \cdots}{P_{w1} P_{w2} \cdots} = 1 \qquad (7.39)$$

The steady-state gain of the system must be unity.

Next, K_2 is given in the partial fraction expansion as

$$K_2 = K_1 \left(\sum \frac{1}{\mathbf{Z}} - \sum \frac{1}{\mathbf{P}} \right)_{s=0} \qquad (7.40)$$

where $\mathbf{Z}$ and $\mathbf{P}$ are the vectors drawn from the zeros and poles of $C(s)$ to the origin $s = 0$. K_1 is not zero; consequently if K_2 is to be zero we must have

$$\sum \frac{1}{\mathbf{Z}}\Big|_{s=0} = \sum \frac{1}{\mathbf{P}}\Big|_{s=0} \qquad (7.41)$$

The poles and zeros of $W(s)$ must be positioned so that the sum of the reciprocal zero vectors is equal to that of the pole vectors. Equations 7.39 and 7.41 are the restrictions made upon $W(s)$ which must hold for zero steady-state ramp error. It is easily shown that $G(s)$ need not have any integrating elements, provided there is freedom to choose $H(s)$.

As a simple example, if $G(s)$ is of the form

$$G(s) = \frac{K_A}{s + \alpha} \qquad (7.42)$$

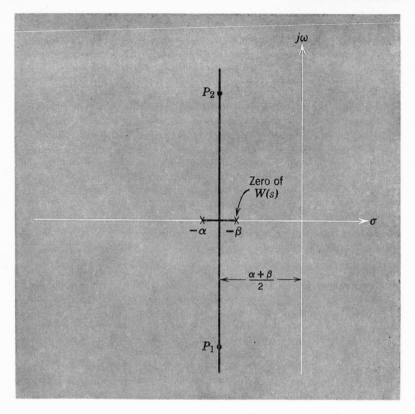

Fig. 7.27. Root locus plot for zero ramp error system.

and if $H(s)$ is given a similar form

$$H(s) = \frac{K_B}{s + \beta} \tag{7.43}$$

the system transfer function will be

$$W(s) = \frac{K_A(s + \beta)}{K_A K_B + (s + \alpha)(s + \beta)} \tag{7.44}$$

A root locus plot for this system is drawn in Fig. 7.27, where β is shown to be slightly less than α. The poles of $W(s)$ are represented by the dots labeled P_1 and P_2. These poles must be placed in a position to satisfy Eq. 7.41 (by adjusting the loop gain $K_A K_B$); it is clear from an examination of the root locus plot that the poles can be so placed. This conclusion is reached as follows:

If the loop gain is adjusted so that both poles of $W(s)$ lie exactly at the point $s = -(\alpha + \beta)/2$, the relationship

$$\sum \frac{1}{P}\bigg|_{s=0} > \sum \frac{1}{Z}\bigg|_{s=0} \qquad (7.45)$$

will hold, since the zero of $W(s)$ lies at $s = -\beta$. Now, if the loop gain is increased so that the poles of $W(s)$ lie far out along the loci at an extreme distance from the origin, the following relationship will hold:

$$\sum \frac{1}{P}\bigg|_{s=0} < \sum \frac{1}{Z}\bigg|_{s=0} \qquad (7.46)$$

Therefore, it is reasonable to expect that if the loop gain is set at some intermediate value, Eq. 7.41 will hold. The reader should verify that for given values of K_A and α, the two conditions specified in Eqs. 7.39 and 7.41, when imposed upon this system, will require that

$$\beta = K_A - \alpha$$
$$K_B = \frac{(K_A - \alpha)^2}{K_A} \qquad (7.47)$$

if the steady-state ramp error is to be zero. $(K_A - \alpha)$ cannot be zero in Eq. 7.47, and, in fact, it should be positive in order to keep $H(s)$ from being unstable (negative β).

Notice that while this system can achieve zero ramp error without a doubly integrating device, Eq. 7.47 requires that K_B and β be set at precise values. Therefore, if K_B or β is misadjusted slightly, the steady-state ramp error will be nonzero. In a doubly integrating, unity feedback system no such requirement for precision in the loop gain or pole location exists as long as the double integration is present.

The third steady-state error coefficient to be defined here is the *parabolic error coefficient*. This constant describes the steady-state system error when the input is a parabolic function, $r(t) = (P/2)t^2$. With this input the system error is

$$\varepsilon(s) = \frac{P}{s^3} [M(s) - W(s)] \qquad (7.48)$$

The final value theorem gives the steady-state parabolic error

$$\varepsilon(t)\bigg|_{t \to \infty} = \lim_{s \to 0} \frac{P}{s^2} [F(s)] = \frac{P}{K_P} \qquad (7.49)$$

where K_P is the parabolic error coefficient and has a finite, nonzero value when the steady-state parabolic error is finite and non-zero. Notice that if this error is to be zero, $F(s)$ will have to have an $(s)^2$ factor to cancel the $(s)^2$ in the denominator of Eq. 7.49. In a unity model, unity feedback system this can easily be shown to mean that $G(s)$ must have a triple integration.

It may also be shown by a consideration of the partial fraction expansion of $C(s)$ that for the unity model system the following three conditions on $W(s)$ must hold in order that the steady-state parabolic error be zero:

$$(i) \; \frac{K_W Z_{w1} Z_{w2} \; \cdots}{P_{w1} P_{w2} \; \cdots} = 1$$

$$(ii) \; \sum \frac{1}{Z_w}\bigg|_{s=0} = \sum \frac{1}{P_w}\bigg|_{s=0}$$

$$(iii) \; \left\{ \frac{d^2}{ds^2}[W(s)] \right\}_{s=0} = 0 \tag{7.50}$$

Since condition (iii) does not have a simple geometric interpretation in terms of vectors, it is less easy to determine where the poles and zeros of $W(s)$ ought to be in order to satisfy this condition than it is for condition (ii), which does have a simple interpretation. The reader can verify, however, that if $W(s)$ is represented as $P(s)/Q(s)$, condition (iii) requires that the following relationship must hold:

$$\left\{ Q^2(s) \frac{d^2 P(s)}{ds^2} + 2P(s)\left[\frac{dQ(s)}{ds}\right]^2 \right\}_{s=0} = \left\{ 2Q(s)\left[\frac{dQ(s)}{ds}\right]\left[\frac{dP(s)}{ds}\right] \right.$$
$$\left. + Q(s)P(s)\frac{d^2 Q(s)}{ds^2} \right\}_{s=0} \tag{7.51}$$

Notice that if the steady-state parabolic error is zero the steady-state ramp error and the steady-state step error will also be zero.

Higher order steady-state error coefficients for inputs of the form t^3, t^4, etc. could be defined in the pattern established here by the definition of the step, ramp, and parabolic error coefficients. In most control system work, however, there is no need for higher order coefficients. The coefficients defined above are related to the *position constant*, the *velocity constant*, and the *acceleration constant*, which were defined for unity feedback, unity model servomechanisms in the early 1940's. These definitions are:

$$\text{Position constant} = \lim_{s \to 0} G(s)$$

$$\text{Velocity constant} = \lim_{s \to 0} sG(s)$$

$$\text{Acceleration constant} = \lim_{s \to 0} s^2 G(s)$$

It is easily shown that in the unity feedback, unity model case these three constants are related to the step-error, ramp-error, and parabolic-error coefficients in the following way:

$$\text{Position constant} = (K_s - 1)$$

$$\text{Velocity constant} = K_r$$

$$\text{Acceleration constant} = K_P \tag{7.52}$$

The names *position, velocity,* and *acceleration* were used originally because most of the early servomechanisms were position-controlling devices; a step input meant a step change in the called-for position, a ramp input meant a step change in the called-for velocity, etc. The steady-state error coefficients defined in this section are more general than the traditional ones in that they are defined for the nonunity model, nonfeedback system, whose controlled quantity may have any physical form—voltage, a fluid level, a temperature, or one of many others, including a mechanical position.

A second set of error coefficients, called the *generalized error coefficients* has been defined and will be included here for the sake of completeness. This set of coefficients is of limited usefulness. We have

$$\varepsilon(s) = R(s)F(s) \tag{7.53}$$

$F(s)$ will have the general form

$$F(s) = \frac{b_0 + b_1 s + b_2 s^2 + \cdots + b_m s^m}{a_0 + a_1 s + a_2 s^2 + \cdots + s^n} \tag{7.54}$$

If the denominator is divided into the numerator, $F(s)$ may be written as

$$F(s) = C_0 + C_1 s + C_2 s^2 + \cdots \tag{7.55}$$

where $C_0, C_1, C_2 \ldots$ are called the generalized error coefficients. If the input is a smoothly varying time function which can be approximated by a power series of finite length, $\varepsilon(s)$ may be written from Eq. 7.53.

As an example, if the input can be represented as

$$r(t) = A + Rt + \frac{P}{2} t^2 \tag{7.56}$$

then

$$R(s) = \frac{A}{s} + \frac{R}{s^2} + \frac{P}{s^3} \tag{7.57}$$

and $\varepsilon(s)$ will be

$$\varepsilon(s) = \left(\frac{A}{s} + \frac{R}{s^2} + \frac{P}{s^3}\right)(C_0 + C_1 s + C_2 s^2 + \cdots) \tag{7.58}$$

which may be expanded to

$$\varepsilon(s) = \frac{C_0 P}{s^3} + \frac{C_0 R + C_1 P}{s^2} + \frac{C_0 A + C_1 R + C_2 P}{s}$$
$$+ (C_1 A + C_2 R + C_3 P) + s(C_2 A + C_3 R + C_4 P)$$
$$+ s^2(C_3 A + C_4 R + C_5 P) + s^3(C_4 A + C_5 R + C_6 P) + \cdots \quad (7.59)$$

Now, the inverse transform of $\varepsilon(s)$ yields an expression for the error as a function of time.

$$\varepsilon(t) = \frac{C_0 P}{2} t^2 + (C_0 R + C_1 P)t + (C_0 A + C_1 R + C_2 P)$$
$$+ \text{(infinite series of impulses)} \quad (7.60)$$

The infinite series of impulses are equivalent to the transient terms in the error response; if these are dropped, Eq. 7-60 will represent the steady-state error of the system.

If the transient terms in $\varepsilon(t)$ persist for a long time, the generalized error coefficients are of little use, since they relate only to the steady-state error. If the input has some exponential components whose time constants are smaller than the system time constants, such a situation will exist.

7.5 CONTROL OF UNSTABLE PLANTS

The forward path of a feedback control system is ordinarily composed of a mechanism or *plant* which is being controlled and a second device, called a controller, which generates the control signal. This general configuration is represented in Fig. 7.28. In many cases the *plant* is beyond the jurisdiction of the controls engineer; consequently, he will be unable to effect any modifications of it in order to improve the performance of the system but must confine his design efforts to

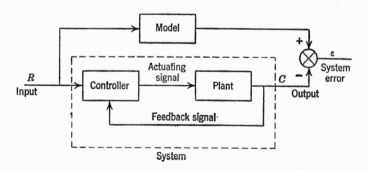

Fig. 7.28. System diagram showing controller and plant.

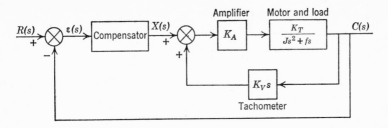

Fig. 7.29. Servomechanism with regenerative velocity feedback.

the controller. In some instances the plant is dynamically unstable—if it is linear its transfer function has one or more poles in the right-half s plane. Examples of such unstable plants are high performance military aircraft under certain conditions of airspeed, altitude, and loading, a servomechanism with regenerative velocity feedback, and some hydraulic or pneumatic control systems having acoustic resonances in the supply lines. In certain short term navigational problems the kinematics of the problem are represented by an unstable transfer function. Although this is not a plant in the usual sense, it does present a similar control problem.

Even though the plant is unstable, the system can be made stable by a suitable design of the controller. The design procedure will be exactly the same as that for a system having a stable plant, the root locus method being especially useful in this type of system. A stable system having an unstable plant has some peculiar properties, however, which warrant special mention. These properties are demonstrated in the following example, which uses a servomotor with regenerative velocity feedback to represent the unstable plant.

A block diagram of the unstable servomechanism is shown in Fig. 7.29. The transfer function of the inner closed loop is

$$\frac{C(s)}{X(s)} = \frac{K_A K_T}{s[Js + (f - K_A K_T K_V)]} \tag{7.61}$$

so that this inner loop will be unstable if the inner loop gain is high enough to make

$$K_A K_T K_V > f \tag{7.62}$$

For illustrative purposes let us assume that $J = 1$, $(K_A K_T K_V - f) = 1$, and $K_A K_T = 1$, so that Eq. 7.61 becomes

$$\frac{C(s)}{X(s)} = \frac{1}{s(s - 1)} \tag{7.63}$$

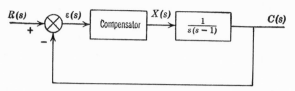

Fig. 7.30.   Block diagram reduced.

The block diagram of the system can then be drawn as in Fig. 7.30, where the unstable inner loop is represented as a single block.

In designing a compensator to stabilize this system we might be tempted to specify a zero at $s = +1$ in order to cancel the pole of $C(s)/X(s)$ at that point. Theoretically, this would be a solution to the stability problem, but it is not a practical solution for the following reason. In a real servomechanism the pole location depends upon the four system parameters K_A, K_T, K_V, and f, the values of which are known only approximately and are subject to slight changes with fluctuations in temperature and the aging of the components. Therefore, the pole will not really be at $s = +1$, but will only be known to be in the *neighborhood* of that point. A compensator with a zero at $s = +1$ will not cancel the pole but will actually create a short branch of the root locus in the right half plane, as shown in Fig. 7.31. The system transfer function will have a dipole in the right half plane, which, of course, means instability.

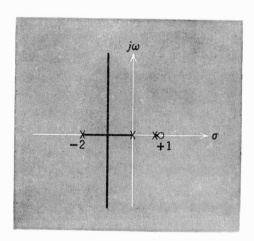

Fig. 7.31.   Effect of inexact cancelation of right half plane pole $\dfrac{X(s)}{\varepsilon(s)} = \dfrac{K(s-1)}{(s+2)}$.

It is possible to stabilize this system using a lead type compensator. As an example, consider the root locus plot for the system with a compensator having a transfer function

$$\frac{X(s)}{\varepsilon(s)} = \frac{K(s + 0.3)}{(s + 4.5)} \tag{7.64}$$

This plot is drawn in Fig. 7.32. The zero at $s = -0.3$ is close enough

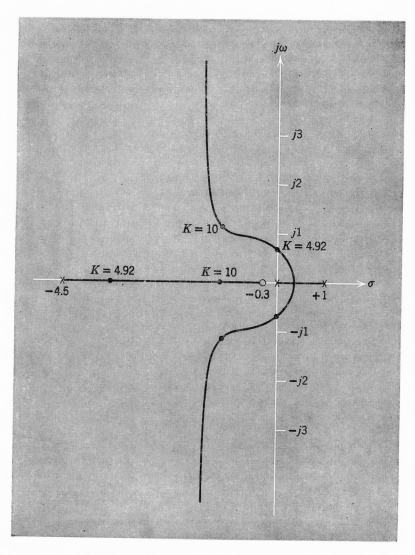

Fig. 7.32. Stabilization of system with lead compensator.

to the origin to draw the loci well into the left half plane. Notice that this system is a conditionally stable one in that the loop gain must be greater than 4.92 to insure stability. The poles of $W(s)$ move from the *right* half plane into the *left* half plane as K is increased, which is the reverse of the usual situation. In this system K would probably be set in the neighborhood of 10, so that the complex poles would be well away from the $j\omega$ axis and at the same time have a reasonably low damping ratio.

The conditional stability property of this system is an important one from a practical standpoint. If the loop gain of the system should ever drop below 4.92 the system would become unstable. In a real system the loop gain is much more likely to decrease because of malfunctions than it is to increase. Vacuum tube or transistor failures, power supply failures, and various other malfunctions can cause the loop gain to drop below the critical value, thereby throwing the system into an unstable oscillation. During warmup or shutdown the loop gain also fluctuates from its operational value to lower levels, so precautions must be taken to prevent instability during these periods.

Perhaps the most important practical consideration is the effect which a saturating element, such as an amplifier or motor, has on the system stability. If the signals in the loop are of small amplitude, so that the saturating element is operating in its linear range, the system will be stable, provided the loop gain is sufficiently high. If the signal should become large enough to saturate the amplifier, however, the system will be operating in its nonlinear region. It is not possible, in general, to use pole-zero analysis for nonlinear systems. However, in most control systems a simple saturating nonlinearity can be approximated as an amplitude dependent gain—the higher the amplitude of the signal the lower the gain of the saturating element. This is demonstrated in Chapter 10. Hence, if the system is driven into saturation far enough, the "gain" will drop below the critical value, and unstable oscillations may occur. Experiment has shown that oscillations of large amplitude will occur in the system shown in Fig. 7.32 when a saturating element is contained in the forward path of the system. In most practical servomechanisms the linear range of signal amplitude is very narrow, corresponding to a small fraction of one degree error in some angular positional control systems. Because of this, the use of conditionally stable systems is avoided whenever possible.

Systems with unstable plants have another interesting property which may prove to be useful in some applications. If the steady-state ramp error for the system shown in Fig. 7.32 is computed it will

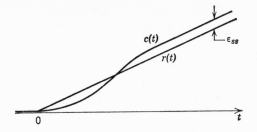

Fig. 7.33. Response of system with unstable plant to ramp input.

be found to be negative. Figure 7.33 shows the response of the system to a ramp input; the steady-state output is *ahead* of the input. The reason for this is that the steady-state gain of the forward path ε to C in Fig. 7.29, is negative because of the single pole in the right half plane. The steady-state error must be negative to support a positive output velocity. If two poles of the forward path transfer function occurred in the right half plane, the steady-state ramp error would be positive. The generalization here is that an odd number of poles and zeros in the right half plane will cause the steady-state ramp error to be negative. It is not necessary, therefore, to have an unstable plant for this phenomenon to occur, nor does an unstable plant guarantee that it will occur.

7.6 CONTROL OF LOAD DISTURBANCES

In many control systems the controlled member, or plant, as it is called in Fig. 7.28, is subject to outside disturbances which influence the dynamic behavior of the output. In a positional servomechanism, for example, the output shaft may have disturbing torques applied to it by mass unbalances, by wind pressure, by dry friction in the bearings, or by other miscellaneous agents. A block diagram representing the disturbance as a sort of input to the plant is drawn to analyze the effects of such load disturbances in a linear system. The response of the system to the disturbance may then be computed in the same way in which the response to a signal input is computed. If both signal and disturbance are present simultaneously, the total response is simply the superposition of the individual responses.

To illustrate a typical system in which load disturbances introduce an error, consider the servomechanism shown in Fig. 7.3, where the load disturbance is considered to be a torque $T_L(t)$ applied to the out-

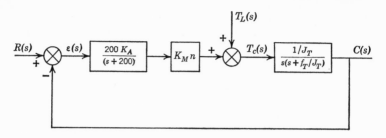

Fig. 7.34. Load torque disturbance on the third order servomechanism.

put shaft. A block diagram showing how the torque disturbance enters the system is drawn in Fig. 7.34. It is important in drawing this diagram to represent the physical situation accurately—that is, to sum the load torque into the block diagram at the point representing output shaft torque. To make the summation properly it is sometimes necessary to redraw the original block diagram in order to expose the point having the same physical dimensions as the load disturbance.

A transfer function relating the system error to the load disturbance can be derived easily from Fig. 7.34. In this derivation the input $r(t)$ is taken to be zero.

$$\frac{\varepsilon(s)}{T_L(s)} = \frac{-\dfrac{1}{J_T}(s + 200)}{s\left(s + \dfrac{f_T}{J_T}\right)(s + 200) + \dfrac{200 K_A K_M n}{J_T}} \tag{7.65}$$

Notice that the denominator of this transfer function is the same as that of the system transfer function, so that the characteristic equation for the system is the same whether T_L or R is considered the input. If the loop gain is adjusted so that the system is stable and a step load torque is applied, the error response will be that shown in Fig. 7.35.

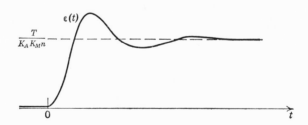

Fig. 7.35. Error response to a step load torque $T_L(s) = -T/s$.

The steady-state error in this example is $T/K_A K_M n$, where T is the magnitude of the load torque. Notice that the steady-state error is inversely proportional to the static gain of the forward path between the error point and the torque summation point. The gain in this part of the loop should be made as high as possible in order to minimize the disturbance-induced error. Of course, loop gain is limited by the system stability considerations, but in some systems it may be possible to redistribute the loop gain so that most of it can be put into the box ahead of the disturbance summing point, and the gain of the box following the summing point will then be reduced to its minimum possible value.

Compensating elements may be used to reduce the sensitivity of the system to load disturbances. For instance, a lag network placed in the error channel of this system would increase the allowable static gain of the forward path and reduce the error sensitivity to load torque. If an integrating element were placed in the error channel, the static error sensitivity would be reduced to zero, since the integrator would build up at its output a signal large enough to cancel the load torque. The steady-state error would then be zero. However, any compensating scheme devised to minimize the effects of load disturbances will influence the dynamic response of the system to other inputs. The designer must be aware of these other influences and must often make appropriate compromises in the design of his compensation scheme in order to satisfy the dynamic response requirements of both the input and the disturbance.

REFERENCES

1. Chestnut and Mayer, *Servomechanisms and Regulating System Design*, Vol. 1, 2nd Edition, Wiley, 1959.
2. Evans, *Control System Dynamics*, McGraw-Hill, 1954.
3. James, Nichols, and Phillips, *Theory of Servomechanisms*, McGraw-Hill, 1947.
4. Seifert and Steig, *Control Systems Engineering*, McGraw-Hill, 1960.
5. Guillemin, *Synthesis of Passive Networks*, Wiley, 1957.

8 Dynamic Analysis of Linear Systems Using the Real Frequency Response Method

8.1 DEFINITION OF THE REAL FREQUENCY RESPONSE

If a linear system is driven by a sinusoidally varying input such as

$$x_1(t) = A_1 \sin \omega t \qquad (8.1)$$

which is switched on to the system at time zero, the output response will be that shown in Fig. 8.1. The output will not be purely sinusoidal during the period of time just after $t = 0$, but it will have a transient component which will die out as time goes by if the system is stable. After a sufficient period of time has elapsed the output will have settled into a steady-state sinusoidal oscillation having the same frequency as the input but not necessarily in phase with the input. The amplitude of the steady-state sinusoidal oscillation is not necessarily the same as that of the input. The output can therefore be represented by the following function:

$$x_0(t) = A_0 \sin (\omega t + \phi) + \text{(Transient terms)} \qquad (8.2)$$

In defining the real frequency response of the system the transient terms are omitted, and only the steady-state part of the output response is considered. Because of this, it is ordinarily assumed that the system being studied by frequency response methods is a stable one. Certainly, if measurements are to be made on a real system, the transients must be decaying in order that the steady-state component of the output be measurable. In a paper analysis, however, the important fact that one or more of the transient terms could be unstable

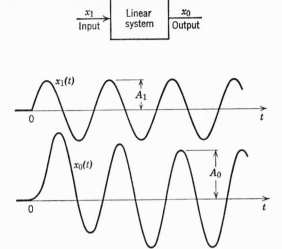

Fig. 8.1. Linear system response to a sinusoidal input.

might be overlooked by an unobservant analyst. In Chapter 9 we take up methods for determining the stability of feedback systems by observations made on only the steady-state sinusoidal portions of the response.

Before going further with the definition of the real frequency response of linear systems let us consider the type of output response which might occur if the system were not linear. It is not possible to make generalizations concerning the response of nonlinear systems to a sinusoidal input. The response obtained is dependent upon the amplitude of the input function and upon the initial state of the system. Although it is not possible to go into the study of nonlinear systems here, it can be said that in many practical types of nonlinear systems the steady-state portion of the output will not be purely sinusoidal, although it will be periodic. Hence, the steady-state portion of the response is said to contain *harmonics*, since it can be expressed as

$$x_0(t) \Big|_{ss} = A_0 \sin(\omega t + \phi) + a_1 \sin 2\omega t + a_2 \sin 3\omega t + \cdots$$
$$+ b_1 \cos 2\omega t + b_2 \cos 3\omega t + \cdots \qquad (8.3)$$

In some nonlinear systems *subharmonics* of the fundamental frequency may also occur. These are terms with the form $\sin(\omega/2)t$, $\sin(\omega/3)t$, etc. However, no such interesting phenomena can be observed in a

ω	A_1	A_0	ϕ
ω_1	A_1	$A_0(\omega_1)$	$\phi(\omega_1)$
ω_2	A_1	$A_0(\omega_2)$	$\phi(\omega_2)$
ω_3	A_1	$A_0(\omega_3)$	$\phi(\omega_3)$
ω_4	A_1	$A_0(\omega_4)$	$\phi(\omega_4)$
ω_5	A_1	$A_0(\omega_5)$	$\phi(\omega_5)$
ω_6	A_1	$A_0(\omega_6)$	$\phi(\omega_6)$
ω_7	A_1	$A_0(\omega_7)$	$\phi(\omega_7)$
ω_8	A_1	$A_0(\omega_8)$	$\phi(\omega_8)$
$\cdot$	$\cdot$	$\cdot$	$\cdot$
$\cdot$	$\cdot$	$\cdot$	$\cdot$
$\cdot$	$\cdot$	$\cdot$	$\cdot$

Fig. 8.2. Record of sinusoidal response measurements.

linear system, in which the response always has the simple form indicated by Eq. 8.2.

The real frequency response may be obtained experimentally in the following manner. Consider the following sequence of measurements made on a stable linear system. A sinusoidal signal generator having an output defined by Eq. 8.1 is switched on to the system at $t = 0$, and the output is allowed to settle into its steady state oscillation. Then the amplitude of the output oscillation A_0 and the phase shift ϕ (see Eq. 8.2) are measured and recorded in the first line of a table such as that shown in Fig. 8.2. The signal generator is then removed from the system, the frequency is changed from ω_1 to ω_2, and the generator is switched back onto the system. The output is again allowed to reach a steady state, and the amplitude and phase shift are measured and recorded in the table opposite ω_2. The signal generator is reset to a new frequency ω_3, and the process is repeated. After many such repetitions the table will contain the amplitude and phase shift response of the system for frequencies covering a broad range.

The data listed in the table might be plotted on a graph as in Fig. 8.3. The ratio $A_0(\omega)/A_1(\omega)$ is called the amplitude ratio of the system, and $\phi(\omega)$ is called the phase shift. If the amplitude ratio and phase shift have been measured at a sufficient number of frequencies, the points on the graph corresponding to each frequency may be joined by a smooth curve, as shown in Fig. 8.3, without introducing a serious error in the data. The real frequency response of the linear system is then defined as being the amplitude ratio and phase shift of the system over the entire frequency range $0 \leqq \omega \leqq \infty$. The real frequency response of a system may also be obtained analytically (see Section 8.2).

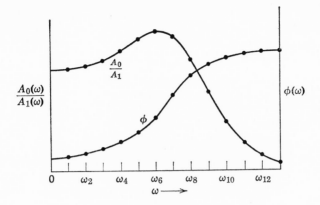

Fig. 8.3. Plot of the data in Fig. 8.2.

Figure 8.3 illustrates only one of three commonly used ways of plotting real frequency response data, the rectangular plot. Two other methods of plotting the data from a table are the polar chart and the Bode chart (also called an attenuation-phase diagram).

A polar chart of real frequency response data is shown in Fig. 8.4. Here the amplitude ratio and phase-shift curves of Fig. 8.3 are combined into a single curve with the frequency appearing as a parameter along the curve. The amplitude ratio is plotted as distance from the

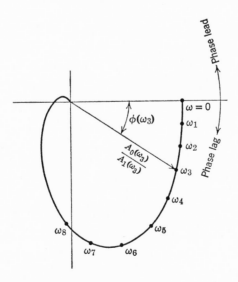

Fig. 8.4. Polar plot of real frequency response data.

origin, and the phase shift is plotted as angular displacement from the right-hand horizontal axis, as indicated by the vector (or phasor) shown for $\omega = \omega_3$ in the figure. If $\phi(\omega)$ is negative the phase shift is said to be a *phase lag*, and if $\phi(\omega)$ is positive it is called a *phase lead*. Leading or lagging phase shift is indicated by the usual electrical engineering convention of taking a counterclockwise angular displacement as positive, as shown in the figure. The polar chart is often preferable to the rectangular plot because it combines both the amplitude ratio and phase-shift data in a single curve.

On a Bode chart, as on a rectangular plot, the amplitude ratio and phase-shift curves are plotted separately against frequency. However, on the Bode chart the frequency axis is logarithmic in order to include a wide range of frequencies on the graph. Also, for reasons of computational convenience made apparent below, the amplitude ratio is not plotted directly; instead, a number proportional to the logarithm of the amplitude ratio is plotted. This number is defined as

$$\left.\frac{A_0(\omega)}{A_1(\omega)}\right|_{db} = 20 \log_{10} \frac{A_0(\omega)}{A_1(\omega)} \tag{8.4}$$

This is said to be the amplitude ratio expressed in decibels. It should be noted that the term decibel is used in electronic engineering as *ten* times the logarithm of the ratio of two power levels. *Twenty* is used by control system engineers (and others) because A_0 and A_1 usually are signal amplitudes, and therefore are proportional to the square root of the power level. The phase-shift curve is plotted on the Bode chart to a linear scale, usually in degrees.

A typical Bode chart is sketched in Fig. 8.5. Notice that because

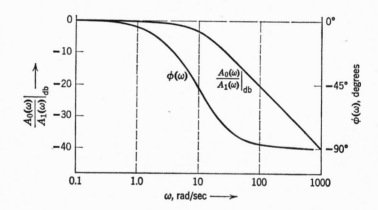

Fig. 8.5. A Bode chart.

of the logarithmic frequency scale it is not possible to plot the curves down to zero frequency. It is impossible, therefore, to represent the entire frequency range, $0 \leq \omega \leq \infty$, on the Bode chart. This rarely creates difficulty, however, since ordinarily it is possible to include on the chart as wide a frequency range as is necessary to represent the important frequency response properties of the system under study. In this example the real frequency response at very low frequencies is apparently unity, inasmuch as the amplitude curve approaches zero decibels (db), signifying an amplitude ratio of one, and the phase shift approaches zero degrees at very low frequencies.

The Bode chart is extremely useful for two reasons. First, because of the logarithmic nature of the coordinates the frequency response characteristics of linear systems may be approximated by a series of

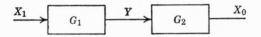

Fig. 8.6. Two linear elements in cascade.

straight line segments drawn on the chart. This technique is developed in Section 8.3. Second, the real frequency response of a system which is composed of two or more cascaded elements may be determined by combining graphically the real frequency response curves of each of the individual elements which have been drawn on Bode charts. An example of such a computation follows.

If two linear elements are in cascade (see Fig. 8.6), the input of the second is the output of the first. Therefore, if the input to the first is a sinusoid given by

$$x_1(t) = A_1 \sin \omega t \qquad (8.5)$$

the steady-state portion of the output of the first block will be of the form

$$y(t) = Y \sin (\omega t + \phi_1) \qquad (8.6)$$

where ϕ_1 is the phase shift of the first element, and Y/A_1 is the amplitude ratio of the first element. The steady-state output of the second element is

$$x_0(t) = A_0 \sin (\omega t + \phi_1 + \phi_2) \qquad (8.7)$$

where ϕ_2 is the phase shift of the second element and A_0/Y is the amplitude ratio of the second element.   The phase shift and amplitude ratio of the entire system, from x_1 to x_0, is found as follows:

$$\text{System phase shift} = \phi_1 + \phi_2$$

$$\text{System amplitude ratio} = \frac{A_0}{A_1} = \left(\frac{Y}{A_1}\right)\left(\frac{A_0}{Y}\right) \qquad (8.8)$$

The system phase shift is simply the sum of the phase shifts of each of the elements, and the system amplitude ratio is the product of the individual amplitude ratios.   It follows directly that the amplitude ratio and phase shift of a system composed of n elements in cascade are given by:

$$\text{System phase shift} = \phi_1 + \phi_2 + \phi_3 + \cdots + \phi_n$$

$$\text{System amplitude ratio} = M_1 M_2 M_3 \cdots M_n \qquad (8.9)$$

where M_1, M_2, etc. are the amplitude ratios for each of the cascaded elements.

On the Bode chart the phase-shift curves are plotted on a linear scale; hence, if the phase-shift curves for two (or more) cascaded elements are drawn on the same Bode chart the overall system phase shift curve may be found simply by adding the individual curves graphically.

If the amplitude ratio curves were also plotted to a linear scale, they could not be *added* graphically to get the overall system curve, since this curve is the product of the individual amplitude curves.   But when the amplitude ratio is expressed in logarithmic form, in decibels, the logarithmic form of the overall system amplitude ratio may be obtained from the *sum* of the logarithmic forms of each of the individual curves.   If M is the overall system amplitude ratio we have, from Eq. 8.9

$$M = M_1 M_2 M_3 \cdots M_n \qquad (8.10)$$

By taking the logarithm of each side and multiplying by 20 we have

$$\begin{aligned}
20 \log_{10} M &= 20 \log_{10} (M_1 M_2 M_3 \cdots M_n) \\
&= 20 (\log_{10} M_1 + \log_{10} M_2 + \cdots + \log_{10} M_n) \quad (8.11)
\end{aligned}$$

As an example, consider Fig. 8.7, in which the two amplitude ratio curves corresponding to the cascaded elements in Fig. 8.6 are drawn in logarithmic form and are added graphically to form the composite

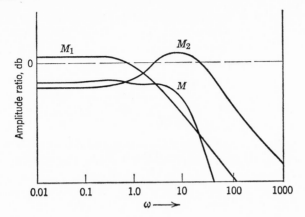

Fig. 8.7. Graphical computation of frequency response curve (amplitude ratio only) of two elements in cascade.

amplitude ratio curve which is labeled M. Similarly, the composite phase-shift curve ϕ is formed by adding graphically the individual phase-shift curves ϕ_1 and ϕ_2.

Now that we have established the definition of the real frequency response of a linear system and have discussed several ways in which real frequency response data may be plotted conveniently, let us consider the reasons for the use of the real frequency response as a method of analysis in the study of the dynamics of linear systems.

First, the frequency response method and the pole-zero method are simply two different ways of applying the same basic principles of analysis (see Section 8.2). Consequently, one method may be used to check the accuracy of the other.

Second, experimental data is often presented to the designer in frequency response form. Many testing organizations use frequency response measurements out of habit and seem to be reluctant to incorporate more direct methods of dynamic measurements, such as the transient response, into their testing procedures. Also, in some experimental situations the frequency response measurements are the only ones which may be made with any degree of accuracy or convenience.

Third, the design specifications for control systems are sometimes stated most explicitly in terms of the frequency response. This is especially true where the input signals are random time functions having known statistical properties.

Fourth, in some systems the analysis required to answer certain design questions is performed more quickly by frequency response techniques than by pole-zero methods. This is particularly true in some multiloop systems and in systems in which a pure time delay element occurs in the loop.

Fifth, some of the analytical procedures which are applicable to non-linear systems are based upon frequency response techniques. To understand these methods it is necessary to be familiar with the frequency response of linear systems.

Sixth, from a purely historical standpoint the frequency response method is important. The analysis of linear feedback systems has been performed by techniques based upon transformation mathematics since 1930. Until 1950 the frequency response method was used almost exclusively. Although Routh first suggested the use of pole-zero methods in 1877, it was not until 1950 that the root locus method began to gain popularity as a tool for analysis.

8.2 REAL FREQUENCY RESPONSE OBTAINED FROM THE TRANSFER FUNCTION

Section 8.1 defined the frequency response of a linear system and demonstrated that the frequency response of a system may be determined experimentally by a lengthy series of measurements. In this section the amplitude ratio and phase shift of a linear system, as functions of the frequency at which they are forced, are found from the transfer function.

Assume that a sinusoidal signal with the form

$$x_1(t) \ = \ A \sin \omega t \qquad (8.12)$$

is switched on to the input of a linear system whose transfer function is $G(s)$, as shown in Fig. 8.8. Assume that $G(s)$ is of the usual form

$$G(s) \ = \ \frac{X_0(s)}{X_1(s)} \ = \ \frac{K(s + Z_1)(s + Z_2) \ \cdot \ \cdot \ \cdot}{(s + P_1)(s + P_2) \ \cdot \ \cdot \ \cdot} \qquad (8.13)$$

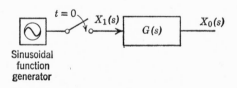

Fig. 8.8. Sinusoidal signal driving a linear system.

where all poles of $G(s)$ are in the left half plane. Now,

$$X_1(s) = \mathcal{L}\{x_1(t)\} = \frac{A\omega}{s^2 + \omega^2} \tag{8.14}$$

Therefore, the Laplace transform of the output is:

$$X_0(s) = \frac{A\omega K(s + Z_1)(s + Z_2) \cdots}{(s^2 + \omega^2)(s + P_1)(s + P_2) \cdots} \tag{8.15}$$

Equation 8.15 may be expanded into partial fractions in the usual fashion.

$$X_0(s) = \frac{\bar{K}_0}{s + j\omega} + \frac{K_0}{s - j\omega} + \frac{K_1}{s + P_1} + \frac{K_2}{s + P_2} \cdots \tag{8.16}$$

Here K_0 is the residue of $X_0(s)$ at the point $s = j\omega$, $\bar{K}_0$ is the residue of $X_0(s)$ at the point $s = -j\omega$, and $\bar{K}_0$ is known to be the complex conjugate of K_0. K_1 is the residue at $s = -P_1$, K_2 the residue at $s = -P_2$, and so forth. All terms in Eq. 8.16, except for the first two, correspond to decaying transients in the time response $x_0(t)$, since all poles of $G(s)$ are in the left half plane. Since we are concerned only with the steady-state portion of the output, we can drop all those terms and write

$$X_0(s)\Big|_{ss} = \frac{\bar{K}_0}{s + j\omega} + \frac{K_0}{s - j\omega} \tag{8.17}$$

where $X_0(s)\Big|_{ss}$ means the Laplace transform of the steady-state portion of $x_0(t)$. Equation 8.17 may be written as

$$X_0(s)\Big|_{ss} = \frac{(\bar{K}_0 + K_0)s}{s^2 + \omega^2} + \frac{j\omega(K_0 - \bar{K}_0)}{s^2 + \omega^2} \tag{8.18}$$

K_0 may be computed by the vector method, as indicated in Fig. 8.9.

$$K_0 = (A\omega K)\left(\frac{\Pi Z}{\Pi P}\right)_{s = j\omega} \tag{8.19}$$

ΠP and ΠZ refer to the poles and zeros of $X_0(s)$. All but one of these poles and zeros are associated with the transfer function, so Eq. 8.19 may just as easily be written as

$$K_0 = \frac{A\omega K}{j2\omega}\left[\frac{Z(j\omega)}{P(j\omega)}\right] \tag{8.20}$$

where $Z(j\omega) = (j\omega + Z_1)(j\omega + Z_2) \cdots$

$$P(j\omega) = (j\omega + P_1)(j\omega + P_2) \cdots \tag{8.21}$$

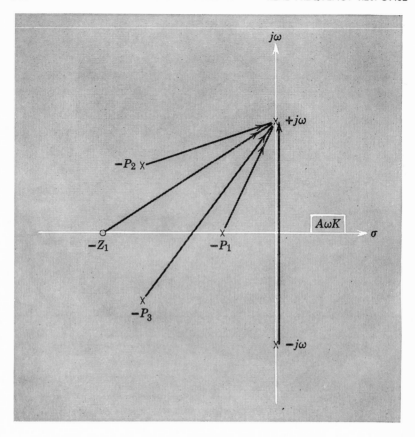

Fig. 8.9.   Computing K_0 by the vector method from a pole-zero map of $X_0(s)$.

Equation 8.20 may be written as

$$K_0 = -j\frac{A}{2}\,[G(j\omega)] \qquad\qquad (8.22)$$

where
$$G(j\omega) = G(s)\Big|_{s=j\omega} \qquad\qquad (8.23)$$

In the general case, K_0 will be a complex number.   Therefore, K_0 may be written as

$$K_0 = a + jb \qquad\qquad (8.24)$$

where the real part of K_0, a, and the imaginary part b may be computed easily for any given pole-zero configuration for $X_0(s)$.   The conjugate of K_0 is, of course,

$$\bar{K}_0 = a - jb \tag{8.25}$$

A substitution of Eqs. 8.24 and 8.25 into 8.18 yields

$$X_0(s)\bigg|_{ss} = \frac{2as}{s^2 + \omega^2} - \frac{2b\omega}{s^2 + \omega^2} \tag{8.26}$$

The steady-state portion of the output is obtained by inversely transforming Eq. 8.26.

$$x_0(t)\bigg|_{ss} = 2a \cos \omega t - 2b \sin \omega t \tag{8.27}$$

This may be rearranged into a single term

$$x_0(t)\bigg|_{ss} = \sqrt{4a^2 + 4b^2} \sin(\omega t + \phi) \tag{8.28}$$

where $\phi = \tan^{-1}(a/-b)$.

Now the amplitude ratio of the system is defined as

$$M = \frac{\sqrt{4a^2 + 4b^2}}{A} \tag{8.29}$$

and the phase shift is

$$\phi = \tan^{-1}\left(\frac{a}{-b}\right) \tag{8.30}$$

But from Eq. 8.24 we see that

$$\sqrt{4a^2 + 4b^2} = 2\sqrt{a^2 + b^2} = 2|K_0| \tag{8.31}$$

and from Eq. 8.22

$$|K_0| = \frac{A}{2}|G(j\omega)| \tag{8.32}$$

Combining Eqs. 8.32, 8.31, and 8.29 we arrive at the very useful relationship

$$M(\omega) = |G(j\omega)| \tag{8.33}$$

The phase shift of the system may also be expressed as a function of $G(j\omega)$. Equation 8.22 gives K_0 as a function of $G(j\omega)$, and Eqs. 8.24 and 8.30 relate the phase shift to K_0. A combination of these three equations will give the relationship

$$\phi(\omega) = \underline{/G(j\omega)} \tag{8.34}$$

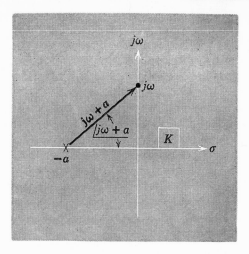

Fig. 8.10. Computing G(jω) from a pole-zero plot of G(s).

Equations 8.33 and 8.34 show that the amplitude ratio and phase shift for a linear system which is driven at a frequency ω may be computed simply by substituting $j\omega$ for s in the transfer function; this gives $G(j\omega)$, a function of the complex variable $j\omega$. $G(j\omega)$ may therefore be expressed as a complex number, $|G(j\omega)|$ @ $\underline{/G(j\omega)}$. It has been demonstrated above that the magnitude of $G(j\omega)$ is the amplitude ratio and the angle of $G(j\omega)$ is the phase shift obtained from a frequency response test made on the system.

The frequency response of a linear system, as defined by $M(\omega)$ and $\phi(\omega)$, may be computed from a pole-zero plot of $G(s)$. Consider as an example the frequency response of a simple lag network whose transfer function is

$$G(s) = \frac{K}{s + a} \tag{8.35}$$

A pole-zero plot of the transfer function is drawn in Fig. 8.10. Here

$$G(j\omega) = \frac{K}{j\omega + a} \tag{8.36}$$

The term $(j\omega + a)$ is the complex number represented by the vector drawn from the pole at $s = -a$ to the point $s = j\omega$. Thus, the magnitude of $G(j\omega)$ is

$$|G(j\omega)| = \frac{K}{|j\omega + a|} \tag{8.37}$$

and the angle of $G(j\omega)$ is

$$\underline{/G(j\omega)} = 0° - \underline{/j\omega + a} \qquad (8.38)$$

Consider the manner in which $|G(j\omega)|$ and $\underline{/G(j\omega)}$, the amplitude ratio and phase shift of the system, vary as ω is varied from zero to infinity. We may do this by thinking of the vector in Fig. 8.10 as an elastic vector whose tip is attached to the point $s = j\omega$. As the point moves along the $j\omega$ axis from the origin up toward $+j\infty$, the elastic vector stretches, starting with length a and becoming continually longer as ω is increased. The angle associated with the vector starts at 0° for $\omega = 0$ and increases continually toward $+90°$ as ω approaches infinity. Since the amplitude ratio is simply inversely proportional to the vector length, the amplitude ratio $M(\omega) = |G(j\omega)|$ is a monotonically decreasing function of ω, as shown in Fig. 8.11. The phase shift $\phi(\omega) = \underline{/G(j\omega)}$ is just the negative of the vector angle, and this is also a monotonic function of ω.

Because the phase shift is negative at all frequencies other than zero, this network is called a *lag* network. Here the steady-state sinusoidal output will *lag* the steady-state input by an angle between 0° and 90°, depending upon the frequency. From Fig. 8.10 it is evident that the phase shift will be exactly $-45°$ at $\omega = a$ rad/sec, and at this frequency the amplitude ratio will be just 0.707 times its value at $\omega = 0$. This frequency is called the *break* frequency or the *corner* frequency for this system, since it is the frequency which approximately divides the response curves into a *low* frequency region and a *high* frequency region. In Section 8.3 the break frequency is used as a key point in sketching Bode diagrams.

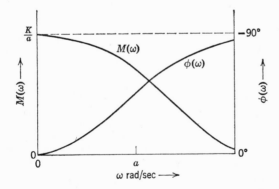

Fig. 8.11.   Rectangular plot of $M(\omega)$ and $\phi(\omega)$ for $G(s) = \dfrac{K}{s + a}$.

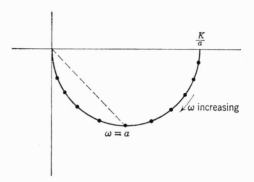

Fig. 8.12. Polar plot of Fig. 8.11.

It is also interesting to note that a polar plot of the curves in Fig. 8.11 will be a semicircle, as shown in Fig. 8.12. The reader should verify this by studying Fig. 8.10 and Eqs. 8.37 and 8.38. Note that the break frequency $\omega = a$ occurs where the phase shift is $-45°$ and the amplitude ratio is $0.707K/a$.

As a second example, consider the frequency response of a system whose transfer function has one pole and one zero

$$G(s) = \frac{K(s + b)}{s + a} \tag{8.39}$$

When $j\omega$ is substituted for s in the transfer function we have

$$G(j\omega) = \frac{K(j\omega + b)}{j\omega + a} \tag{8.40}$$

$G(j\omega)$ may be evaluated by means of *elastic vectors* in the manner of the previous example. Assume that $b < a$, so that the pole-zero plot of $G(s)$ is that shown in Fig. 8.13. Here the term $(j\omega + b)$ is the complex number represented by the vector drawn from the zero at $s = -b$ to the point $s = j\omega$, and $(j\omega + a)$ is represented by the vector drawn from the pole to the $s = j\omega$ point. The magnitude and angle of $G(j\omega)$ are related to these two vectors in the following way.

$$M(\omega) = |G(j\omega)| = \frac{K|j\omega + b|}{|j\omega + a|} \tag{8.41}$$

$$\phi(\omega) = \underline{/G(j\omega)} = \underline{/j\omega + b} - \underline{/j\omega + a} \tag{8.42}$$

To find the frequency response functions $M(\omega)$ and $\phi(\omega)$, again consider the two vectors to be elastic and observe the manner in which they stretch as ω is varied from zero to infinity.   Consider first the variations in the lengths of the vectors.   At $\omega = 0$ the vector $(j\omega + b)$ has a length b, and as ω is increased its length also increases.   Similarly, at $\omega = 0$ the vector $(j\omega + a)$ has a length a which increases as ω is increased.   However, because b is less than a, the vector $(j\omega + b)$ will increase by a *larger percentage* than will the vector $(j\omega + a)$ for a given change in ω.   This difference in the percentage increase between the two vectors is most pronounced at $\omega = 0$, and the difference diminishes as ω is increased.   In fact, when ω is very large, the two vectors are nearly the same length, and the percentage increase for a given change in ω is nearly the same for both.   The amplitude ratio is determined by measuring the vectors at each frequency and dividing their lengths as indicated in Eq. 8.41.   Because of the differences in the percentage change in the vector lengths, $M(\omega)$ will be an increasing function of ω, since the vector with the larger percentage increase is in the numer-

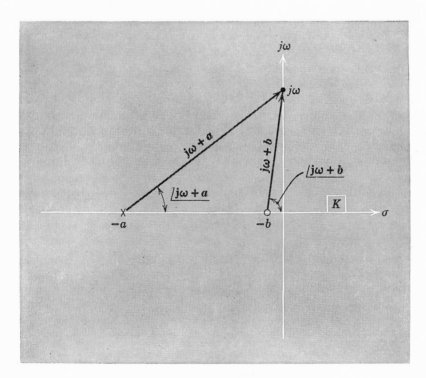

Fig. 8.13.   Computing $G(j\omega)$ from pole-zero plot of $G(s)$.

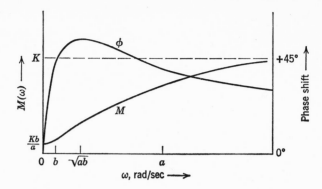

Fig. 8.14. Rectangular plot of $M(\omega)$ and $\phi(\omega)$, $G(s) = \dfrac{K(s + b)}{(s + a)}$.

ator of Eq. 8.41. $M(\omega)$ is plotted in Fig. 8.14. Notice that the zero frequency, or d-c, amplitude ratio is Kb/a, and that as ω approaches infinity the amplitude ratio approaches K, since the two vectors are nearly equal.

The phase shift for this system may also be computed by considering the movements of the elastic vectors.   It is apparent that for all values of ω except $\omega = 0$ the angle of $(j\omega + b)$ is larger than that of $(j\omega + a)$. At $\omega = 0$ both angles are 0, and as ω approaches infinity both angles approach $+90°$.   The phase shift is therefore always positive, starting at $0°$ for $\omega = 0$, increasing to a maximum, and then decreasing again toward 0 as ω becomes very large. $\phi(\omega)$ is plotted in Fig. 8.14, along with $M(\omega)$.   This system is said to have a *leading* phase shift, since $\phi(\omega)$ is always positive.   Figure 8.13 indicates that at $\omega = b$ the angle of $(j\omega + b)$ is $+45°$ and the angle of $(j\omega + a)$ is less than $+45°$. Hence $\phi(\omega)$ at $\omega = b$ must be less than 45°.   If a is very much larger than b, $\phi(\omega)$ at $\omega = b$ will be close to, but not quite, 45°.   The phase shift is the same at $\omega = a$ as at $\omega = b$, and the maximum phase shift occurs at the intermediate frequency, $\omega = \sqrt{ab}$.

The relationship between the maximum phase shift, the frequency at which it occurs, and the constants a and b is more evident in a polar plot of $G(j\omega)$, which turns out to be a semicircle (Fig. 8.15).   From this plot it may be shown that

$$\phi(\omega)\Big|_{\text{max}} = \phi(\sqrt{ab}) = \tan^{-1}\left[\frac{a - b}{2\sqrt{ab}}\right] \qquad (8.43)$$

As a third example, consider the frequency response of an underdamped second order system whose transfer function has a constant numerator.

$$G(s) = \frac{K}{s^2 + 2\zeta\omega_n s + \omega_n^2} \tag{8.44}$$

To evaluate $G(j\omega)$ by the "elastic vector" method, locate the poles of $G(s)$ on the s plane, as shown in Fig. 8.16. Here the pole-zero plot is shown for ζ in the neighborhood of 0.3. When $\omega = 0$ the two vectors are the same length, so that the amplitude ratio is K/ω_n^2. The phase shift, given by $\underline{/G(j\omega)}$, is $-(\alpha + \beta)$ in this system where α and β are the angles associated with the two "elastic vectors." At $\omega = 0$ $(\alpha + \beta)$ is 0°. As ω is increased from zero, the "upper" vector shrinks in length until the $s = j\omega$ point is just abreast of the upper pole; it then grows indefinitely in length. The "lower" vector simply increases in length from its initial value. The amplitude ratio of the system is inversely proportional to the product of the two vector lengths.

In this system the amplitude ratio as a function of frequency will exhibit a resonant peak because of the way in which the vector lengths change with frequency. This is shown in the rectangular plot of Fig. 8.17. The frequency at which the peak in the amplitude curve occurs is called the *resonant frequency* and is denoted as ω_r. The value of the amplitude ratio at the resonant frequency is called M_P, for peak magnitude. Figure 8.17 also shows the phase shift plotted as a function of frequency. It is easy to see from Fig. 8.16 that the phase shift begins at zero for $\omega = 0$ and becomes progressively larger (lagging), approaching $-180°$ as ω approaches infinity.

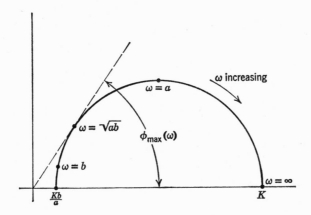

Fig. 8.15. Polar plot of Fig. 8.14.

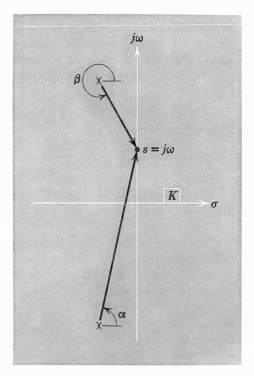

Fig. 8.16.   Computing $G(j\omega)$ for an underdamped second order system.

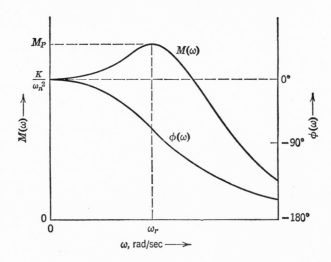

Fig. 8.17.   Rectangular plot of frequency response characteristics of underdamped second order system.

It is possible to discover some interesting properties of the frequency response of this second order system by making a quantitative study of the pole-zero plot shown in Fig. 8.16.   This plot is redrawn in Fig. 8.18. We recall that the poles of the second order transfer function are located at the points $s = -\zeta\omega_n \pm j\omega_0$, where ω_0 is the frequency of the damped oscillations resulting when the input is a step or an impulse, and ω_n is the undamped natural frequency (that is, the frequency at which the output would oscillate in response to a step or impulse input if there were no damping in the system).   The distance from a pole to the origin was found to be ω_n, so if a circle of radius ω_n and centered at the origin is constructed, it will pass through the poles, as shown in the sketch.   This circle intercepts the $j\omega$ axis at the point $s = j\omega_n$, so it is

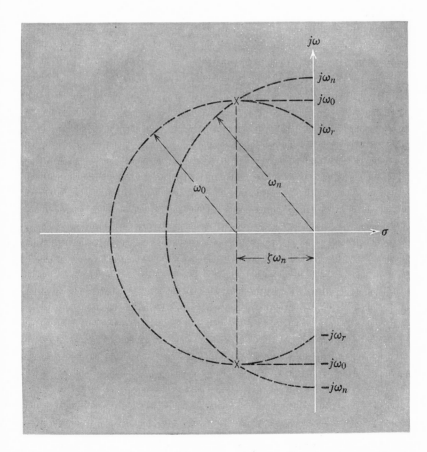

Fig. 8.18.   Defining ω_n, ω_0, ω_r, for a second order system, from the pole-zero plot.

obvious that ω_n is always greater than ω_0 when the damping ratio is greater than zero.

Now, if a quantitative study of the frequency response of this system is made by means of the geometrical relationships indicated in Fig. 8.16, it will be seen that the resonant frequency ω_r will occur where a circle of radius ω_0, centered at $s = -\zeta\omega_n$, intersects the $j\omega$ axis. The geometrical constructions shown in Fig. 8.18 are obvious when we recall that ω_r is the frequency at which the product of the two "elastic vectors" in Fig. 8.16 is a minimum.

Several important facts about second order systems are now apparent. The resonant frequency is seen to be less than ω_0, the transient oscillating frequency, except when $\zeta = 0$. Furthermore, when $\zeta = 0.707$ the resonant frequency is 0, and when $\zeta > 0.707$ there will be no resonant frequency—that is, the $M(\omega)$ vs. ω curve will have no peak but will be monotonically decreasing. The differences in the magnitudes of ω_n, ω_0, and ω_r are quite pronounced in a well-damped system (when ζ is in the neighborhood of 0.5), but for very lightly damped systems (when ζ is less than 0.1) these three characteristic frequencies are quite close to the same value. Because of this, many electronics engineers who are accustomed to working only with very lightly damped ("high Q") tuned circuits do not make any distinction between these three frequencies, lumping them all under the name *natural frequency*, or some other general sounding title. The control systems engineer, on the other hand, usually works with well-damped systems, and it is important for him to understand the distinction between these three frequencies. A graph showing the variation of ω_0 and ω_r as a function of ζ is drawn in Fig. 8.19.

Observe in Fig. 8.18 that the phase shift of the second order system,

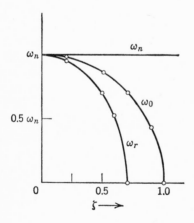

Fig. 8.19. ω_0 and ω_r as functions of ζ in the second order system.

$-(\alpha + \beta)$, is exactly $-90°$ at $\omega = \omega_n$. This is true for all values of the damping ratio, including those greater than unity.

All these relationships, which were obtained by geometrical observations, may of course be derived analytically as well. When $j\omega$ is substituted for s in $G(s)$,

$$G(j\omega) = \frac{K}{(\omega_n{}^2 - \omega^2) + j2\zeta\omega_n\omega} \tag{8.45}$$

The amplitude ratio and phase shift are derived as

$$M(\omega) = |G(j\omega)| = \frac{K}{[(\omega_n{}^2 - \omega^2)^2 + (2\zeta\omega_n\omega)^2]^{1/2}} \tag{8.46}$$

$$\phi(\omega) = \underline{/G(j\omega)} = -\tan^{-1}\frac{2\zeta\omega_n\omega}{\omega_n{}^2 - \omega^2} \tag{8.47}$$

By applying the rules of calculus to Eq. 8.46 we find that the frequency at which $M(\omega)$ is a maximum is

$$\omega_r = \omega_n\sqrt{1 - 2\zeta^2} \qquad \zeta < 0.707 \tag{8.48}$$

and that the peak magnitude is

$$M_P = M(\omega_r) = \frac{K}{2\zeta\omega_n{}^2\sqrt{1 - \zeta^2}} \qquad \zeta < 0.707 \tag{8.49}$$

It is apparent from Eq. 8.48 that ω_r goes to zero as ζ approaches 0.707, and from Eq. 8.47 that the phase shift at $\omega = \omega_n$ is $-90°$ for all values of ζ. Thus the conclusions arrived at from a study of the geometry of the pole-zero plot are verified analytically. Further consideration is given to the frequency response of second order systems in Section 8.3.

The three examples treated above show that the frequency response of a linear system may be derived directly from the transfer function. More correctly, the frequency response is simply a special form of the transfer function obtained by substituting $j\omega$ for s in $G(s)$. The frequency response, then, may be considered to be a description of the transfer function, since it is an indirect way of describing the locations of the poles and zeros of the transfer function. It is considered by many to be a less effective tool for describing the dynamic properties of the system than is the transfer function, which may just as easily be used to show the pole and zero locations directly.

An evaluation of the frequency response method in this light may be made by considering the problem of determining the exact shape of a solid object which has an intricate set of holes and slots cut into it. The most direct method of determining its shape is simply to examine the bare object. However, if the object were covered by a cloth, it would also be possible to determine its size and shape by feeling through the cloth for the holes and slots. Similarly, the exact dynamic properties of a linear system are obtained most directly from the transfer function itself, which shows the exact locations of the poles and zeros. However, it is also possible to determine the dynamic properties of the system by moving along the $j\omega$ axis and sensing $M(\omega)$ and $\phi(\omega)$, which *depend* upon the pole and zero locations but which do not show these locations directly. Hence, the frequency response method is an indirect way of dealing with the transfer function. Even though the frequency response method is a less direct approach to dynamic analysis than is the pole-zero method, it is an important and useful technique and should be well understood by control system engineers.

8.3 ASYMPTOTIC APPROXIMATION TO REAL FREQUENCY RESPONSE CURVES

This section describes a very useful technique for obtaining the approximate frequency response characteristics for linear systems. The Bode diagram must be used for plotting the amplitude and phase shift curves when this technique is employed.

Consider, as a first example, the transfer function for a pure differentiating device:

$$G(s) = s \qquad (8.50)$$

The frequency response of this device is obtained by substituting $j\omega$ for s in the transfer function. The amplitude and phase shift will be

$$M(\omega) = |G(j\omega)| = \omega$$
$$\phi(\omega) = \underline{/G(j\omega)} = +90° \qquad (8.51)$$

A table in Fig. 8.20 lists the values for $M(\omega)$, $M_{db}(\omega)$, and $\phi(\omega)$ for various values of ω. Since $M(\omega)$ is simply ω itself, $M(\omega)$ will increase

ω	$M(\omega)$	$M_{db}(\omega)$	$\phi(\omega)$ degrees
0	0	$-\infty$	$+90°$
0.1	0.1	-20	$+90°$
0.5	0.5	-6.02	$+90°$
1.0	1.0	0	$+90°$
2.0	2.0	$+6.02$	$+90°$
5.0	5.0	$+13.94$	$+90°$
10.0	10.0	$+20$	$+90°$
100.0	100.0	$+40$	$+90°$
∞	∞	∞	$+90°$

Fig. 8.20. Frequency response data for G(s) = s.

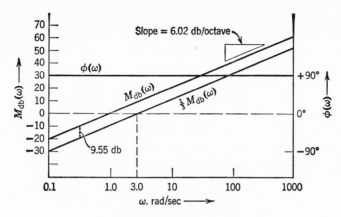

Fig. 8.21. Bode plot of $G(j\omega) = j\omega$ and $G(j\omega) = \frac{1}{3}j\omega$.

linearly when ω is increased. On the logarithmic scales used in the Bode plot $M_{db}(\omega)$ will also be a straight line function, as shown in Fig. 8.21. The slope of this curve is measured as the change in decibel level between two frequency points which are separated by a given distance along the abscissa. This distance cannot be measured in radians per second because a given distance at the low frequency end of the scale will represent a change of very few radians per second, while the same distance at the high frequency end will represent a change of very many radians per second. However, a given distance along the abscissa will represent the same *percentage* change in frequency, no matter where that distance is taken along the frequency scale. Therefore, the slope of the $M_{db}(\omega)$ curve is expressed in decibels per percentage change in frequency. A change in frequency of 100 percent—from $\omega = 1$ to $\omega = 2$, for example— is called an octave, so in this system the $M_{db}(\omega)$ curve has a slope of 6.02 db/octave. A change in frequency by a factor of 10—from $\omega = 1$ to $\omega = 10$, for example—is called a decade, so in this system the $M_{db}(\omega)$ curve has a slope of 20 db/decade. Either the octave or the decade measure may be used. Since the phase shift is constant at $+90°$, its curve is simply a flat line at $\phi(\omega) = +90°$.

If the transfer function in Eq. 8.50 is multiplied by a constant, it becomes

$$G(s) = Ks \qquad (8.52)$$

and the amplitude and phase shift will be

$$M(\omega) = \big|G(j\omega)\big| = K\omega$$

$$\phi(\omega) = \underline{/G(j\omega)} = +90° \qquad (8.53)$$

A table of frequency response data for this system would be the same as that shown in Fig. 8.20, except that the numbers in the $M(\omega)$ column would be K times those shown, and the numbers in the $M_{db}(\omega)$ column would be those in Fig. 8.20 plus $20 \log_{10} K$. From this we conclude that if a transfer function is multiplied by a constant, the phase shift of the system is unaffected but the amplitude ratio is increased (or decreased) by the constant factor. On the Bode chart this increase (or decrease) shows up in the amplitude curve as a vertical shift by the number of decibels corresponding to the constant multiplier. In this system if the constant K is $\frac{1}{3}$, for example, the amplitude curve on the Bode plot would be shifted downward 9.55 db, since

$$20 \log_{10} \left(\tfrac{1}{3}\right) = -9.55 \tag{8.54}$$

This shift is shown in Fig. 8.21, where it may be noted that the shifted curve passes through the zero db line for $\omega = 3$.

As a second example of the straight line Bode plot, consider the transfer function

$$G(s) = \frac{K}{s} \tag{8.55}$$

whose frequency response is defined by

$$M(\omega) = |G(j\omega)| = \frac{K}{\omega}$$

$$\phi(\omega) = \underline{/G(j\omega)} = -90° \tag{8.56}$$

Here the amplitude ratio is inversely proportional to ω, so that at $\omega = K$ $M(\omega) = 1$ (0 db). The slope of the $M_{db}(\omega)$ curve will be -20 db/decade, or -6.02 db/octave, as shown in Fig. 8.22, which has been drawn for $K = 4$. The phase shift is again constant at $-90°$ in this example.

As a third example consider the transfer function of a "double integrator."

$$G(s) = \frac{K}{s^2} \tag{8.57}$$

For this transfer function the frequency response is given by

$$M(\omega) = |G(j\omega)| = \frac{K}{\omega^2}$$

$$\phi(\omega) = \underline{/G(j\omega)} = -180° \tag{8.58}$$

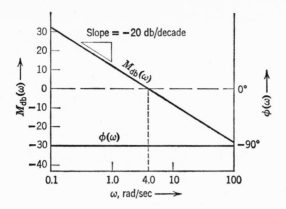

Fig. 8.22. Bode plot of $G(j\omega)$. $G(j\omega) = \dfrac{4}{j\omega}$.

Again, the Bode plot for $M_{db}(\omega)$ is a straight line having a negative slope (since $M(\omega)$ decreases with an increase in ω), but the slope will be -40 db/decade, since an increase of one decade in ω causes $M(\omega)$ to change by a factor of 100. The amplitude and phase curves are drawn on the Bode plot for $K = 4$ in Fig. 8.23. A comparison of the curves in Fig. 8.21, 8.22, and 8.23 indicates that the Bode plot for a transfer

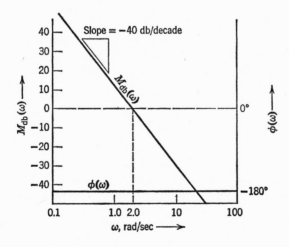

Fig. 8.23. Bode plot of $G(j\omega)$. $G(j\omega) = \dfrac{4}{(j\omega)^2}$.

function of the form

$$G(s) = K(s)^n \qquad (8.59)$$

where n is an integer will have the following properties:

(a) $M_{\mathrm{db}}(\omega)$ will be a straight line having a slope of $(20n)$ decibels per decade. Of course, if n is negative the slope will be negative.

(b) $M_{\mathrm{db}}(\omega)$ will cross the zero db line at the frequency $\omega = K^{-1/n}$.

(c) $\phi(\omega)$ will be constant at $90n°$.

We now consider transfer functions having Bode plots which are not straight lines, but which may be approximated by straight lines. We do this by considering the *asymptotic behaviour* of such transfer functions—that is, their properties at extremely low and extremely high frequencies.

Let the transfer function have the form

$$G(s) = K(s + a) \qquad (8.60)$$

so that the frequency response is given by

$$G(j\omega) = K(j\omega + a) \qquad (8.61)$$

and the amplitude and phase shift functions are

$$M(\omega) = |G(j\omega)| = K(\omega^2 + a^2)^{\frac{1}{2}}$$

$$\phi(\omega) = \underline{/G(j\omega)} = \tan^{-1}\frac{\omega}{a} \qquad (8.62)$$

Now, consider the behavior of $M(\omega)$ when the frequency is very low—that is, when $\omega \ll a$. At these low frequencies $M(\omega)$ will be approximately

$$M(\omega) \cong Ka \qquad \omega \ll a \qquad (8.63)$$

This is a straight line of zero slope with a decibel value of $20 \log_{10}(Ka)$, as shown in the Bode diagram in Fig. 8.24.

Next, consider $M(\omega)$ for very high frequencies—that is, for $\omega \gg a$. At these high frequencies $M(\omega)$ will be approximately

$$M(\omega) \cong K\omega \qquad \omega \gg a \qquad (8.64)$$

This is a straight line having a slope of 20 db/decade and passing through the $20 \log_{10}(Ka)$ point at $\omega = a$ (Fig. 8.24). Thus the two straight lines intersecting at $\omega = a$ comprise an approximation to the amplitude ratio curve $M_{\mathrm{db}}(\omega)$.

We have seen here that this approximation is very good at very low and at very high frequencies, but let us now investigate the error at

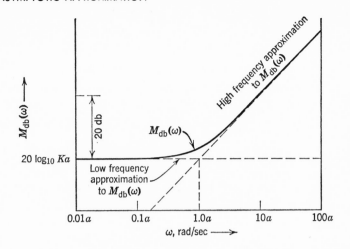

Fig. 8.24. Straight line approximations to $|G(j\omega)|_{db}$ on Bode chart. $G(j\omega) = K(j\omega + a)$.

frequencies in the neighborhood of $\omega = a$. At $\omega = a$ we have

$$M(\omega)\Big|_{\omega=a} = K(a^2 + a^2)^{\frac{1}{2}} = \sqrt{2}\,Ka \qquad (8.65)$$

So in terms of decibels we have

$$M_{db}(\omega)\Big|_{\omega=a} = 20\log_{10}(Ka) + 20\log_{10}\sqrt{2} \qquad (8.66)$$

But $\qquad 20\log_{10}\sqrt{2} = 3.01 \qquad (8.67)$

The Bode plot actually passes through a point which is 3.01 db above the intersection of the two straight line approximations. ($\omega = a$ is called the *break frequency* or the *corner frequency* of this transfer function.)

At a frequency one octave below the break frequency—that is, at $\omega = a/2$—the amplitude ratio is

$$M(\omega)\Big|_{\omega=a/2} = K\left(\frac{a^2}{4} + a^2\right)^{\frac{1}{2}} = \sqrt{\tfrac{5}{4}}\,Ka \qquad (8.68)$$

which, expressed in decibels, is

$$M_{db}(\omega)\Big|_{\omega=a/2} = 20\log_{10}(Ka) + 20\log_{10}\sqrt{\tfrac{5}{4}} \qquad (8.69)$$

But $\qquad 20\log_{10}\sqrt{\tfrac{5}{4}} = 0.969 \qquad (8.70)$

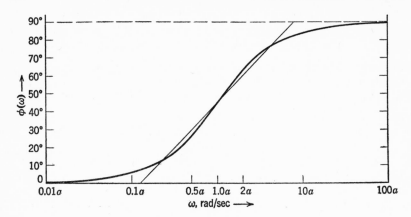

Fig. 8.25.   Phase shift curve for $/G(j\omega) = /j\omega + a$.

Hence, the Bode plot passes through a point which lies 0.969 db above the straight line asymptote at $\omega = a/2$.

Similarly, at a frequency one octave above the break frequency, at $\omega = 2a$, the Bode plot will pass through a point which is 6.99 db above the low frequency asymptote or 0.97 db above the high frequency asymptote. When the asymptotes are sketched and these three points at $\omega = a/2$, a, and $2a$ are spotted on the graph, it is usually possible with the aid of a French curve to sketch in for $M_{db}(\omega)$ an accurate curve which will cover a wide range of frequencies, both above and below the break frequency. This is done in Fig. 8.24. In many problems it is not necessary to have an extremely accurate graph, and the deviations of the straight line asymptotes from the actual $M_{db}(\omega)$ curve may be taken simply as 1, 3, and 1 db instead of the more accurate 0.969, 3.01, and 0.97 db at the three frequencies considered above.

A plot of the phase-shift curve given by Eq. 8.62 is an arctangent curve, as shown in Fig. 8.25. At the break frequency the phase shift is exactly 45°. At $\omega = a/2$ it is about 26.57°, and at $\omega = 2a$ it is about 63.43°. A straight line may be drawn through these three points on the phase-shift curve. This line will intersect the $\phi(\omega) = 0$ line (which may be considered to be the low frequency asymptote) at $\omega = 0.184a$, and it will intersect the $\phi(\omega) = 90°$ line (the high frequency asymptote) at $\omega = 5.43a$. These two frequencies, $0.184a$ and $5.43a$, may be considered to be *break frequencies* in the $\phi(\omega)$ curve. A simple calculation will show that the phase shifts at these two frequencies are 10.435° and

79.565°.   These figures form a basis for making a straight line approximation to the phase-shift curve.   Using Eq. 8.62 we could derive
other straight line approximations to the phase-shift curve.   For
example, the tangent to the $\phi(\omega)$ curve at $\omega = a$ could be used to
approximate the midfrequency phase-shift curve.

As a further example of the straight line approximation technique,
consider the transfer function

$$G(s) = \frac{K(s + a)}{s + b} \tag{8.71}$$

This transfer function may be decomposed so that it is the product of
three transfer functions:

$$G(s) = \left(\frac{Ka}{b}\right)\left(\frac{s + a}{a}\right)\left(\frac{b}{s + b}\right) \tag{8.72}$$

It is a simple matter to draw a straight line approximation to the
amplitude ratio for each of these three simple transfer functions.
This is done in Fig. 8.26, where it is assumed that $a > b$ and that
$Ka/b > 1$.   Notice that the zero frequency amplitude of both the
$(s + a)/a$ and the $b/(s + b)$ terms is 1 (0 db).

It is often convenient to factor the transfer function so that each of
the frequency dependent terms has a zero frequency gain of unity.
The asymptotes for the $(s + a)/a$ term are drawn in exactly the same

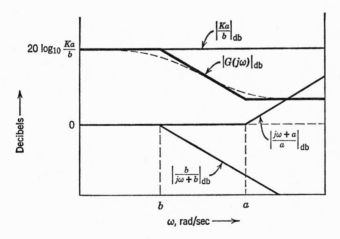

Fig. 8.26.   Asymptotic approximation to $|G(j\omega)| = \left|\dfrac{K(j\omega + a)}{(j\omega + b)}\right|$.

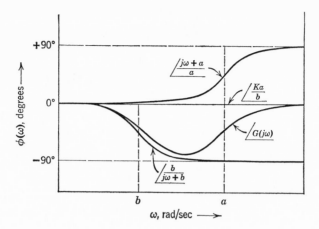

Fig. 8.27. Phase shift curve for $G(j\omega) = \dfrac{K(j\omega + a)}{(j\omega + b)}$.

way as in the previous example (Fig. 8.24). The low frequency asymptote for the $b/(s + b)$ term is also the 0 db line, but the high frequency asymptote has a negative slope of 20 db/decade and passes through the 0 db line at $\omega = b$. A composite straight line approximation to $|G(j\omega)|$ may now be formed simply by adding the three component approximations. This composite curve is drawn in heavy lines in Fig. 8.26. The actual magnitude curve will lie close to this composite straight approximation, as indicated by the dotted lines.

The phase-shift curves for this transfer function are sketched in Fig. 8.27. Notice that the phase shift for the $b/(s + b)$ term is negative or *lagging*, and that for the $(s + a)/a$ term is positive or *leading*. The phase shift of the constant term is zero, of course. The composite phase-shift curve is formed by adding the three individual curves in the same manner as the composite amplitude curve was formed in Fig. 8.26.

If a transfer function is composed of several first order poles and zeros, the composite frequency response curve may be drawn in the fashion described in the foregoing example. One straight line approximation is required for each of the individual components at the break frequency corresponding to that component. The break frequency is numerically equal to the pole or zero value, and the high frequency asymptote breaks *up* for the component contributed by a zero of $G(s)$, and it breaks *down* for the component contributed by a pole of $G(s)$.

For example, the straight line approximation to the amplitude characteristic for this transfer function

$$G(s) = \frac{40(s + 1)(s + 24)}{(s + 2)(s + 6)(s + 40)} \qquad (8.73)$$

is sketched on the Bode chart in Fig. 8.28. The dotted line shows approximately where the actual magnitude curve would lie. A phase-shift curve for this transfer function may be constructed from five individual phase shift curves, each corresponding to one of the break frequencies of $G(s)$.

If a transfer function should contain a quadratic factor having complex roots it cannot be decomposed to a product of individual first order terms, and a straight line approximation to the frequency response characteristics will not be quite as simple as it is when only first order terms are present.

Consider the second order transfer function

$$G(s) = \frac{\omega_n{}^2}{s^2 + 2\zeta\omega_n s + \omega_n{}^2} \qquad (8.74)$$

This is the same as Eq. 8.44 if K is taken to be $\omega_n{}^2$. The amplitude and phase-shift expressions for $G(j\omega)$ are given in Eqs. 8.46 and 8.47. Both $M(\omega)$ and $\phi(\omega)$ depend upon ζ and ω_n as well as upon ω. It is convenient to normalize these expressions with respect to ω_n by intro-

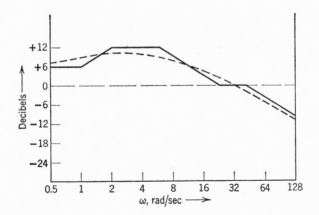

Fig. 8.28. Amplitude ratio curve (approximation) for $G(s) = \dfrac{40(s + 1)(s + 24)}{(s + 2)(s + 6)(s + 40)}$.

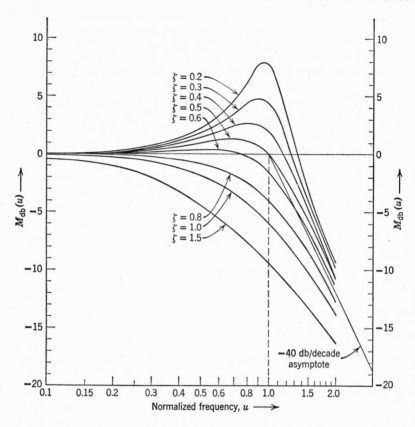

Fig. 8.29. Bode plot of amplitude ratio of second order transfer function.

ducing a normalized frequency u

$$u = \frac{\omega}{\omega_n} \tag{8.75}$$

so that the amplitude and phase-shift functions become

$$M(u) = \frac{1}{[(1 - u^2)^2 + (2\zeta u)^2]^{\frac{1}{2}}} \tag{8.76}$$

$$\phi(u) = -\tan^{-1}\left(\frac{2\zeta u}{1 - u^2}\right) \tag{8.77}$$

Now the amplitude and phase shift depend upon only two variables, ζ and u. $M(u)$ and $\phi(u)$ are accurately plotted for various values of ζ on Bode charts in Figs. 8.29 and 8.30. The high frequency asymptote for all curves in Fig. 8.29 is a straight line passing through the zero db line at $u = 1$ and having a slope of -40 db/decade. Notice also that the resonant frequency is zero for $\zeta = 0.707$, and that it increases toward $u = 1$ as ζ is decreased.

When the normalized frequency response curves for the second order transfer function are available it is possible to make an asymptotic approximation to the frequency response characteristics of any transfer function which is the ratio of two algebraic polynomials in s, since this type of transfer function may always be factored into first and second order terms.

To illustrate the use of the second order curves in making a Bode plot of a transfer function containing a pair of complex poles, consider the following example:

$$G(s) = \frac{50(s + 4)}{s(s^2 + 4s + 100)} \tag{8.78}$$

This can be factored into four terms.

$$G(s) = (2)\left(\frac{s + 4}{4}\right)\left(\frac{1}{s}\right)\left(\frac{100}{s^2 + 4s + 100}\right) \tag{8.79}$$

The first three of these terms may be sketched onto the Bode plot very

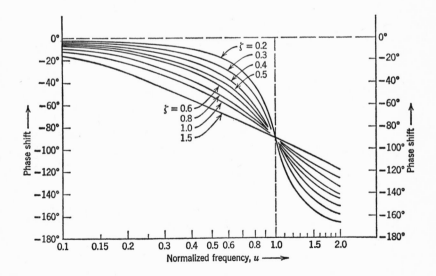

Fig. 8.30. Bode plot of phase shift of second order transfer function.

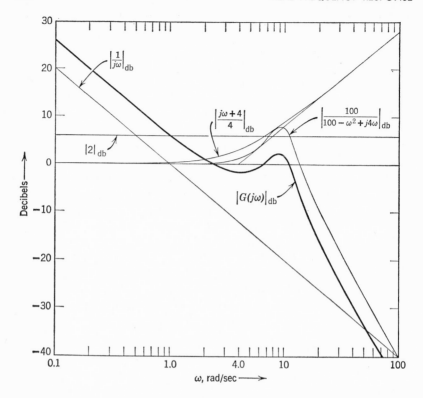

Fig. 8.31. Constructing the amplitude ratio curve for $G(s) = \dfrac{50(s + 4)}{s(s^2 + 4s + 100)}$.

quickly, as shown in Fig. 8.31. The quadratic term is sketched, using the normalized curves in Fig. 8.29. This quadratic term has an ω_n of 10 rad per sec and a ζ of 0.2; $u = 1$ in Fig. 8.29 corresponds to $\omega = 10$ in Fig. 8.31. Thus, the quadratic term will appear as shown, and the composite amplitude curve is formed as the sum of the four individual curves. The phase-shift curve would be formed in a similar manner; it is not shown here.

It should be noted that if the transfer function should have a pair of complex zeros, the curves in Figs. 8.29 and 8.30 may be used to plot the component of the frequency response corresponding to the zeros. The amplitude curves would be the negative of those given in Fig. 8.29, and the phase shift would be the negative of that given by Fig. 8.30.

The examples given in this section demonstrate that it is possible to approximate frequency response curves for a transfer function of any order simply by decomposing it into the product of simple functions. The asymptotic approximations made on the Bode plot require much less time than any other method which might be used to compute the frequency response of a transfer function. In the next two sections some further properties of the frequency response characteristics of linear systems are described.

8.4 MINIMUM PHASE TRANSFER FUNCTIONS

A minimum phase transfer function is one whose poles and zeros all lie in the left-half s plane. The designation *minimum phase* for a particular class of transfer functions in contrast to *nonminimum phase* transfer functions is discussed in Section 8.5.

It was shown in Section 8.2 that the frequency response of a transfer function may be evaluated by substituting $j\omega$ for s in the transfer function. This substitution may be made graphically by the *vector method*, as illustrated in Fig. 8.13. It may be surmised from this vector plot that because both the amplitude and phase-shift properties of the transfer function depend upon the locations of the poles and zeros, certain general relationships exist between the amplitude and phase-shift characteristics of a minimum phase transfer function. Such relationships have been explored exhaustively by Bode and others. Since a full presentation of these relationships would require more space than is available here, this discussion is limited to a statement of one or two of the practical implications of the theorems which Bode put forth regarding the amplitude and phase-shift properties of minimum phase transfer functions.

One of the more practical findings of the study of minimum phase transfer functions is that the amplitude and phase-shift characteristics are interdependent. Therefore, if the amplitude characteristic for a particular transfer function is specified over the entire frequency range $0 < \omega < \infty$, it will not be possible to choose the phase-shift characteristic; we must simply accept whatever phase-shift characteristic results. Conversely, if we specify the phase shift we must accept whatever amplitude characteristics result. However, if we specify the amplitude characteristic over only a portion of the frequency range, we then give ourselves some freedom in choosing the phase shift characteristic over another portion of the frequency range. In doing this we must of course accept those amplitude characteristics which result over the portion of the frequency range for which we did not specify the amplitude characteristic. Some examples in Chapter

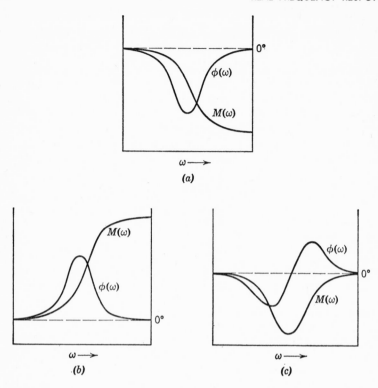

Fig. 8.32. Amplitude and phase shift properties of minimum phase transfer functions; (a) lag, (b) lead, (c) lag-lead.

9 illustrate the way in which this principle applies in the design of net-works for improving the performance of servomechanism systems.

A quantitative statement, or theorem, relating the amplitude and phase-shift characteristics is

$$\int_0^\infty \phi(\omega)\, d\omega = K[M(\infty) - M(0)] \qquad (8.80)$$

where $\phi(\omega)$ is the phase-shift characteristic of the transfer function, $M(\infty)$ is the amplitude ratio at $\omega = \infty$, and $M(0)$ is the amplitude ratio at $\omega = 0$. K is a constant. Equation 8.80 states that the area under the phase-shift curve is proportional to the difference between the infinite frequency amplitude ratio and the zero frequency amplitude ratio. Figure 8.32 shows the amplitude and phase-shift characteristics of three minimum-phase transfer functions. The first is a *lag* type function; the phase shift is negative, so the area under the $\phi(\omega)$ curve is also negative. This dictates that $M(\infty)$ be less than $M(0)$. The second is a *lead* type function; the phase shift is positive, so Eq. 8.80 dictates that $M(\infty)$ be greater than $M(0)$. The third example is a *lag-lead* function. Here $M(0)$ and $M(\infty)$ are equal. Therefore, the negative area under the phase-shift curve must equal the positive area, the net area being zero.

A second quantitative relationship which is useful in frequency response analysis relates the phase shift of a transfer function at a given frequency to the slope of the amplitude curve over the entire frequency range. The statement is this:

$$\phi(\omega_0) = \frac{1}{\pi} \int_{-\infty}^{\infty} \left(\frac{dM}{du}\right) W(u) \, du \qquad \text{radians} \qquad (8.81)$$

In this expression u is a normalized frequency given by

$$u = \log_e \frac{\omega}{\omega_0} \qquad (8.82)$$

ω_0 is the frequency at which the phase shift is measured, and $W(u)$ is a *weighting function* given by

$$W(u) = \log_e \left(\coth \frac{|u|}{2}\right) \qquad (8.83)$$

$W(u)$ is plotted versus u and ω in Fig. 8.33. dM/du, the slope of the

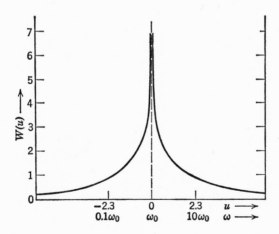

Fig. 8.33.   W(u) plotted vs. u and ω.

amplitude ratio curve plotted as a function of u, will be 1 if the slope of the $M(\omega)$ curve is 20 db/decade; it will be 2 if the slope of the $M(\omega)$ curve is 40 db/decade, and so on.

Equation 8.81 is interpreted in the following manner. The phase shift of a transfer function at a given frequency ω_0 is related to the slope of the amplitude ratio curve. This relationship is such that the slope of the amplitude curve in the immediate neighborhood of ω_0 has much more influence (or weight) upon the magnitude of the phase shift than does the slope at frequencies remote from ω_0. In fact, in systems where the amplitude curve does not have any abrupt changes in slope near ω_0, the contribution to the integral of dM/du at remote frequencies is almost negligible, so that the phase shift at ω_0 is nearly proportional to the slope of the amplitude curve at ω_0.

An extreme case of this sort is the transfer function

$$G(s) = \frac{K}{s} \tag{8.84}$$

whose amplitude curve, plotted on a Bode chart, has *no* change in slope over the entire frequency range (Fig. 8.22). dM/du in this case is -1, and Eq. 8.81 reduces to

$$\phi(\omega_0) = -\frac{1}{\pi} \int_{-\infty}^{\infty} W(u) \, du \qquad \text{radians} \tag{8.85}$$

The definite integral has a value $\pi^2/2$, so the phase shift at ω_0 is $-90°$; Since ω_0 may represent any frequency the phase shift is the same at all frequencies.

As another example of the interpretation of Eq. 8.81, consider the transfer function

$$G(s) = K(s + a) \tag{8.86}$$

Its amplitude curve is shown in Fig. 8.24. Assume that we wish to compute the phase shift of this transfer function at $\omega_0 = 2a$. dM/du is plotted against ω in Fig. 8.34. The weighting function $W(u)$ is also plotted on the same chart, as is the product $W(u) (dM/du)$. The phase shift at $\omega_0 = 2a$ is the integral of this product, or the area under the curve, shown as the shaded portion of the graph. It is apparent from this sketch that if the dM/du curve were considered to be flat—that is, if dM/du were a constant at the value which it assumes when $\omega = 2a$— the product curve would be symmetrical about ω_0. Therefore, the

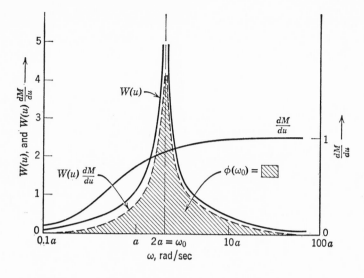

Fig. 8.34. Computing $\phi(\omega_0)$ from Eq. 8.81. $G(s) = K(s + a)$, $\omega_0 = 2a$.

shaded area to the left of ω_0 would be slightly greater than it is in Fig. 8.34, and the shaded area to the right of ω_0 would be slightly less than it is here. However, the total area would be approximately the same. Therefore, in this particular system, the phase shift at any frequency may be considered to be approximately proportional to the slope of the amplitude curve at that frequency. Equation 8.81 reduces to

$$\phi(\omega_0) \cong \frac{\pi}{40} \frac{dM}{d\omega}\bigg|_{\omega = \omega_0} \text{ radians} \qquad (8.87)$$

where $dM/d\omega$ is expressed in decibels per decade.

Equation 8.87 may not be applied to systems in which an abrupt change occurs in the slope of the amplitude curve in the immediate neighborhood of ω_0. Consider, for example, a second order system with a low damping ratio—say, 0.2. Equation 8.87 applied at the resonant frequency will give the phase shift as 0°; at a frequency just below resonance it would give a phase shift of nearly $+150°$; and at a frequency just above resonance it would give a phase shift of nearly $-300°$. The actual phase shift in the *neighborhood* of resonance lies in the region of $-30°$ to $-120°$. Figure 8.35 shows a graphical calculation, made with the use of Eq. 8.81, of the phase shift in a second order system ($\zeta = 0.2$) at the resonant frequency, which is

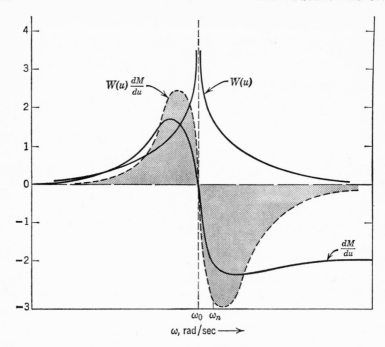

Fig. 8.35. Computing $\phi(\omega_0)$ from Eq. 8.81. $G(s) = \dfrac{\omega_n{}^2}{s^2 + 0.4\omega_n s + \omega_n{}^2}.$ $\omega_0 \sim 0.95\omega_n$.

approximately $0.95\omega_n$. This calculation illustrates clearly why Eq. 8.87 does not hold when dM/du changes abruptly in the neighborhood of the frequency at which the phase shift is being computed.

Equation 8.87 will hold at *extreme* frequencies—that is, at frequencies which are either very much lower or very much higher than any of the *break* frequencies or resonant frequencies in the system, because $dM/d\omega$ is always approximately constant at the extreme frequencies. Consider, for example, an nth order transfer function having m zeros. m is less than or equal to n:

$$G(s) = \frac{K[s^m + a_1 s^{m-1} + \cdots a_m]}{s^n + b_1 s^{n-1} + \cdots + b_n} \qquad (8.88)$$

The frequency response is given by

$$G(j\omega) = \frac{K[(j\omega)^m + a_1(j\omega)^{m-1} + \cdots + a_m]}{(j\omega)^n + b_1(j\omega)^{n-1} + \cdots + b_n} \qquad (8.89)$$

At very high frequencies $G(j\omega)$ will be approximately

$$G(j\omega) \cong K(j\omega)^{m-n}$$

because for very large values of ω $[a_1(j\omega)^{m-1} + \cdots + a_m]$ will be much smaller than $K(j\omega)^m$, and $[b_1(j\omega)^{n-1} + \cdots + b_n]$ will be much smaller than $(j\omega)^n$. Therefore, the amplitude and phase shift will be

$$|G(j\omega)| \cong \frac{K}{\omega^{n-m}} = M(\omega)$$

$$\underline{/G(j\omega)} \cong (-90°)(n - m) = \phi(\omega) \qquad (8.90)$$

The slope of the $M(\omega)$ curve on the Bode chart will be about $-20(n - m)$ db/decade. Equation 8.90 shows that Eq. 8.87 will indeed hold at the extreme frequencies.

Equations 8.90, 8.87, 8.81, and 8.80 state several relationships between the amplitude and phase shift of minimum phase transfer functions which are useful in experimental work with minimum phase systems. They indicate, for example, that if the amplitude ratio is measured over a wide range of frequencies the phase shift curve may be constructed without making additional measurements. It is usually easier to make accurate amplitude measurements than accurate phase-shift measurements, but if both are made, these relationships are useful in checking the data for errors. A smoothly rising amplitude curve, for example, should be accompanied by a positive phase shift. Unless the measured phase shift is positive and of approximately the magnitude indicated by Eq. 8.87, something is amiss. Perhaps a sharp resonant peak in the amplitude curve was overlooked during the measuring process. Perhaps an error has occurred in the instrumentation or in the interpretation of the experimental records; this might occur if the system under test is driven into its nonlinear range. Or perhaps the system under consideration is a nonminimum phase system.

8.5 NONMINIMUM PHASE TRANSFER FUNCTIONS

A nonminimum phase transfer function, as it was defined in Section 4.5, is one having poles or zeros in the right-half s plane. If there is a pole in the right half plane the system will be unstable, a fact which is usually of greater significance than the fact that the system is a nonminimum phase system.

The amplitude and phase shift properties of nonminimum phase transfer functions are most easily studied with the aid of the s plane

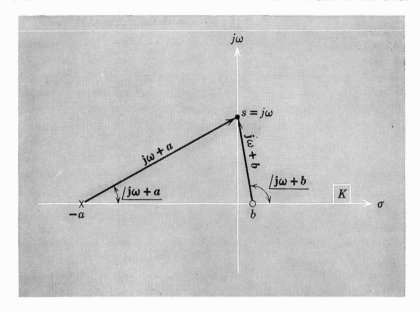

Fig. 8.36. Pole-zero plot for a simple nonminimum phase system.

vector method illustrated in Fig. 8.13. Let us consider a simple
example, one which has a single zero in the right-half s plane.

$$G(s) = \frac{K(s - b)}{(s + a)} \tag{8.91}$$

A pole-zero plot for this transfer function is drawn in Fig. 8.36. The
frequency response is given by $G(j\omega)$:

$$G(j\omega) = \frac{K(j\omega - b)}{(j\omega + a)} \tag{8.92}$$

The amplitude ratio and phase shift are given by

$$M(\omega) = \frac{K|j\omega - b|}{|j\omega + a|} = \frac{K\sqrt{\omega^2 + b^2}}{\sqrt{\omega^2 + a^2}} \tag{8.93}$$

$$\phi(\omega) = \underline{/j\omega - b} - \underline{/j\omega + a}$$

$$= \tan^{-1}\frac{\omega}{-b} - \tan^{-1}\frac{\omega}{a}$$

$$= 180° - \tan^{-1}\frac{\omega}{b} - \tan^{-1}\frac{\omega}{a} \tag{8.94}$$

It is useful at this point to compare Fig. 8.36 with Fig. 8.13. Notice that the amplitude ratio of the nonminimum phase transfer function is identical to that of the minimum phase transfer function. This is true because the amplitude ratio depends only upon the lengths of the two vectors shown in the diagrams and not upon their angles. The phase-shift characteristic of the nonminimum phase system is determined by the angles of the two vectors, and it is apparent that this characteristic is quite different from that of the minimum phase system. In the minimum phase system the phase shift is always 0° at $\omega = 0$, since all of the poles and zeros lie in the left half plane. (Poles on the $j\omega$ axis are excluded from the present discussion.) In this system,

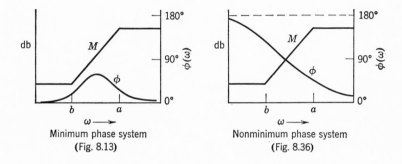

Fig. 8.37. Bode charts corresponding to Figs. 8.13 and 8.36.

however, the phase shift at $\omega = 0$ is 180°, and it decreases to 0° as ω approaches infinity.

The Bode charts for the minimum and nonminimum phase systems are drawn in Fig. 8.37. The origin of the term *minimum phase* is indicated in these two charts. The phase shift on the first chart is the least possible (minimum phase) corresponding to the given amplitude curve, while that in the second chart is greater than the least possible (nonminimum phase). If a similar comparison is made with a higher order system having more than one zero in the right-half s plane, the phase shift will be even more nonminimum phase than that shown in this example.

Zeros in the right-half s plane may give a transient response which has interesting properties. Consider the responses (to a unit step input) of the two systems which are compared in Fig. 8.37. These responses are computed in the conventional manner and appear in

Fig. 8.38. The steady-state value of the nonminimum phase system is negative; this is what we would expect from the frequency response curve which shows a zero frequency phase shift of 180°. The final value theorem may also be applied here to compute the steady-state output to a step input. If the system transfer function is of the general form

$$G(s) = \frac{K(s + Z_1)(s + Z_2) \cdots}{(s + P_1)(s + P_2) \cdots} \tag{8.95}$$

the final value of the output in response to a unit step input is

$$\text{Final value} = \frac{KZ_1Z_2 \cdots}{P_1P_2 \cdots} \tag{8.96}$$

From this we conclude that the final value will be negative if an odd number of zeros occur in the right-half s plane, and it will be positive if an even number of zeros occur there. All of the poles are in the left half plane, so that P_1, P_2 $\cdots$ are all positive numbers.

If a transfer function has one or more poles but no zeros in the right-half s plane a frequency response function may be obtained by substituting $j\omega$ for s in the transfer function, as it is done in a stable system. The frequency response characteristics will exhibit nonminimum phase properties somewhat similar to those in the example treated above. An investigation of this type is suggested as an exercise for the reader.

Some control systems include an element within the control loop which is unstable when isolated from the rest of the system. When the Nyquist stability test is applied to this type of system the frequency response curve for the unstable element must be plotted. It is therefore worthwhile investigating the amplitude and phase-shift properties of unstable elements.

It is possible to measure the frequency response characteristics of

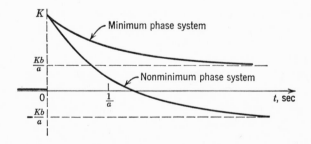

Fig. 8.38.   Transient responses of the two systems compared in Fig. 8.37.

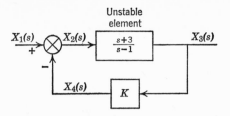

Fig. 8.39.   Circuit for making frequency response measurements on an unstable element.

unstable elements by using them as a part of a feedback system which is made to be stable.   As a simple example, assume that it is desired to make experimental frequency response measurements on a system component which has an unstable transfer function

$$G(s) = \frac{s+3}{s-1} \qquad (8.97)$$

If a loop is closed around this element (Fig. 8.39), the whole system will be stable, provided that K is greater than $\frac{1}{3}$.   When the whole system is stabilized with K set higher than $\frac{1}{3}$, a sinusoidal forcing function may be applied at X_1.   This will induce some transients as well as the steady-state oscillations at X_2, X_3, and X_4, but the transients will all die out eventually, leaving the system in a state of sinusoidal oscillation. X_2 and X_3 are then measured; X_2 is the input to the unstable element, and X_3 is its output.   The procedure is then repeated over and over, using many different frequencies for the forcing function at X_1.   Of course it is important to force the system at X_1 and to make the measurements at X_2 and X_3.   An attempt to force the system at X_2 would in effect disable the feedback mechanism which is essential to the stability of the system.

8.6   INTERPRETATION OF THE REAL FREQUENCY RESPONSE OF A LINEAR SYSTEM IN TERMS OF ITS TRANSIENT RESPONSE

It has been demonstrated in Chapters 2 through 7 that the transient response of a linear system may be computed in a straightforward manner and without undue labor simply by taking the inverse transform of the product of the transfer function and the transform of the input function.   Several graphical techniques based on pole-zero maps were developed to facilitate this procedure.   In Section 8.2 it was demonstrated that the real frequency response of a linear system is simply a special representation of the pole-zero plot—for any given pole-zero plot only one frequency response function occurs and vice-versa. We may therefore conclude that the transient response of a given system is uniquely related to its frequency response.

During the design or testing of a control system we are sometimes presented with some frequency response data from which we may wish to compute, or at least to estimate, what the transient response would be if a step input were to be applied to the system. The obvious way of making such an estimate is simply to determine from the frequency response data where the poles and zeros of the transfer function lie, and then to interpret the pole-zero plot in the conventional way. In many systems the determination of the pole and zero locations is a fairly simple matter of curve fitting, by trial and error, on the Bode plot. We make use of the asymptotic approximations described in Section 8.3 to build up a frequency response curve composed of several components, each having the proper break frequency, or, if an underdamped second order term is required, having the proper ω_n and ζ. With some trial-and-error juggling of the break frequencies it is usually possible to find a very close fit to the curve.

Difficulties in this curve-fitting process will arise, of course, if the frequency response data which are available were taken when the system was operating in its nonlinear region. In designing tests it is advisable to sample the waveform of the system output as well as its amplitude and phase in order to be sure that the oscillation is sinusoidal.

During the 1940's control system designers developed several rules of thumb which were used to relate the frequency response of a system to its transient response. These rules were based upon experimental observations and were developed because the methods of transient analysis based upon pole-zero plots were less well understood than they are today, and it was consequently more difficult to show the exact relationship between the frequency and transient responses. These rules of thumb pertain to such things as the relationship between the *bandwidth* of the system as described by its frequency response and the rise time as described by the transient response, and to the relationship between the M_P of the frequency response curve and the percentage overshoot of the transient response. Also in use were some rather vague rules pertaining to the relationship of the *bumpiness* of the frequency response curve to certain properties of the transient response, such as small amplitude high frequency oscillations or small amplitude long time constant components, which give the transient response a *long tail*. Most of these rules of thumb are essentially valid, and their foundations rest firmly upon easily demonstrated (by pole-zero methods) relationships. However, in certain special cases the rules cannot be applied to give a sufficiently precise answer to the problem at hand. Some of these rules of thumb are listed in Section 9.3.

As a very simple example of the relationship between the frequency response and the transient response of a linear system, consider a first order transfer function

$$G(s) = \frac{a}{s + a} \tag{8.98}$$

Let a be variable. Observe the manner in which the frequency response curve and the transient response (to a unit step input) are affected by a change in a. The comparison is made in Fig. 8.40 for a set at "low," "medium," and "high" values. Note that the fastest transient response corresponds to the broadest frequency response. The fast transient response is a more faithful reproduction of the input step than are the slower transient responses, so that this is often said to be a "higher fidelity" output. The broad frequency response, then, corresponds to "high fidelity" systems; the frequency response is a

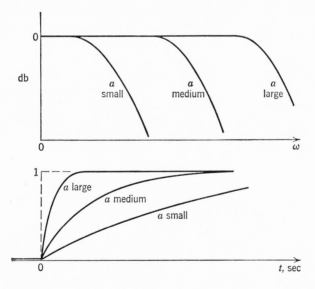

Fig. 8.40. Comparison of frequency response and transient response of first order system, $G(s) = \frac{a}{s + a}$.

more popular way of describing the fidelity of some systems (such as audio amplifiers) than is the transient response, although both methods are obviously equivalent.

A comparison of the frequency response of a second order system and its transient response may be made by studying Figs. 8.29 and 3.35. A relationship exists between the percentage overshoot in the time response and the M_P of the frequency response. The percentage overshoot is given in Eq. 3.148, and M_P is given in Eq. 8.49. The relationship between percentage overshoot and M_P is not a linear one; rather, it depends upon the damping ratio of the system. It is interesting to note that an overshoot occurs in response to a step input for all damping ratios less than unity, but the frequency response curve will not exhibit a resonant peak unless the damping ratio is less than 0.707.

It would be excellent practice at this point for the reader to study the relationship between the frequency response and transient response of some more complicated systems than those discussed here, because for systems of higher order than two no simple relationship between M_P and percentage overshoot can be derived. A useful schedule for such a study would be to consider:

1. First order system with a zero—both lead and lag.

2. Second order system with a zero.

3. Third order system with one real pole and a lightly damped pair of poles.

4. Higher order systems, especially those with one or more pairs of complex poles and/or zeros.

A study such as this will help the reader to understand clearly the relationship between the frequency response and the time response.

This study will be valuable in at least one other respect. It will show the reader the similarity between the techniques developed in Chapters 3 and 4 for sketching the transient response as a composite of individual time functions and the Bode chart approximation technique in this chapter for sketching the frequency response as a composite of individual functions. It is important that the control system engineer be able to utilize either of these techniques in the dynamic analysis of linear systems.

REFERENCES

1. Scott, *Linear Circuits, Part 2, Frequency Domain Analysis*, Addison-Wesley, 1960.
2. Chestnut and Mayer, *Servomechanisms and Regulating System Design*, Vol. 1, 2nd ed., Wiley, 1959.
3. Bode, *Network Analysis and Feedback Amplifier Design*, Van Nostrand, 1945.

9 Control Loop Design Using Real Frequency Response Methods

9.1 INTRODUCTION

In Chapter 7 we studied the problem of selecting poles, zeros, and the gain constant of the loop transfer function $G(s)$ which would satisfy given requirements for the poles, zeros, and gain constant of the system transfer function $W(s)$. In Chapter 9 we are concerned with the problem of selecting the proper form of the loop frequency response function $G(j\omega)$ which will satisfy given requirements for the system frequency response function $W(j\omega)$.

Some system design specifications are written using frequency response data to define the dynamic response requirements. It is convenient, therefore, to be able to analyze the system using frequency response techniques throughout. In some instances the frequency response method is actually more convenient than the pole-zero method.

A unity feedback system of standard form is shown in Fig. 9.1.

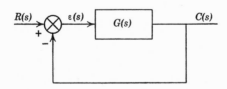

Fig. 9.1. Unity feedback system.

349

The system transfer function is

$$\frac{C(s)}{R(s)} = W(s) = \frac{G(s)}{1 + G(s)} \tag{9.1}$$

If $j\omega$ is substituted for s in Eq. 9.1, the frequency response of the system will be expressed in terms of the frequency response of the loop elements

$$W(j\omega) = \frac{G(j\omega)}{1 + G(j\omega)} \tag{9.2}$$

The interrelationship between $G(j\omega)$ and $W(j\omega)$ may be clearly illustrated by a polar plot of $G(j\omega)$. Assume that $G(s)$ is of the following form, which is typical of servomechanisms:

$$G(s) = \frac{K}{s(s + \alpha)(s + \beta)} \tag{9.3}$$

The frequency response of the loop elements is then

$$G(j\omega) = \frac{K}{j\omega(j\omega + \alpha)(j\omega + \beta)} \tag{9.4}$$

which is plotted in Fig. 9.2. At very high frequencies the phase shift

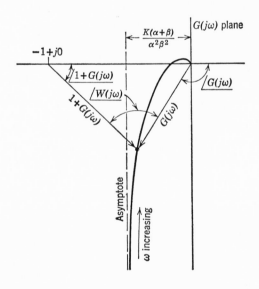

Fig. 9.2.   Polar plot of $G(j\omega) = \dfrac{K}{j\omega(j\omega + \alpha)(j\omega + \beta)}$.

of $G(j\omega)$ approaches $-270°$, and the amplitude approaches zero. At very low frequencies the $G(j\omega)$ curve approaches the asymptote shown in Fig. 9.2. This asymptote is determined by writing $G(j\omega)$ in terms of a real and an imaginary component

$$G(j\omega) = \text{Re}\,[G(j\omega)] + j\,\text{Im}\,[G(j\omega)] \tag{9.5}$$

The real and imaginary components of $G(j\omega)$ may be computed from Eq. 9.4. They are

$$\text{Re}\,[G(j\omega)] = \frac{-K(\alpha + \beta)}{(\alpha^2 + \omega^2)(\beta^2 + \omega^2)}$$

$$\text{Im}\,[G(j\omega)] = \frac{K(\omega^2 - \alpha\beta)}{\omega(\alpha^2 + \omega^2)(\beta^2 + \omega^2)} \tag{9.6}$$

As ω approaches zero the real part of $G(j\omega)$ approaches $-K(\alpha + \beta)/\alpha^2\beta^2$, but the imaginary part approaches $-\infty$. In terms of the amplitude ratio and phase shift, at very low frequencies we have:

$$\underline{/G(j\omega)} \rightarrow -90°$$

$$|G(j\omega)| \rightarrow \infty \tag{9.7}$$

A vector drawn from the origin to the curve represents $G(j\omega)$; the length of the vector is the amplitude ratio, the angle of the vector is the phase shift, and the curve defines the way in which $G(j\omega)$ varies with frequency. A vector drawn from the point $-1 + j0$ to the curve will therefore represent $1 + G(j\omega)$. But the system frequency response is simply the ratio $G(j\omega)/[1 + G(j\omega)]$ (from Eq. 9.2).

It is quite a simple matter, therefore, to compute $W(j\omega)$ graphically from the polar plot of $G(j\omega)$. The amplitude ratio and phase shift of the system frequency response are:

$$|W(j\omega)| = \frac{|G(j\omega)|}{|1 + G(j\omega)|}$$

$$\underline{/W(j\omega)} = \underline{/G(j\omega)} - \underline{/1 + G(j\omega)} \tag{9.8}$$

At very low frequency both the $G(j\omega)$ and $1 + G(j\omega)$ vectors will be very long and their angles will be almost equal, so the system amplitude ratio will be very close to unity and the phase shift virtually zero. As the frequency is increased the amplitude ratio will decrease slightly, since the $G(j\omega)$ vector is always shorter than the $1 + G(j\omega)$ vector. As the frequency is increased beyond the region where $\underline{/G(j\omega)} \cong -130°$ the amplitude ratio decreases more rapidly with frequency, since $G(j\omega)$ decreases toward zero while $1 + G(j\omega)$ decreases toward unity. A

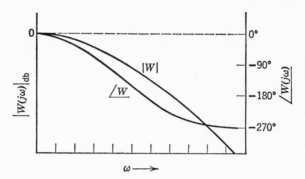

Fig. 9.3. W(jω) plotted from Fig. 9.2.

Bode plot of $W(j\omega)$ in Fig. 9.3 shows the amplitude ratio of $W(j\omega)$ as a function of frequency. Notice that the phase shift of the system transfer function is the angle formed by the intersection of the $G(j\omega)$ and $1 + G(j\omega)$ vectors. At very low frequency this angle is nearly zero, and it approaches $-270°$ as the frequency approaches infinity.

Figures 9.2 and 9.3 are drawn for a system in which the term $K(\alpha + \beta)/\alpha^2\beta^2$ is approximately 0.5. Consider how $G(j\omega)$ and $W(j\omega)$ will change if this term is increased. If K is increased the effect on $G(j\omega)$ will be simply to increase its magnitude without altering its phase shift. Hence a polar plot of $G(j\omega)$ will have the same shape as that in Fig. 9.2 but will be expanded radially.

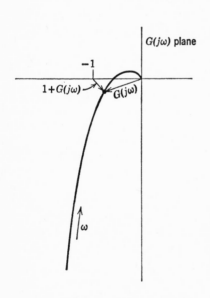

Fig. 9.4. Polar plot of G(jω) for increased K.

A polar plot of $G(j\omega)$ for the increased loop gain is drawn in Fig. 9.4. It is evident that the system frequency response can exhibit a resonant peak in the amplitude curve because in the region of the point $-1 + j0$ the $1 + G(j\omega)$ vector becomes shorter than the $G(j\omega)$ vector, but at high frequency the $G(j\omega)$ vector is the shorter of the two. A Bode plot of the system frequency response is drawn in Fig. 9.5, showing the resonant peak which occurs because the frequency response locus passes close to the $-1 + j0$ point. The frequency at which the peak occurs—the resonant frequency—is denoted by ω_r, and the maximum amplitude ratio is called M_P. If the loop gain is increased further until the frequency response locus of $G(j\omega)$ passes just to the right of the -1 point, the resonant peak in $W(j\omega)$ will be extremely high. In fact, it will approach infinity as K is increased and the locus is made to pass closer and closer to the -1 point. If K is set so that the locus of $G(j\omega)$ passes directly through the -1 point, the resonant peak will be an infinite one. This means that if the system were forced at the resonant frequency the oscillations of the output would build up indefinitely instead of building up to a fixed level. [In any real (nonlinear) system the oscillations would not build up beyond the saturation limit of the output member.] We also see in the next section that the value for K which places the $G(j\omega)$ locus on the -1 point is the critical value of loop gain for system stability.

If the loop gain is increased beyond the stability point, the -1 point will lie *inside* the $G(j\omega)$ locus, as shown in Fig. 9.6. A Bode plot for $|W(j\omega)|$ and $\underline{/W(j\omega)}$ may be constructed from Fig. 9.6 in the same manner as those constructed for lower values of K in Fig. 9.5 and 9.3. The Bode plot for $W(j\omega)$ corresponding to Fig. 9.6 is drawn in Fig. 9.7. Notice that the amplitude curve is qualitatively similar to that in Fig. 9.5, but the phase-shift curve is quite different. The reason for the oddly shaped phase-shift curve is that the system is unstable; the poles of $W(s)$ in the right-half s plane give the system nonminimum phase shift characteristics.

It must be remembered that the frequency response curves for a system describe only the *steady-state* sinusoidal response of the system.

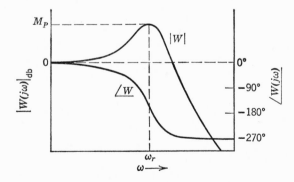

Fig. 9.5. Bode plot of $W(j\omega)$ corresponding to Fig. 9.4.

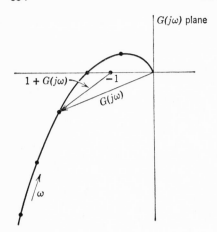

Fig. 9.6.   G(jω) for K increased beyond the stability point.

The sinusoidal *steady-state* portion of the response in an unstable system may be computed using the techniques developed in Chapter 8; however, the *steady-state* frequency response has little practical use in an unstable system because of the overriding consideration of the instability itself. Any experimental frequency response measurements must be made on a stable system, since all the switching transients must die out before the steady-state oscillations can be measured. To obtain experimentally the frequency response curves shown in Fig. 9.7 we would employ a feedback arrangement similar to that shown in Fig. 8.39, but having a more complex feedback element to make the system stable. Unfortunately, it is less easy to determine the stability of a system from an inspection of $W(j\omega)$ than it is from an inspection of the pole locations of $W(s)$. However it can be done through application of the Nyquist stability criterion.

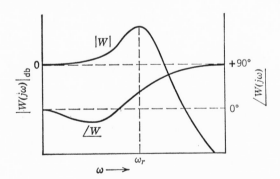

Fig. 9.7.   Bode plot for W(jω) corresponding to Fig. 9.6.

9.2   NYQUIST STABILITY CRITERION

The Nyquist stability criterion is applied in feedback control system analysis to determine how many poles of the system transfer function $W(s)$ lie in the right-half s plane.   In a unity feedback system this determination is made from an inspection of $G(j\omega)$, which is usually drawn on a polar plot.   The Nyquist criterion is based upon a theorem of complex variable mathematics due to Cauchy.   It is advisable to review that theorem before applying it to the stability analysis of control systems.   Fortunately, the theorem is simple enough so that it may be applied by a person who has had no formal training in complex variable theory, provided he is willing to accept the theorem without formal proof.

Cauchy's theorem is stated most effectively with the aid of graphs. Let $F(s)$ be a function of s in the same form as a transfer function, a ratio of two algebraic polynomials in s; s is a complex variable and is represented graphically by the s plane, which is subdivided by the real axis and the imaginary axis.   Since $F(s)$ is a function of the complex variable s, it is itself complex, and it may be represented on a complex plane called the $F(s)$ plane.

To draw a graph of a function of a complex variable we need two planes—one for the variable s, and one for the function $F(s)$.   This is similar to the graphing of the function of a real variable where only two axes are required—a variable axis and a function axis, usually placed together on the same plane.   An example of the graph of a function of a complex variable appears in Fig. 9.8.   Here the function under

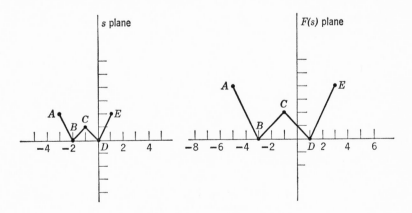

Fig. 9.8.   Conformal map for $F(s) = 2s + 1$.

consideration is $F(s) = 2s + 1$.   Consider point A in the s plane, at $s = -3 + j2$; this value for s substituted into $F(s)$ gives $F(s_A) = -5 + j4$, which is plotted on the $F(s)$ plane as point A.   If points B, C, D, and E are also substituted into $F(s)$, the corresponding values for $F(s)$ will be as shown in this table.

Point	s	$F(s) = 2s + 1$
A	$-3 + j2$	$-5 + j4$
B	$-2 + j0$	$-3 + j0$
C	$-1 + j1$	$-1 + j2$
D	$0 + j0$	$1 + j0$
E	$+1 + j2$	$+3 + j4$

These points are plotted on the $F(s)$ plane.   Both sets of points are connected by straight line segments.   Any point lying on the W-shaped curve in the s plane will have a corresponding point on the curve in the $F(s)$ plane, which also happens to be W shaped because of the simple form of $F(s)$.   The "W" curve in the $F(s)$ plane is twice as large as that in the s plane because of the factor 2 appearing in $F(s)$. Point D, which is at the origin in the s plane, is shifted by the $+1$ term in $F(s)$, so that it lies at $+1 + j0$ in the $F(s)$ plane.   The correspondence of a curve in the s plane to one in the $F(s)$ plane, as illustrated here, is called a conformal map of the s plane curve on the $F(s)$ plane. If $F(s)$ has several poles and zeros a simple curve in the s plane will map into a more elaborate curve in the $F(s)$ plane.

Cauchy's theorem is concerned with the conformal mapping of a closed curve in the s plane onto the $F(s)$ plane; the $F(s)$ plane curve will also be a closed curve.   Consider the closed, square curve in the s plane shown in Fig. 9.9, and the function $F(s) = 3(s + 1)/(s + 3)$. The square curve is mapped conformally onto the $F(s)$ plane, using the given function to compute the points corresponding to A, B, C, D, and all the intermediate points.   The conformal map is the closed curve shown on the $F(s)$ plane. $F(s)$ may be evaluated for any given point on the square curve by making a plot of the poles and zeros of $F(s)$ on the s plane and using a Spirule to compute $F(s)$ as the ratio of vector products.   A *sense* may be assigned to the square curve by indicating with an arrow that the curve passes through points A, B, C, and D in this sequence.   The conformal map will also have a *sense* which in this example is counterclockwise, the same as the sense of the s plane curve. It is shown below that the sense of both curves is not always the same,

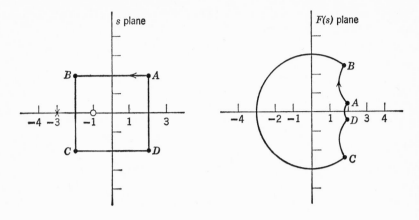

Fig. 9.9. Conformal map of a closed curve onto the F(s) plane. $F(s) = \dfrac{3(s+1)}{(s+3)}.$

but depends upon $F(s)$. A counterclockwise sense will be taken as the positive direction, and a clockwise sense will be negative.

Cauchy's theorem follows:

A closed curve with a positive sense drawn in the s plane which encloses P poles of $F(s)$ and Z zeros of $F(s)$ and which does not pass through any poles or zeros of $F(s)$ will map onto the $F(s)$ plane as a closed curve which encircles the origin of the $F(s)$ plane N times where $N = Z - P$.

An *encirclement* of the origin may be defined in the following way. Draw a line from the origin of the $F(s)$ plane to a point on the curve which has been mapped onto the $F(s)$ plane. Allow the point to move along the curve in the direction indicated by the sense of the curve. As the point makes a complete circuit of the curve, returning to its initial position, the line connecting the origin and the point will have experienced a rotation. If the net rotation of the line is 2π radians counterclockwise, the curve is said to have encircled the origin once in the positive direction.

Cauchy's theorem is illustrated in Fig. 9.9. The square curve encloses one zero and no poles of $F(s)$. Therefore, $Z = 1$ and $P = 0$, so, according to the theorem, $N = Z - P = 1$, and the closed curve in the $F(s)$ plane encircles the origin once in the positive sense.

It is quite easy to see why Cauchy's theorem holds. Consider

Fig. 9.9. $F(s)$ may be represented in polar form as

$$F(s) = |F(s)| \ @ \ \underline{/F(s)} \tag{9.9}$$

where $$|F(s)| = \frac{3|s + 1|}{|s + 3|} \tag{9.10}$$

and $$\underline{/F(s)} = \underline{/s + 1} - \underline{/s + 3} \tag{9.11}$$

Now, $\underline{/F(s)}$ is the angle between the line drawn from the origin of the $F(s)$ plane to a point on the $F(s)$ plane curve and the positive real axis of the $F(s)$ plane.   Therefore, to determine the number of encirclements of the origin we simply observe how $\underline{/F(s)}$ changes as the point moves along the closed curve.   In Fig. 9.9, for example, as the point moves from A to B to C to D and back to A, the net contribution to $\underline{/F(s)}$ of the $\underline{/s + 3}$ term in Eq. 9.11 is $0°$ because the pole at $s = -3$ is *outside* the contour. $\underline{/s + 3}$ at point A is $21.8°$; it increases to $63.5°$ at C, decreases to $-21.8°$ at D and increases to $+21.8°$ again at A, the net value being zero.   The zero at $s = -1$ is *inside* the contour, so there will be a net contribution of $+360°$ to $\underline{/F(s)}$ from the term $\underline{/s + 1}$.   At A $\underline{/s + 1}$ is $+33.7°$; it increases to $116.5°$ at B, continues to increase as we move to C and to D and back to A, at which time $\underline{/s + 1}$ is $393.7°$, just 2π radians more than it was when the point was at its initial position.

Cauchy's theorem is further illustrated in Fig. 9.10, where again $F(s) = 3(s + 1)/(s + 3)$.   Contour a encloses both the pole and the zero, so $Z = 1$, $P = 1$, and N will be 0; the conformal map of a does not encircle the origin of the $F(s)$ plane.   Contour b encircles only the pole, so $P = 1$, $Z = 0$, and $N = -1$, indicating that b will encircle the origin of the $F(s)$ plane once in the negative sense.   Contour c does not enclose any poles or zeros of $F(s)$, so $P = 0$, $Z = 0$, and $N = 0$; c does not encircle the origin of the $F(s)$ plane.

Nyquist's stability criterion is simply a special application of Cauchy's theorem.   In a unity feedback system the system transfer function is

$$W(s) = \frac{G(s)}{1 + G(s)} \tag{9.12}$$

and the stability question is: How many poles of $W(s)$ lie in the right-half s plane?   Since a zero of $[1 + G(s)]$ is a pole of $W(s)$, an equivalent question is: How many zeros of $[1 + G(s)]$ lie in the right-half s plane?

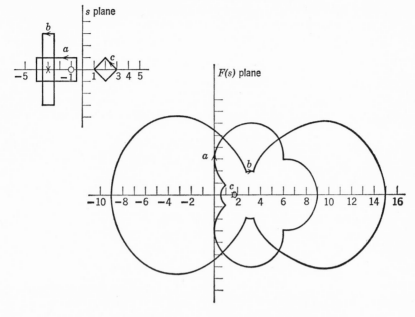

Fig. 9.10. Illustrating Cauchy's theorem with $F(s) = \dfrac{3(s + 1)}{(s + 3)}$.

Cauchy's theorem is applied to the function $[1 + G(s)]$ to determine how many of its zeros lie in the right-half s plane. $G(s)$ is the transfer function of the forward path elements; it is assumed to be known in factored form. Notice that the poles of $G(s)$ are also the poles of the function $[1 + G(s)]$; if we draw a closed contour in the s plane encircling a known number of poles of $[1 + G(s)]$ (the locations of these poles are known from the factored form of $G(s)$), and if we make a conformal map of that contour in the $[1 + G(s)]$ plane, counting the encirclements N, we can determine how many zeros of $[1 + G(s)]$ are enclosed in the s plane contour through Cauchy's equation, $Z = N + P$. Of course, the s plane contour will be chosen so that it encircles the entire right half plane.

An example will illustrate the use of the real frequency response curve $G(j\omega)$ as the contour whose encirclements are counted. Assume that the stability of a unity feedback, third order servomechanism having

$$G(s) = \frac{K_R}{s(s + 1)(s + 2)} \tag{9.13}$$

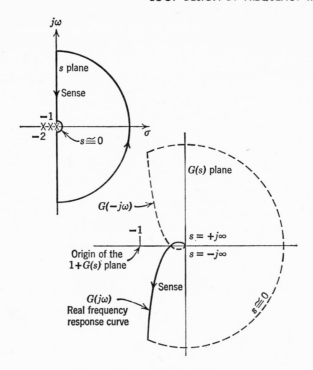

Fig. 9.11.   Illustrating Nyquist's criterion, third order servomechanism.

is to be determined.   (Routh's rule tells us immediately that $K_R < 6$
for stability.)   The poles and zeros of $G(s)$ are first plotted on the
s plane (Fig. 9.11).   There are no finite zeros in this particular example.
A contour is drawn enclosing the entire right-half s plane, but not
passing through any poles or zeros of $G(s)$.   This contour is simply the
imaginary axis of the s plane, except for the point at the origin where a
pole of $G(s)$ appears.   The contour is represented as having a positive
sense, running from $+j\infty$ to $-j\infty$, and then closing on itself with the
infinite semicircle.   The pole at the origin cannot lie on the contour,
so a tiny semicircular detour is made in the contour around this point.
It does not matter whether the detour is made to enclose the pole or to
exclude the pole from within the contour; it is excluded in this example.
Now, the contour in the s plane encloses no poles of $G(s)$, and consequently no poles of $1 + G(s)$.   Therefore, a conformal map of this
contour onto the $1 + G(s)$ plane will encircle the origin of the $1 + G(s)$
plane N times, where $N = Z$ and Z is the number of zeros of $1 + G(s)$

lying within the s plane contour. If the system is to be stable, we must have no zeros of $1 + G(s)$ inside the contour; hence, N must be zero.

The conformal map of the positive $j\omega$ axis on the $G(s)$ plane is simply the real frequency response, plotted on polar coordinates! This is shown in Fig. 9.11 where the loop gain K_R is taken as 2. At very large values of $+j\omega$, $G(j\omega)$ is practically zero with a phase shift of nearly $-270°$. As ω decreases, the conformal map traces out the real frequency response of $G(s)$, as indicated by the sense arrow. As ω approaches zero the magnitude of $G(j\omega)$ approaches infinity and the phase shift approaches $-90°$. The tiny semicircular detour around the origin maps onto the $G(s)$ plane as the very large semicircle. It is important that this large semicircle be drawn in its proper position, as dictated by the conformal map. The negative $j\omega$ axis (called the negative real frequency axis) will produce a conformal map on the $G(s)$ plane which is the mirror image, in the horizontal axis, of the real frequency response curve, as shown by the dotted lines.

Cauchy's theorem calls for the contour from the s plane to be mapped onto the $1 + G(s)$ plane, not the $G(s)$ plane. However, we used the $G(s)$ plane in Fig. 9.11 because the contour lying along the $j\omega$ axis happens to map into the real frequency response curve $G(j\omega)$, which is readily determined analytically or experimentally. Fortunately, the conformal contour has exactly the same size and shape when plotted in the $1 + G(s)$ plane as it has when plotted in the $G(s)$ plane. In fact, when the $G(s)$ and $1 + G(s)$ planes are superimposed so that the conformal contours coincide, the origin of the $1 + G(s)$ plane lies at the point $-1 + j0$ in the $G(s)$ plane. Hence, an encirclement by the contour of the $-1 + j0$ point in the $G(s)$ plane is equivalent to an encirclement of the origin of the $1 + G(s)$ plane. In Fig. 9.11 the contour does not enclose the $-1 + j0$ point; consequently Cauchy's equation yields

$$Z = N + P = 0 + 0 = 0 \qquad (9.14)$$

which shows the system to be stable.

Consider the alteration of the contour in Fig. 9.11 if K_R is increased to 10. The only effect of this change upon $G(j\omega)$ is to increase its magnitude. This increase is easily represented simply by changing the scale factor of the $G(s)$ plane; the -1 point is moved inward toward the origin (Fig. 9.12). Now the contour encircles the -1 point two times in a positive sense; Cauchy's equation tells us that the system is unstable, with two poles of $W(s)$ lying in the right-half s plane. The critical value for K is easily determined from this plot as the value

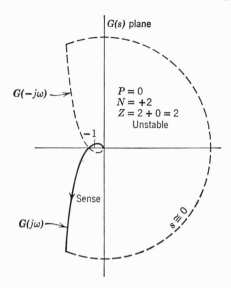

Fig. 9.12. Nyquist plot for third order servomechanism, $K_R = 10$.

required to place the -1 point right on the contour. In this case, $K_R = 6$ is the critical value.

We may now formalize the procedure to be followed in applying the Nyquist stability criterion in a unity feedback system.

(*i*) Determine $G(s)$ in factored form. If there are no poles of $G(s)$ on the $j\omega$ axis, plot $G(j\omega)$ for $+j\infty > \omega > -j\infty$ on a polar graph.

(*ii*) If $G(s)$ has poles on the $j\omega$ axis, construct tiny detours around these poles as shown in Fig. 9.11. Draw the conformal map of this contour. This map will match $G(j\omega)$ exactly except in the neighborhood of the $j\omega$ axis poles.

(*iii*) Count the number of poles of $G(s)$ lying within the s plane contour. This number, P, will be zero unless $G(s)$ has a pole in the right-half s plane, or unless a tiny detour has been made around a pole which places it inside the contour.

(*iv*) Count the number of times the $G(j\omega)$ contour encircles the -1 point as ω is varied from $+j\infty$ *to* $-j\infty$. This number is N. Form $Z = N + P$. If Z is zero the system is stable. If Z is greater than zero the system is unstable. (If Z is negative a mistake has been made in determining N or P.)

Two more examples are presented here to illustrate the application of the Nyquist test. Consider a system which has a double integration in the forward path.

$$G(s) = \frac{K_R}{s^2(s + 10)} \qquad (9.15)$$

A tiny detour is made in the s plane contour to avoid the two poles at the origin. The $G(j\omega)$ contour is shown in Fig. 9.13; the exact location of the -1 point on this plot depends upon K_R. However, for any positive value for K_R the -1 point will lie along the negative horizontal axis, and N will be $+2$. Since P is zero we have $Z = +2$—two poles of $W(s)$ in the right half plane.

If a series compensator is placed in the loop, deflecting the real frequency response curve so that it passes below the -1 point, the system will be stable. A compensator with a single zero will accomplish this, provided the zero lies inside the pole at $s = -10$. Figure 9.14 shows the Nyquist contour for the compensated system with a zero at $s = -2$, and for $K_R = 50$. Now $N = 0$, $Z = 0$, and the system is stable.

As the next example, consider a system with an unstable forward path. Assume that the transfer function is

$$G(s) = \frac{K_R}{s(s - 10)} \qquad (9.16)$$

The pole in the right half plane might be the result of an unstable feedback loop inside the $G(s)$ block; it might be caused by some uninten-

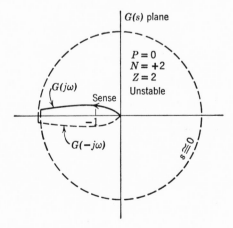

Fig. 9.13. Nyquist plot for doubly integrating system. $G(s) = \dfrac{K_R}{s^2(s + 10)}$.

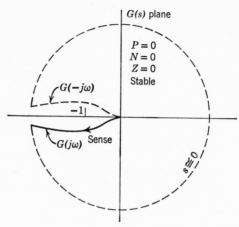

Fig. 9.14. Compensated doubly integrating system. $G(s) = \dfrac{50(s + 2)}{s^2(s + 10)}$.

tional feedback such as regenerative flow forces in a hydraulic servo valve, or it might simply represent a natural unstable situation in the device being controlled, such as a divergent line of sight angle in a head-on fire control problem. Figure 9.15 shows the $G(j\omega)$ contour where the tiny detour around the origin has been made in the usual

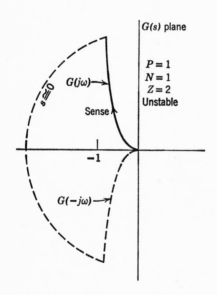

Fig. 9.15. Nyquist plot for $G(s) = \dfrac{K_R}{s(s - 10)}$.

way—in a manner which leaves the pole at the origin outside the
s plane contour. Now we have $P = 1$, since one pole of $G(s)$ [hence a
pole of $1 + G(s)$] is enclosed by the s plane contour. The frequency
response locus encircles the -1 point $+1$ times as ω is taken from
$+j\infty$ to $-j\infty$; Z is 2, indicating that there are two poles of $W(s)$ in
the right-half s plane.

To render this system stable we can put a series compensating element into the loop. A lead network type of compensator is used so
that the forward path transfer function becomes

$$G(s) = \frac{K_R(s + 2)}{s(s - 10)(s + 20)} \qquad (9.17)$$

Now the Nyquist plot is altered (Fig. 9.16) so that the $G(j\omega)$ locus will
encircle the -1 point once in the negative direction. Z is now zero,
and the system is stable. Figure 9.16 is drawn for $K_R = 500$. If K_R
is lowered to less than 250, the -1 point will lie to the left of the point
at which $G(j\omega)$ crosses the axis. In that case N will be $+1$, and the

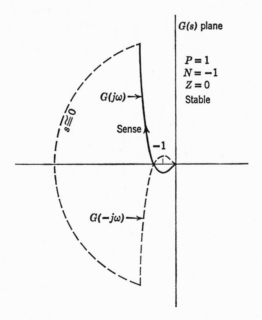

Fig. 9.16. Nyquist plot for $G(s) = \dfrac{500(s + 2)}{s(s - 10)(s + 20)}$.

system will be unstable.   This conditionally stable control system has some properties which are quite different from the ordinary control system.   These properties were discussed in Chapter 7.

In most ordinary control systems the forward path element is stable. The P term in the Nyquist equation is then zero, and stability is determined simply by observing whether or not $G(j\omega)$ encircles the -1 point. However, when $G(s)$ has one or more right half plane poles it is necessary to apply the Nyquist criterion in its complete form, and the $G(j\omega)$ locus must be made to encircle the -1 point P times in the negative direction if the system is to be stable.   If we develop the habit of using only the simplified form ($P = 0$) of the Nyquist criterion, we may become confused when we have to handle a system in which $G(s)$ is unstable.

The root locus method may be used to work all the examples treated in this section, and the stability boundaries for loop gain may be checked using Routh's rule.   It is suggested that the reader work through these examples using the root locus method in order to verify the conclusions presented here.   The root locus method is a more direct way of determining system stability than is the Nyquist method since the poles of $W(s)$ appear directly in the root locus analysis. Because of this many engineers prefer the root locus method when a choice between the two is possible.   However, since it is sometimes easier or more expedient to obtain a plot of $G(j\omega)$ than to obtain a root locus plot, the controls engineer should be familiar with both methods of analysis.

In a nonunity feedback system having $H(s)$ as the transfer function of the feedback path, the system transfer function is

$$W(s) = \frac{G(s)}{1 + G(s)H(s)} \tag{9.18}$$

Stability is determined using the Nyquist method by treating the loop transfer function $G(s)H(s)$ in the way in which $G(s)$ was treated in the unity feedback case. $G(j\omega)H(j\omega)$ is plotted on the $G(s)H(s)$ plane; P is the number of poles of $G(s)H(s)$ in the right-half s plane, and N is the number of encirclements made by the $G(j\omega)H(j\omega)$ locus around the -1 point. Z, of course, has to be zero for stability.

9.3   SETTING LOOP GAIN FOR SPECIFIED M_P

In Chapter 6 we used the root locus method to set the loop gain so that the poles and zeros of $W(s)$ would lie at suitable locations in the

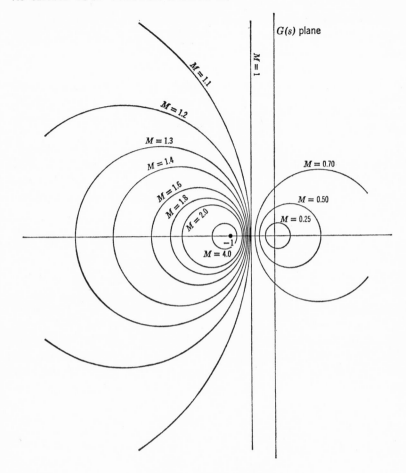

Fig. 9.17. Loci of constant M.

s plane. In this section we develop a method for setting the loop gain so that the system frequency response $W(j\omega)$ will conform to a specified M_P. Section 9.1 presented a qualitative, geometric illustration of the relationship between $W(j\omega)$ and $G(j\omega)$. Now we set up a quantitative procedure for measuring $W(j\omega)$ from a polar plot of $G(j\omega)$.

If we search the $G(j\omega)$ plane for all points for which the ratio of $|G(j\omega)|$ to $|1 + G(j\omega)|$ is constant (see Fig. 9.2), we find that these points form a circular locus, as shown in Fig. 9.17. At every point on the $M = 2$ circle, for example, the ratio $|G(j\omega)|/|1 + G(j\omega)|$ is 2. It can be shown that the M circles may be constructed with centers on the horizontal axis at

$$\text{Center} = \frac{M^2}{1 - M^2} \qquad (9.19)$$

(so that the center of the $M = 2$ circle is at -1.333) and with radii given by

$$\text{Radius} = \left| \frac{M}{M^2 - 1} \right| \qquad (9.20)$$

(so that the radius of the $M = 2$ circle is 0.667). If a frequency response locus of $G(j\omega)$, with frequency points spotted, is drawn over a grid of M circles, the amplitude of the system frequency response $M(\omega)$ may be read directly off the M circle grid. The M circle grid provides the quantitative means for relating the loop frequency response locus $G(j\omega)$ to the system frequency response $M(\omega)$ (amplitude only).

It is possible to construct a coordinate grid similar to the M circles for relating system phase shift to $G(j\omega)$. If $\phi(\omega)$ is the system phase shift function (see Fig. 9.2)

$$\phi(\omega) = \underline{/W(j\omega)} \qquad (9.21)$$

and if the tangent of $\phi(\omega)$ is defined as

$$N = \tan \phi(\omega) \qquad (9.22)$$

we may locate points on the $G(j\omega)$ plane where N is constant. These points also form circular loci, called N circles. It may be shown that the N circles are all centered on the line $\text{Re}\,[G(j\omega)] = -\frac{1}{2}$ at the point

$$\text{Center} = -\tfrac{1}{2} + j\frac{1}{2N} \qquad (9.23)$$

The radius of the N circle is

$$\text{Radius} = \frac{\sqrt{N^2 + 1}}{|2N|} \qquad (9.24)$$

The N circle corresponding to $\phi(\omega) = -45°$ ($N = -1$) is centered at $-\frac{1}{2} - j\frac{1}{2}$ and has a radius of 0.707. A grid of N circles is drawn in Fig. 9.18. Notice that all the N circles pass through the origin of the $G(j\omega)$ plane and the -1 point.

To find the proper setting of the loop gain for a specified value of

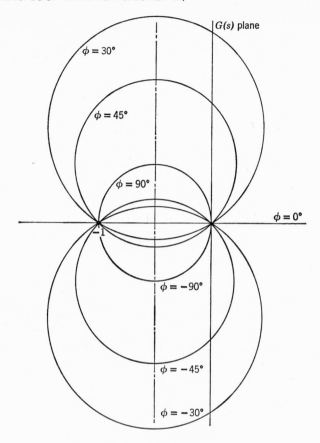

Fig. 9.18.   Grid of N circles.

system M_P it is necessary simply to plot $G(j\omega)$ on the polar plane with K_R set at some arbitrary value and then to adjust K_R so that the $G(j\omega)$ locus just touches the desired M circle.   An abbreviated method for doing this, one which eliminates the need for drawing a whole grid of M circles, is demonstrated by the following example.

Let us find the proper value for K in a third order, unity feedback system where $G(s)$ is of the form

$$G(s) = \frac{K_R}{s(s + 200)(s + 250)} \tag{9.25}$$

M_P will be 1.4.   First, K_R is set at an arbitrary value, say 10^6 in this

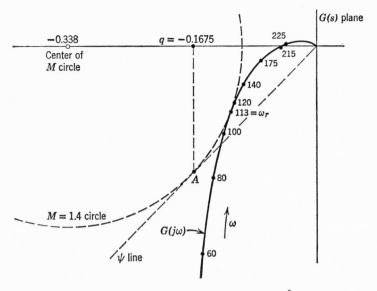

Fig. 9.19. Setting K_R for $M_P = 1.4$, $G(s) = \dfrac{10^6}{s(s + 200)(s + 250)}$.

case, and $G(j\omega)$ is plotted accurately on a polar plot (Fig. 9.19).   Next, a line is drawn from the origin at an angle ψ from the horizontal axis, where ψ is given by

$$\psi = \sin^{-1}\frac{1}{M_P} = 45.6° \tag{9.26}$$

Now, a circle centered on the horizontal axis and tangent to both the ψ line and the $G(j\omega)$ locus is constructed by a series of trial-and-error constructions.   This series usually converges to the right point after three or four trials.   In this case the proper circle is centered at -0.338, as shown in Fig. 9.19.   The point at which the newly constructed circle is tangent to the ψ line (point A in Fig. 9.19) is projected upon the horizontal axis, intersecting it at the point -0.1675, called point q in Fig. 9.19.

   The object of this geometrical construction may now be made clear. If the scale factor of this plot is changed so that the point q becomes the -1 point, the circle which was constructed will be the $M = 1.4$ circle, and, since this is tangent to the $G(j\omega)$ curve, the M_P of the system will be 1.4.   In order to change the scale factor, K_R will have to be increased by a factor 5.97 over the arbitrary value 10^6.   Hence, the proper value for K_R is 5.97×10^6.

The resonant frequency may also be read directly from Fig. 9.19 as the frequency at which $G(j\omega)$ is tangent to the $M = 1.4$ circle. ω_r is about 113 rad/sec in this case.

In addition to specifications for M_P and ω_r the system designer uses the *gain margin* and the *phase margin* of his system as design quantities. The gain margin is simply the factor by which K_R must be changed in order to render the system unstable. In this example, with $K_R = 5.97 \times 10^6$, the gain margin is 3.76. Figure 9.20 shows this graphically. In an ordinary system the gain margin is expressed as a number greater than one. In a conditionally stable system, such as that in Fig. 9.16, the gain margin would be expressed as a number less than one, since the gain in that system has to be lowered in order to drive the system unstable. In a more complex conditionally stable system instability will occur if the gain is lowered *or* raised, in which case there would be two gain margins.

The phase margin is defined as the difference between 180° and $\underline{/G(j\omega)}$ at the frequency for which $|G(j\omega)| = 1$ (in this instance, 102 rad/sec). In this system, with $K_R = 5.97 \times 10^6$, the phase margin is 41°, as shown in Fig. 9.20.

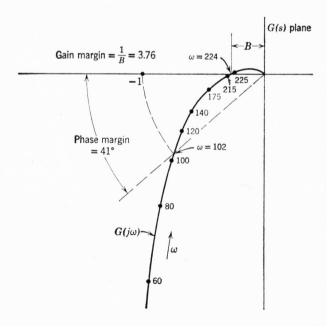

Fig. 9.20. Definition of phase margin and gain margin, $K_R = 5.97 \times 10^6$.

During the early 1940's, when servomechanism theory was being developed and before the advent of the more precise pole-zero methods for dynamic analysis, system designers developed several "rules of thumb" which were used as guides in specifying the values for M_P, ω_r, gain margin, and phase margin. These rules of thumb evolved out of experience with low-ordered servomechanism systems, and were used only as rough guides to design. Today these rules are still useful as approximate design tools, but for more precise design work, and for work with complex systems the pole-zero methods or the more detailed and precise frequency response methods must be used. Three of these rules of thumb are listed below.

We should keep in mind that although rules as these can be useful in many cases it is much more useful to understand the principles of dynamic analysis upon which these rules are based than it is simply to know the rules.

1. If M_P is kept between 1.0 and 1.7 the transient response will be "acceptable" for most systems—that is, it will not be overdamped nor will it oscillate excessively.

2. If the $G(j\omega)$ locus is "well behaved" in the region of the -1 point —that is, if it has no sharp curves or bends—and if the gain margin is greater than about 3 and the phase margin is greater than about $35°$, the M_P will lie in the "acceptable" range. In some systems a gain margin of less than 3 will give an acceptable M_P if the phase margin is sufficiently large. However, a deficiency in phase margin cannot be overcome easily by a large gain margin.

3. The transient speed of response is related to ω_r in a roughly inverse ratio. It is possible to obtain an approximate idea of the relationship between ω_r and the speed of response by looking at the curves for a second order system. If M_P is in the "acceptable" range—say, $M_P = 1.4$—then a rise time of 1 sec corresponds roughly to $\omega_r = 2$ rad/sec.

The graphical technique of setting K_R for a desired M_P (demonstrated in Fig. 9.19) is not very useful because of the computational time required to plot $G(j\omega)$. The Bode chart may be utilized to advantage here if, instead of M_P, the gain can be set to give a specified phase margin or gain margin. Figure 9.21 shows a Bode plot of $G(j\omega)$ for the third order system. K_R is at its design level, 5.97×10^6. This plot may be constructed quickly using the asymptote method. Notice that the phase margin may be read directly off the Bode chart at the frequency at which the amplitude curve crosses the 0 db line ($\omega = 102$), and the gain margin may be read (in decibels) at the fre-

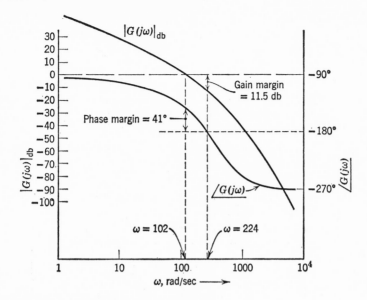

Fig. 9.21. Bode plot of G(jω), K_R = 5.97 $\times$ 10^6.

quency at which the phase-shift curve crosses the $-180°$ line ($\omega = 224$)
Now a change in K_R will be reflected on the Bode chart simply as a
vertical displacement of the $|G(j\omega)|$ curve; the phase shift curve is
unaffected by changes in K_R. It is easy to shift the $|G(j\omega)|$ curve by
plotting it on a transparent oversheet and sliding that sheet up or
down, observing its effect on the gain and phase margins. If K_R is
halved, for example, to $K_R = 2.98 \times 10^6$, the gain margin is increased
by a factor of two (6 db). If the $|G(j\omega)|$ curve is displaced downward
by 6 db to reflect this change in gain, the phase margin will be increased
to 62°, occurring at $\omega = 56$ rad/sec.

One of the Bode relationships which was developed in Chapter 8 is
useful in studying Fig. 9.21. Recall that if the amplitude curve for a
given transfer function is gently sloping without resonant peaks the
phase shift will be approximately proportional to the slope of the curve,
a 90° phase shift for a 6 db/octave slope. Therefore, if the slope
of the amplitude curve is shallower than -12 db/octave at the point
where the curve crosses the 0 db line, the phase shift will be less than
180° and the phase margin will be positive—that is, the system will be
stable. If the slope is steeper than -12 db per octave at the point
where the curve crosses the 0 db line the phase margin is likely to be
negative. This is another rule of thumb which is useful only in some

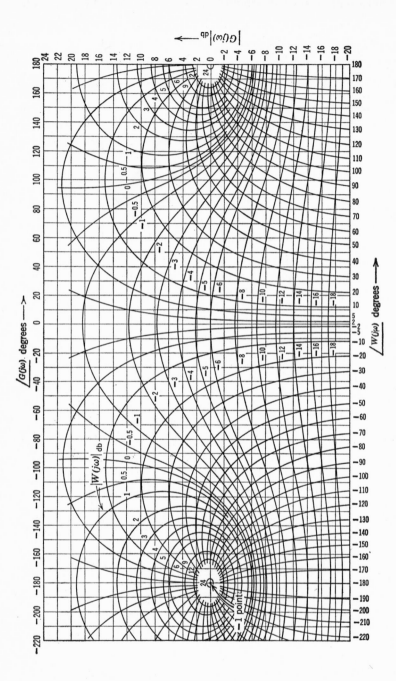

Fig. 9.22. Nichol's chart for system in which $W(s) = \dfrac{G(s)}{1 + G(s)}$

374

simple systems, particularly in those in which the $G(j\omega)$ locus is well behaved in the region of the -1 point.

If we wish to have control over M_P directly and at the same time to observe the effect of changes in gain on the phase margin and gain margin, we can plot $G(j\omega)$ on a special kind of graph known as the Nichols chart. The Nichols chart is arranged so that $G(j\omega)$ is plotted on rectangular coordinates, the phase shift $\underline{/G(j\omega)}$ being plotted as the abscissa, and the amplitude ratio $|G(j\omega)|$, expressed in decibels, plotted as the ordinate, as shown in Fig. 9.22. On the Nichols chart, a kind of conformal map of the polar $G(j\omega)$ chart, the M circles and N circles appear as elliptically shaped contours. The scale for $|G(j\omega)|$ in decibels runs along the right-hand side of the chart, and the scale for $\underline{/G(j\omega)}$ in degrees runs along the top of the chart. The point at which $\underline{/G(j\omega)} = -180°$ and $|G(j\omega)| = 0$ db corresponds to the -1 point in the polar plane. The M contours, which are centered about this point, are labeled in decibels rather than by numerical magnitude; the 0 db contour corresponds to $M = 1$, the 6 db contour corresponds to $M = 2$, etc. The N contours, which cross the M contours orthogonally, are labeled in degrees along the bottom edge of the chart.

The Nichols chart may be used to set the loop gain for a desired M_P. At the same time the resonant frequency, gain margin and phase margin, as well as the low frequency and high frequency characteristics of $W(j\omega)$, may be read directly off the chart. Furthermore, the Bode chart asymptotic approximation technique may be used in conjunction with the Nichols chart to eliminate lengthy numerical calculations of $G(j\omega)$.

Let us use the Nichols chart in the third order system example. $G(j\omega)$ is available in decibel form on the Bode chart in Fig. 9.21. The magnitude and phase of the $G(j\omega)$ curve is read at several different frequencies from the Bode chart; these points are plotted on the Nichols chart. Figure 9.23 shows the appearance of the $G(j\omega)$ locus on the Nichols chart. Notice that the phase margin and gain margin appear very clearly on this chart and that the $G(j\omega)$ locus touches the $M = 2.92$ db contour, corresponding to $M_P = 1.4$, at the resonant frequency. $W(j\omega)$ may now be plotted by reading its amplitude and phase shift at each frequency from the M and N contours. Figure 9.24 shows $W(j\omega)$ so plotted on a Bode chart.

The utility of the Nichols chart lies in the plotting of the amplitude of $G(j\omega)$ on the ordinate of the rectangular grid so that a change in K_R is reflected simply as a vertical shift in the $G(j\omega)$ curve. For example, suppose that we wished to know how K_R should be adjusted so that

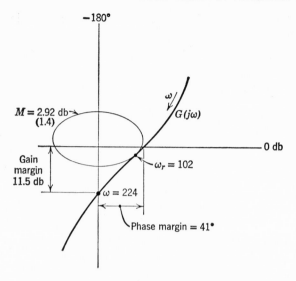

Fig. 9.23.   G($j\omega$) plotted on Nichol's chart from Fig. 9.21.

M_P will be 1.1 instead of 1.4.   First we must locate the M contour corresponding to a magnitude of 1.1; this is the $M = 0.83$ db contour. Next, we shift the $G(j\omega)$ curve vertically (using the transparent overlay scheme) so that it is tangent to the $M = 0.83$ db contour.   In this example the curve will be shifted downward 3.86 db.   Therefore, the new value for K_R should be 3.86 db lower than 5.97×10^6, so $K_R =$

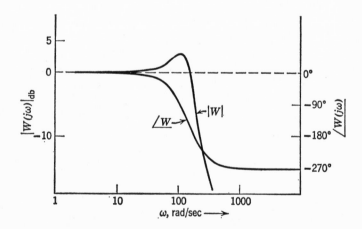

Fig. 9.24.   Bode plot of W($j\omega$), read from Nichol's chart plot of G($j\omega$) (Fig. 9.23).

3.82×10^6 for an M_P of 1.1. This new setting for K_R increases the gain margin to 15.36 db and the phase margin to 56°.

The Nichols chart may also be used in a nonunity feedback system, but the M_P cannot be read directly from the M contours. If $G(j\omega)H(j\omega)$ is treated just as is $G(j\omega)$ in the unity feedback case, the M and N contours will give the amplitude and phase shift of $B(j\omega)/R(j\omega)$, not $W(j\omega)$ (see Fig. 5.9). To find $W(j\omega)$ we can plot $B(j\omega)/R(j\omega)$ on a Bode chart (taking the data off the Nichols chart) and also $H(j\omega)$ on the same Bode chart. $W(j\omega)$ is then constructed by subtracting the amplitude for $H(j\omega)$ from that of $B(j\omega)/R(j\omega)$ and the phase shift of $H(j\omega)$ from that of $B(j\omega)/R(j\omega)$. M_P and ω_r may then be read off the Bode chart. If these are not satisfactory, an adjustment will be made in K_R on the Nichols chart, a new $B(j\omega)/R(j\omega)$ curve drawn, and a new $W(j\omega)$ curve constructed. Usually only one or two adjustments need be made to set K_R for a desired M_P in this fashion.

In nonunity feedback systems it is sometimes convenient to describe the system characteristics by $1/W(j\omega)$, since a polar plot of $1/G(j\omega)$ added to a polar plot of $H(j\omega)$ will yield a polar plot of $1/W(j\omega)$. The M circles and N circles are easily laid out on this polar plot. The reader may wish to pursue this *inverse polar plot* approach further, using one of the several books which describe it in detail.

9.4 SERIES COMPENSATION OF THE THIRD ORDER SERVOMECHANISM

In Chapter 7 the compensatory effects of lag, lead, and lag-lead networks upon the third order servomechanism were described by means of the root locus method. In this section that analysis is repeated, using the real frequency response approach to the compensation problem.

$G(j\omega)$, the loop frequency response function for the third order servomechanism, is plotted on the Nichols chart in Fig. 9.23. This is the *uncompensated* $G(j\omega)$, with K_R set for an M_P of 1.4, a slightly higher value than that used in Chapter 7 for the uncompensated system, since that value was set to satisfy a pole location specification. If K_R is readjusted here to 5.4×10^6, the $G(j\omega)$ curve will be shifted downward by 0.86 db and will then be tangent to the $M = 2.4$ db contour, giving $M_P = 1.32$, a resonant frequency of 97 rad/sec, a gain margin of 4.15, and a phase margin of 46°. If a lag network with a pole at $s = -4$ and a zero at $s = -25$ is placed in cascade with $G(j\omega)$, the loop transfer function will be

$$\frac{C(s)}{\varepsilon(s)} = \frac{K_R(s + 25)}{s(s + 4)(s + 200)(s + 250)} \qquad (9.27)$$

The $C(j\omega)/\varepsilon(j\omega)$ locus may be constructed by plotting the frequency response curve for the lag network on the Nichols chart along with $G(j\omega)$ and adding the amplitude and phase-shift values of the two curves at each frequency. This construction is illustrated in Fig. 9.25, which is drawn for $K_R = 5.4 \times 10^6$. If the composite curve is shifted downward slightly to correspond to $K_R = 4.56 \times 10^6$ (the value used in Chapter 7), then M_P will be 1.59, ω_r will be 81, the phase margin will be 35°, and the gain margin 4.

The effect of the lag compensator upon this system is apparent in Fig. 9.25. A compensating element with the transfer function $(s + 25)/(s + 4)$ has a steady-state (zero frequency) gain of 6.25, indicating that the physical compensating device placed in the loop must have amplification as well as lagging frequency response characteristics. The amplification at low frequency is the desirable property of the lag compensator, since this increases the torque constant to 185×10^7 dyne-cm/rad. However, the low frequency gain is accompanied by phase lag, which makes the $C(j\omega)/\varepsilon(j\omega)$ curve lie to the left of the $G(j\omega)$ curve. The pole and zero of the lag network are chosen so that the *bulge* in the $C(j\omega)/\varepsilon(j\omega)$ curve occurs at a low frequency. Consequently, this curve will not pass through a region of high M_P. In the frequency range near resonance the phase lag contributed by the compensator is quite small, so that it does not push the $C(j\omega)/\varepsilon(j\omega)$ curve into the region of the -1 point.

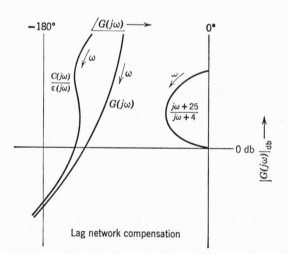

Fig. 9.25. Constructing $\dfrac{C(j\omega)}{\varepsilon(j\omega)}$ as the sum of $G(j\omega)$ and $\dfrac{j\omega + 25}{j\omega + 4}$. $K_R = 5.4 \times 10^6$.

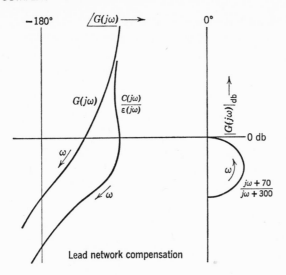

Fig. 9.26. Constructing $\dfrac{C(j\omega)}{\varepsilon(j\omega)}$ as the sum of $G(j\omega)$ and $\dfrac{j\omega + 70}{j\omega + 300}$. $K_R = 5.4 \times 10^6$.

If we use the frequency response approach to design series compensators in order to achieve specified design ends, we must accomplish our purpose without permitting the frequency response locus to pass too close to the -1 point. In this example the design goal was an improvement in the low frequency gain; this was realized by making the compensator zero larger than the compensator pole. The undesirable effect of phase lag was introduced, but a judicious choice of the critical frequencies of the compensator (making them small with respect to the break frequencies in $G(j\omega)$) placed the phase lag above the region of the -1 point.

The design aim in view in the analysis of the lead compensator in Chapter 7 was an improvement in the speed of response of the system. Interpreted in terms of frequency response, this improvement indicates a higher resonant frequency in $W(j\omega)$, and it must be realized without a sacrifice in stability—that is, without an excessively high M_P. Consider the effect of the addition of a lead compensator with a transfer function $(s + 70)/(s + 300)$ upon this system. The $C(j\omega)/\varepsilon(j\omega)$ curve is again constructed on the Nichols chart (Fig. 9.26). The lead compensator curve, when combined with $G(j\omega)$, makes the $C(j\omega)/\varepsilon(j\omega)$ curve bulge out to the right, since the compensator adds phase lead and also attenuation.

If the pole and zero of the compensator are chosen so that the maximum phase lead will occur at a frequency in the same range as the resonant frequency of the uncompensated system, the bulge in $C(j\omega)/\varepsilon(j\omega)$ will be such that when the curve is raised (by increasing K_R) it touches the M_P contour at a higher frequency than does the uncompensated $G(j\omega)$ curve. In this example if K_R is increased to 20.35×10^6 the resonant frequency will be 185 rad/sec, M_P will be 1.0, the gain margin will be 4.5, and the phase margin will be 66°. Thus the lead compensator gives the desired improvement in the resonant frequency.

If the design aim is to increase both the steady-state gain of the loop elements and the resonant frequency of $W(j\omega)$, the lag and lead compensators may be combined in series. The particular compensator function used here is

$$\frac{(s+30)(s+150)}{(s+5)(s+900)}$$

which may be realized with a very simple R-C network. The poles and zeros of this compensator are chosen so that the maximum attenuation in the compensator will occur near the resonant frequency of the uncompensated system; this will permit the gain to be increased a maximum amount. Also, the phase shift is leading at frequencies higher than this value, causing the $C(j\omega)/\varepsilon(j\omega)$ curve to bulge to the right and permitting even more increase in gain and a higher resonant frequency. Figure 9.27 shows the effect of the lag-lead controller

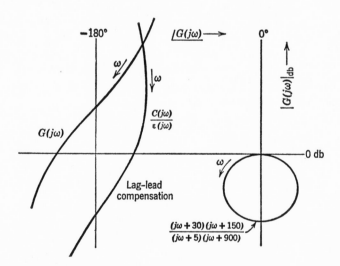

Fig. 9.27. Constructing $\dfrac{C(j\omega)}{\varepsilon(j\omega)}$ as the sum of $G(j\omega)$ and $\dfrac{(j\omega+30)(j\omega+150)}{(j\omega+5)(j\omega+900)}$. $K_R = 64.5 \times 10^6$.

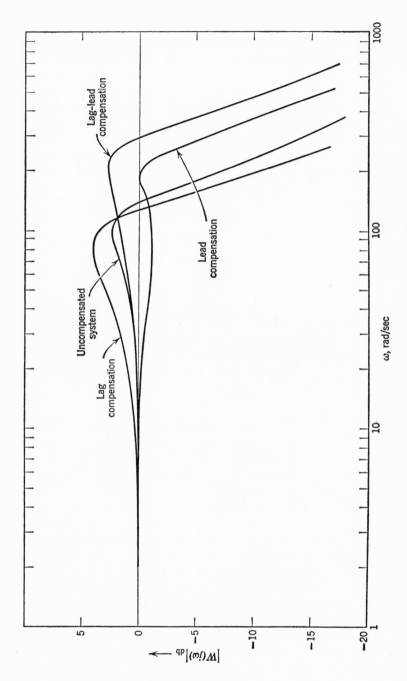

Fig. 9.28. $W(i\omega)$ (amplitude ratio only) for the four systems.

381

upon this system. M_P, ω_r, and the other performance quantities realized with this compensation are listed in the following table along with the transient response quantities determined in Chapter 7.

System (see Fig. 7.11)	K_R	M_P	ω_r, rad/sec	Gain Margin	Phase Margin	Percent- age Overshoot	K_T, dyne- cm/rad
Uncompen- sated	5.4 $\times 10^6$	1.32	97	4.15	46°	23%	35 $\times 10^7$
Lag com- pensation	4.56 $\times 10^6$	1.59	81	4.0	35°	45%	185 $\times 10^7$
Lead com- pensation	20.35 $\times 10^6$	1.0	185	4.5	66°	2%	30.8 $\times 10^7$
Lag-lead compen- sation	64.5 $\times 10^6$	1.36	210	4.4	42°	33%	418 $\times 10^7$

The system frequency response for each of the four systems in the table is drawn on the Bode chart in Fig. 9.28. It is instructive to compare this data with the transient response curves for the four systems appearing in Fig. 7.12.

9.5 INNER LOOP COMPENSATION OF THIRD ORDER SERVOMECHANISM

The analysis of a multiloop system may be accomplished as a series of single loop analyses, the closed-loop transfer function (or frequency response) of one loop becoming the open-loop function for the next loop, beginning with the innermost loop and working toward the final outer loop. However, when the problem is one of designing a compensating element to go into one of the inner loops in order to improve the performance of the whole system the procedure is less explicit than it is in the analysis problem. If the system has only two loops it is usually possible to arrive at a satisfactory design in a short series of trial-and-error analyses of the loops. Sometimes a more complex system may be reduced essentially to a two loop system by rearranging the block diagram of the system so that all the fixed elements appear in the inner loops; these are then evaluated as a single block. If this is not feasible, high speed computers are often brought to bear on the problem to reduce the time required for calculation of the frequency response curves.

It will be instructive to consider the compensation of the third order

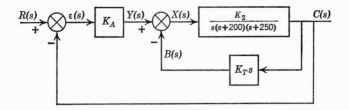

Fig. 9.29. Third order servomechanism with tachometer feedback.

servomechanism by tachometer feedback, using frequency response curves. A block diagram of the system is drawn in Fig. 9.29. Let us assume that $K_2 = 2550$ and that the static outer loop gain should be such that $K_A K_2 = 25.5 \times 10^6$, or that $K_A = 10,000$. This is the same problem which was solved in Chapter 7 by the root locus method. In the present case, let us assume that K_T should be set so that the system M_P will be 1.4.

First, draw the inner loop frequency response curve on a Nichols chart with K_T set arbitrarily at 10 (Fig. 9.30). The closed loop contours will give $B(j\omega)/Y(j\omega)$, which we now draw on a Bode chart (Fig. 9.31), along with $C(j\omega)/B(j\omega)$, the inverse of the tachometer frequency response function. Now it is easy to construct graphically the inner loop transfer function $C(j\omega)/Y(j\omega)$ by adding the amplitude curves to one another and also adding the phase-shift curves. Next, draw the outer loop frequency response locus $C(j\omega)/\varepsilon(j\omega)$ on a Nichols

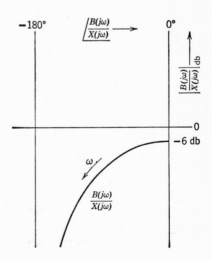

Fig. 9.30. Nichol's chart for inner loop.

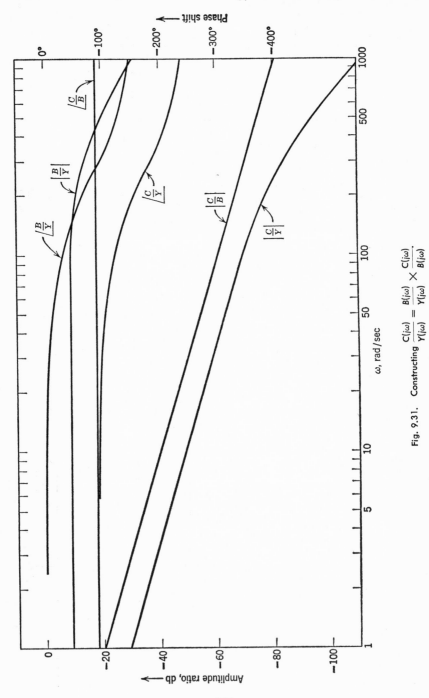

Fig. 9.31. Constructing $\dfrac{C(j\omega)}{Y(j\omega)} = \dfrac{B(j\omega)}{Y(j\omega)} \times \dfrac{C(j\omega)}{B(j\omega)}$

384

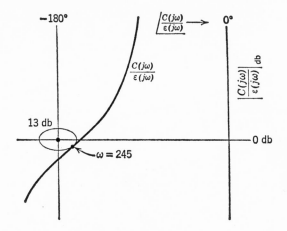

Fig. 9.32.   Nichol's chart plot of $\dfrac{C(j\omega)}{\epsilon(j\omega)}$ for $K_T = 10$, $K_A = 10,000$.

chart in order to compute the closed-loop frequency response.   This plot appears in Fig. 9.32, where it is seen that the system M_P is very high—about 4.5, and the resonant frequency is 245 rad/sec.   Clearly, $K_T = 10$ does not satisfy the design requirements.

A study of Figs. 9.30, 9.31, and 9.32 will indicate the change which must be made in K_T in order to reduce the M_P to 1.4.   Consider first the effect of a reduction in K_T upon these curves.   If K_T is reduced to 5, for example, $|C(j\omega)/B(j\omega)|$, which is inversely proportional to K_T, will increase by 6 db.   (See Fig. 9.31.) $|B(j\omega)/Y(j\omega)|$ will also be less, but the decrease in this curve will be less than 6 db—not enough to off-set the increase in $|C(j\omega)/B(j\omega)|$.   Consequently, the amplitude ratio of the outer loop will suffer a net increase, which will make the M_P even higher than 4.5 and possibly even drive the system into instability.

On the other hand, if K_T is increased, the effect upon the inner loop frequency response $|C(j\omega)/Y(j\omega)|$ will be improved in two respects.   First, $|C(j\omega)/B(j\omega)|$ will be lowered on the Bode chart by an amount greater than the amount by which $|B(j\omega)/Y(j\omega)|$ is raised, thereby effecting a net decrease in the $|C(j\omega)/\epsilon(j\omega)|$ curve.   Second, the $|B(j\omega)/Y(j\omega)|$ curve will be flat to a higher frequency and will have less phase shift in the frequency range near the -1 point in Fig. 9.32.   These two effects will combine to reshape the outer loop frequency locus so that it passes through an acceptable region on the Nichols chart.

Having determined qualitatively that K_T should be increased from $K_T = 10$ rather than decreased, we may turn to the task of determining the proper value for K_T by making a series of trial-and-error plots in which K_T is set at a new value, say, $K_T = 50$. Figure 9.30 is redrawn for this new value; Fig. 9.31 is redrawn from the new Nichols chart, and finally Fig. 9.32 is constructed from the Bode chart of $C(j\omega)/Y(j\omega)$. This is a somewhat tedious process, but the labor can be minimized if the curves are computed only for the band of frequencies which are on the outer loop locus near the critical point—that is, where M_P occurs. The following table presents the results of a series of trial-and-error measurements which were made following the procedure outlined above.

K_T	M_P	ω_r rad/sec
10	4.5	245
25	1.97	255
30	1.65	255
33.9	1.4	255
35	1.34	255
40	1.15	265
50	1.0	0

A second and more direct way of finding the right value for K_T is to redraw the block diagram of the system so that the tachometer appears in the outer loop (see Fig. 7.24). This approach is more direct than the trial-and-error method because only one parameter, K_T, is adjusted in this problem.

If the inner loop of a two loop system is unstable, as in the example analyzed in Chapter 7 (see Fig. 7.29) it is necessary to use the complete form of the Nyquist criterion in analyzing the stability of the whole system. In this example the inner loop block diagram could be represented as shown in Fig. 9.33. When the minus sign is inside the feedback block the summing point appears as a conventional degenerative summing point. The frequency response of the inner loop elements is

$$\frac{B(j\omega)}{e_A(j\omega)} = \frac{(-K_vK_AK_T)/J}{j\omega + f/J} \qquad (9.28)$$

which is plotted on polar coordinates in Fig. 9.34. If the loop gain is

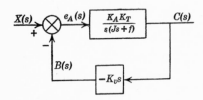

Fig. 9.33. Inner loop of unstable servomechanism (Fig. 7.29).

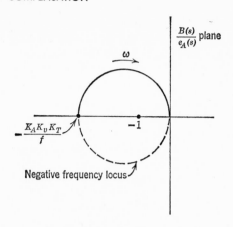

Fig. 9.34. Nyquist plot for Fig. 9.33.

set so that

$$K_v K_A K_T > f \qquad (9.29)$$

the Nyquist locus will enclose the -1 point one time, and since there are no poles of $B(s)/e_A(s)$ in the right half plane, there will be one pole of $C(s)/X(s)$ in the right half plane.

The frequency response curve for $C(j\omega)/X(j\omega)$ may be derived from the Nichols chart. If, for example, $J = 1$, $f = 3$, $K_v = 4$, $K_A = 1$, and $K_T = 1$, Equation 9.28 will be

$$\frac{B(j\omega)}{e_A(j\omega)} = \frac{-4}{(j\omega + 3)} \qquad (9.30)$$

and the Nichols chart plot will appear as in Fig. 9.35. The *closed-loop*

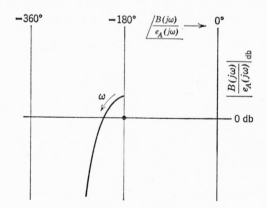

Fig. 9.35. Nichol's chart plot of Fig. 9.34.

amplitude and phase-shift contours are used to find $B(j\omega)/X(j\omega)$. The inner loop frequency response $C(j\omega)/X(j\omega)$ is derived from $B(j\omega)/X(j\omega)$ by subtracting the amplitude and phase shift curves of $-(j\omega)K_v$ from $B(j\omega)/X(j\omega)$ in the usual fashion. A plot of $C(j\omega)/X(j\omega)$ on a polar chart appears in Fig. 9.36.

If a simple gain is used as a compensator (see Fig. 7.29), Fig. 9.36 may be used to determine the overall system stability. For any gain setting the frequency response locus encircles the -1 point $+1$ time for ω moving from $+\infty$ toward $-\infty$. From the analysis of the inner loop we know that $C(s)/\varepsilon(s)$ has one pole in the right half plane, so that in the Nyquist formula $N = +1$, $P = 1$, and

$$Z = N + P = 2 \qquad (9.31)$$

Since there are two poles of the system transfer function in the right half plane, the system is unstable. This may be very easily verified by a root locus plot.

Nyquist's equation shows that the frequency response locus must encircle the -1 point once in the negative sense ($N = -1$) if the system is to be stable. A compensator with a phase lead characteristic will provide the properly shaped locus for such an encirclement. If a compensator having the following form

$$\frac{X(s)}{\varepsilon(s)} = \frac{K(s + 0.3)}{(s + 4.5)} \qquad (9.32)$$

is used, the polar plot of the loop frequency response will be that shown in Fig. 9.37. If K is set at 10 the -1 point will be in the position shown. A comparison of this plot with Fig. 9.36 indicates the effect of the lead compensator. Now the encirclement of the -1 point is -1 for ω moving from $+\infty$ toward $-\infty$, and the Nyquist formula shows

$$Z = -1 + 1 = 0 \qquad (9.33)$$

There are no poles of the system transfer function in the right-half s plane.

The reader may verify the result of the Nyquist theory in this case simply by referring to Fig. 7.32, which shows a root locus plot of this same system. The gain margin here is 0.492, indicating that the system will become unstable if the loop gain is *reduced* by a factor of $1/0.492$. This is the conditional stability characteristic which is discussed in Chapter 7. Notice in Fig. 9.37 that a reduction in loop gain by a factor greater than 2.04 will place the -1 point outside the little loop formed by the frequency response locus. The encirclement would then be $N = +1$, making the system unstable.

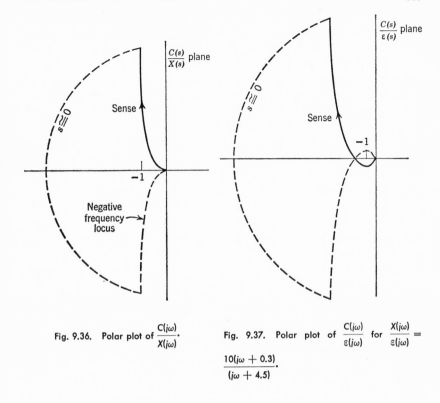

Fig. 9.36. Polar plot of $\dfrac{C(j\omega)}{X(j\omega)}$.

Fig. 9.37. Polar plot of $\dfrac{C(j\omega)}{\varepsilon(j\omega)}$ for $\dfrac{X(j\omega)}{\varepsilon(j\omega)} = \dfrac{10(j\omega + 0.3)}{(j\omega + 4.5)}$.

This example has illustrated the application of the complete form of the Nyquist criterion. In most systems having unstable inner loops, especially those having multiple poles in the right half plane, it is easier to apply the root locus method of analysis than the Nyquist method. The positions of the poles of both inner loop and outer loop are clearly shown by the root locus method; consequently, less opportunity exists for misinterpreting the graph. Nyquist plots are more difficult to interpret, since the pole positions do not appear directly on the plot.

9.6 SYSTEMS WITH DEAD TIME

Some control systems employ an element within the loop which is characterized by a delay or *dead time*. The block diagram in Fig. 9.38 represents such an element. Here the input is shown as a transient function $f(t)$ beginning at time zero. The output is completely *dead* for τ seconds, at which time it reproduces the input function exactly,

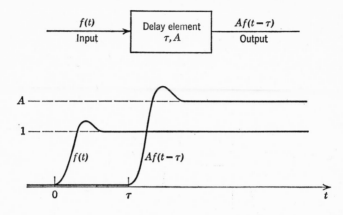

Fig. 9.38.   Definition of delay element.

except for a change in amplitude characterized by a gain A.   Notice
that this phenomenon is not the same as a *time lag*.   An element
represented by *time lag* will produce some distortion (in shape as well
as size) of the input signal.   Electrical networks with lumped R, L,
and C parameters or mechanical systems with lumped masses and
springs are described by ordinary differential equations and give rise
to the *time lag* type of response.   On the other hand, electrical transmission lines whose R, L, and C parameters cannot be considered to be
lumped in one point in space but are *distributed* evenly along the line,
or fluid power lines in which the pressure wave travels slowly are
described by partial differential equations and give rise to the *dead time*
type of response.   A transportation lag, which might occur in a continuous process, is also an example of a dead time element.

A transfer function is easily derived for the dead time element.   The
reader will recall from Chapter 2 that the Laplace transform of a
delayed time function is

$$\mathcal{L}\{Af(t-\tau)\} = A\epsilon^{-\tau s}F(s) \qquad (9.34)$$

where
$$\mathcal{L}\{f(t)\} = F(s) \qquad (9.35)$$

The transfer function is still the ratio of the Laplace transforms of the
output and input, so

$$G(s) = A\epsilon^{-\tau s} \qquad (9.36)$$

This is a fundamentally different kind of transfer function from those
with which we have been working.   It is a transcendental function of s
rather than an algebraic function of s and it has no poles or zeros in the

finite portion of the s plane. A rigorous mathematical treatment of transcendental transfer functions cannot be given here, but these functions may be incorporated into the analysis of the control loop, using either the root locus approach (which involves the so-called *phase angle loci*) or the frequency response method, employing the Nyquist stability criterion. Only the frequency response approach is given here.

If $j\omega$ is substituted for s in the transfer function, we have

$$G(j\omega) = A\epsilon^{-j\omega\tau} \qquad (9.37)$$

so that the amplitude and phase shift are given as

$$|G(j\omega)| = A$$

$$\underline{/G(j\omega)} = -\omega\tau \qquad (9.38)$$

The dead time element is characterized in the real frequency domain by a constant amplitude ratio A and a phase shift which is proportional to the frequency. A polar plot of $G(j\omega)$ is a circle with radius A, as shown in Fig. 9.39. The phase lag increases indefinitely as the frequency increases. Notice that the dead time τ is the constant of proportionality relating the phase lag to the frequency.

Now, consider the effect of a dead time element in a control loop

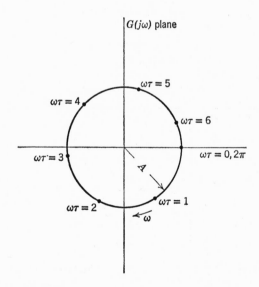

Fig. 9.39.   Frequency response locus for $G(j\omega)$; $G(s) = A\epsilon^{-\tau s}$.

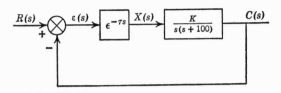

Fig. 9.40. Second order system with a dead time element in loop.

upon the system stability. A simple example is shown in Fig. 9.40, where a dead time element exists in the error channel of an otherwise second order system. This dead time might be caused by a tape recording device which records the error signal on the tape with one recording head, reading it off the tape and sending it to the system through a second head located a short distance away from the recording head. The dead time, which is the tape transport interval between heads, depends upon the tape speed and the spacing between the heads. A Nyquist plot for this system with zero dead time is shown in Fig. 9.41a. In Fig. 9.41b the effect of adding a dead time of 8 msec is shown. Because the dead time contributes a phase shift proportional to frequency (Fig. 9.39), the product of the two frequency response curves will be the spiral curve.

Here system stability may be determined by Nyquist's rule. Since no poles of $C(s)/\varepsilon(s)$ occur in the right-half s plane, P will be zero in

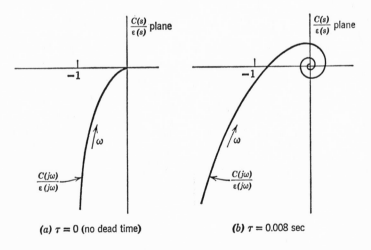

(a) $\tau = 0$ (no dead time)   (b) $\tau = 0.008$ sec

Fig. 9.41. Nyquist plot for second order system with dead time, $K = 10,000$.

the Nyquist equation.   The $C(j\omega)/\varepsilon(j\omega)$ locus must not enclose the -1 point if the system is to be stable.   When $K = 10{,}000$ and $\tau = 0.008$ the system is stable (the negative frequency locus has been omitted in the figure), but it is clear that the dead time has decreased the margin of stability to a precarious level.   When $\tau = 0$ the phase margin is $51.8°$ ($\omega = 78.6$ rad/sec).   When $\tau = 0.008$ sec the phase shift of the dead time element at $\omega = 78.6$ rad/sec is $-36.3°$, reducing the phase margin to only $15.5°$.   The gain margin is infinite when $\tau = 0$, but it decreases to 1.4 when $\tau = 0.008$ sec.   When $\tau = 0.008$ sec $W(j\omega)$ will exhibit a high resonant peak ($M_P = 4.3$) in its amplitude curve.   Judging from this, the transient response would be excessively oscillatory.   As an exercise, the reader should determine how long a dead time is required to drive the system completely unstable.   The answer is approximately 11.7 msec.

REFERENCES

1. Churchill, *Introduction to Complex Variables and Applications*, McGraw-Hill, 1948.
2. Nyquist, "Regeneration Theory," *Bell System Technical Journal*, January 1932.
3. Chestnut and Mayer, *Servomechanisms and Regulating System Design*, Vol. 1, 2nd Edition, Wiley, 1959.
4. Brown and Campbell, *Principles of Servomechanisms*, Wiley, 1948.
5. Gille, Pelegrin, and Decaulne, *Feedback Control Systems*, McGraw-Hill, 1959.
6. Chu, "Feedback Control System with Dead Time Lag on Distributed Lag by Root-Locus Method," *Trans. AIEE*, Vol. 70, Part II, 1951.

10 Advanced Topics

10.1 INTRODUCTION

The discussion in the preceding chapters has been limited to simple linear control systems having lumped and constant parameters. Also, it has been assumed that the variable physical quantities in the systems under consideration are continuous functions of time (not switched, sampled, or otherwise interrupted) and that the input signals are explicit functions of time (such as the step, the ramp, or the sine wave). These are called deterministic functions, a nondeterministic function being a random function of time which cannot be described as an explicit function. Limiting the scope of the first nine chapters has made it possible to develop thoroughly the operational techniques used in solving sets of ordinary linear differential equations having constant coefficients. This combination of operational techniques, called *linear servomechanism theory*, has been demonstrated by applying it to simple feedback systems. The systems studied here are, in fact, idealistically simple. Almost any real system will have associated with it equipment which renders the analysis of the system more complicated than the analyses presented in the first nine chapters. It is therefore desirable for an engineer to build upon the foundation of this introductory material by studying more advanced topics.

This chapter introduces briefly three advanced topics which have become so important in recent years that they are really fundamental to control system engineering. They are "advanced" only in their relation to the introductory material of this book. The topics discussed in Sections 10.2, 10.3, and 10.4 are ordinarily covered in the first year of graduate study in engineering colleges. The few paragraphs presented here simply point out the importance of the subjects and introduce, in a brief and qualitative way, the basic problems of analysis involved. A number of references are listed at the end of this chapter to facilitate further study in these areas. The discussion of *a-c* carrier servomechanisms in Section 10.5 is not an advanced topic; it is presented here for those readers who wish to know why a distinction is sometimes made between *d-c servomechanisms* and *a-c servomechanisms*. Several other topics closely allied with control system engineering are not included here for lack of space. These include network synthesis, fundamentals of communication theory, logical design of high speed computers, and construction of control system components. Classical mechanics, thermodynamics, aerodynamics, and nuclear physics could also be included in the list of topics with which the well-rounded systems engineer should have some familiarity.

10.2 OPTIMUM DESIGN OF LINEAR SYSTEMS

The design specifications for a control system may be presented in several forms. A given design may be judged acceptable on the basis of the accuracy of the system [as reflected in $\varepsilon(t)$], the size, weight, or cost of the hardware required to implement the design, the energy efficiency of the system, or the system reliability, measured in terms of the length of time which the system can be expected to remain operable between breakdowns. Other nonphysical aspects of the design, such as the length of time required to get the system into mass production, or the realizable financial return on the investment, are often important considerations in reaching a final design decision.

Because of the many factors influencing the design of a control system the word *"optimum"* must be used very carefully in the design process. Obviously, since it is not possible to realize the ultimate in accuracy, size, weight, cost, reliability, etc. in a single design, some compromise is always necessary.

One approach to design is the derivation of *trading curves* which show quantitatively the interrelationship between the several design factors. From these curves, for example, the "cost" of system accuracy in terms of size, weight, or energy efficiency may be determined. It is also possible to formulate a composite *figure of merit*, a combination of several design factors, and to arrive at that combination of design variables which gives the optimum value to the figure of merit (usually a maximum or a minimum).

Most formal literature on the optimum design of control systems is concerned with techniques for optimizing the system accuracy. Accuracy measurements are usually based upon the system error in response to a given input and with given disturbances entering the system at various places. The disturbances, called *noise*, are often random fluctuations in voltage, torque, temperature, etc. The system error, as shown in Fig. 7.28, is defined as the difference between the desired output and the actual output. When noise is present in the system it is not possible to have zero error, and the optimization process is then one of minimizing the error in the presence of noise.

In most systems it is important to keep the error as small as possible at all times. Consider, for example, the importance of this factor in an automatically controlled milling machine whose cutting head is moved by servomechanisms in response to electrical guidance signals. In some systems, often called *final value control systems*, the error is important only at specific instants (or intervals) of time. For example, in a guidance system for a long range military missile the error at the instant of impact is the important thing; any deviation from the desired trajectory during flight is unimportant unless it should influence the terminal error.

In formulating a design figure of merit it is desirable to have the quantity representing performance expressed as a function of the system parameters so that a given set of system parameters will give the figure of merit a specific numerical value. In systems where the error is important during all operating time the figure of merit is usually an integral function of the error. An example is

$$Q_1(t_1,t_2) = \int_{t_1}^{t_2} \varepsilon(t)\, dt \qquad (10.1)$$

where the interval t_1 to t_2 is the operating time of the system. For a given set of system parameters, a given interval $(t_2 - t_1)$, and a given input signal, Q_1 will have a specific numerical value.

The figure of merit should be a function the numerical value of which is related to the performance it is intended to measure. Ordinarily this requires that the figure of merit be at a minimum (or maximum) when the system is at its optimum performance. Notice that Q_1 in Eq. 10.1 is not such a function, since $\varepsilon(t) \equiv 0$ (the optimum performance) will give $Q_1 = 0$, but $\varepsilon(t) = E \sin \omega t$ will also give $Q_1 = 0$ if t_1 and t_2 happen to occur at the same point in the sinusoidal cycle. For this reason the error performance measures are usually integrals of a rectified function of the error. Some examples follow:

$$Q_2(t_1,t_2) = \int_{t_1}^{t_2} \left|\varepsilon(t)\right| dt \qquad (10.2)$$

$$Q_3(t_1,t_2) = \int_{t_1}^{t_2} \varepsilon^2(t)\, dt \qquad (10.3)$$

$$Q_4(t_1,t_2) = \int_{t_1}^{t_2} (t - t_1)\left|\varepsilon(t)\right| dt \qquad (10.4)$$

$$Q_5(t_1,t_2) = \int_{t_1}^{t_2} t\varepsilon^2(t)\, dt \qquad (10.5)$$

The limits on these integrals are usually taken to be $t_1 = 0$ and $t_2 = \infty$ where the input signal is first applied at $t = 0$. Q_2, Q_3, Q_4 and Q_5 are all positive functions, and they are minimal (zero) only when the error is zero over all time. In this respect they have the desirable characteristics of performance figures of merit. However, these figures may or may not be appropriate as performance figures of merit for a particular system with specific design goals. This point is discussed further in the following paragraphs.

If the input signal or disturbance is a random function of time (also called a stochastic function) it must be represented analytically by its statistical properties. If it is a *stationary* function (the statistical properties remaining fixed with respect to time), two basic statistical properties—the probability density function of the amplitude and the autocorrelation function—are used in analysis. A background of mathematical statistics is essential to a discussion of random signals; consequently, the discussion here is limited to nonrandom signals. However, most general aspects of optimum design apply as well to systems with random inputs as they do to systems with deterministic inputs; the differences occur in the details of the analysis involved.

The integral of the error squared (ISE) to a step or impulse input is one performance measure which is often used in optimum design. An example is Q_3 in Eq. 10.3. It usually takes the following form:

$$\text{ISE} = \int_0^\infty \varepsilon^2(t)\, dt \qquad (10.6)$$

If the signals are random the mean square error (MSE), the counterpart of ISE, is used.

$$\text{MSE} = \lim_{T \to \infty} \frac{1}{2T} \int_{-T}^{T} \varepsilon^2(t)\, dt \qquad (10.7)$$

Of course, ISE must be finite in order to be useful, so that $\varepsilon(t)$ must approach zero as $t \to \infty$. All poles of $\varepsilon(s)$, therefore, must be in the left-half s plane.

ISE has come into general use primarily because it is a function amenable to analysis, and not because it is inherently an excellent measure of performance. Although it is an appropriate measure of performance in some systems it has been shown to be of little value in others. The analytical utility of ISE stems from a theorem in complex variable mathematics due to Parseval which states that if $\varepsilon(s)$ has all its poles in the left-half s plane ISE may be evaluated as follows:

ISE = Sum of the residues of $[\varepsilon(s)\varepsilon(-s)]$ at the left half
plane poles of $[\varepsilon(s)\varepsilon(-s)]$ (10.8)

As a simple example, let

$$\varepsilon(t) = A\epsilon^{-\alpha t} \tag{10.9}$$

so that
$$\text{ISE} = \int_0^\infty A^2 \epsilon^{-2\alpha t}\, dt = \frac{A^2}{2\alpha} \tag{10.10}$$

The application of Parseval's theorem gives us

$$\varepsilon(s) = \frac{A}{s + \alpha}$$

$$\varepsilon(-s) = \frac{A}{-s + \alpha} \tag{10.11}$$

so that
$$\varepsilon(s)\varepsilon(-s) = \frac{A^2}{(s + \alpha)(-s + \alpha)} \tag{10.12}$$

There is only one pole of $\varepsilon(s)\varepsilon(-s)$ in the left half plane. The residue of $\varepsilon(s)\varepsilon(-s)$ at that pole is

$$(s + \alpha)\varepsilon(s)\varepsilon(-s)\Big|_{s=-\alpha} = \frac{A^2}{2\alpha} \tag{10.13}$$

which is ISE.

Formulas for ISE based upon Eq. 10.8 have been derived and published for error functions up to the tenth order. [$\varepsilon(s)$ has ten poles.] (See references 1 and 2.) These formulas give ISE as algebraic functions of the coefficients of numerator and denominator polynomials in $\varepsilon(s)$. The formulas are long and cumbersome for fifth and higher order error functions, but they are very easy to program into a high speed digital computer for numerical evaluation. In fact, this is the only practical way to evaluate ISE.

Optimum design using ISE as the performance measure is a problem of finding the right combination of system parameters to make the ISE function a minimum. For simple systems this can be accomplished by making a few plots of ISE as a function of the variable parameters (using the digital computer for evaluating the formula) and picking the optimum combination. For more complex systems more formal methods of minimization—methods of steep descent, for example—may be employed to find the optimum value of system parameters. Logical operations for varying the parameters can also be programmed into the computer so that the optimum point is found automatically by the computer.

Sometimes the mathematically optimum setting of system parameters corresponds to unrealistic physical requirements on the system.

For example, in a servomechanism the optimum setting for the amplifier gain and the compensating poles and zeros might result in a very
narrow linear band in the error-torque channel; that is, a very small
error will cause the motor to saturate.   To account for this in the
optimization procedure it is necessary to incorporate a *constraint* condition into the ISE function.   When one or more constraints are
placed upon the minimization procedure the analysis becomes a problem in the calculus of variations and is sometimes too involved to be of
practical use.

Optimum design methods for linear systems are systematic and
analytical and therefore offer some advantages over the trial-and-error
techniques described in Chapters 7, 8, and 9.   Once the optimum
design condition is obtained there is no question that another trial
setting of the parameters might improve the error.   Furthermore, the
inherent limitations of the system performance are often obvious when
the figure of merit is expressed analytically.   Consequently, an unrealizable design specification can be discovered early with analytical
techniques, whereas much floundering might occur before the same
discovery is made with the trial-and-error procedures.

However, since the analytical design methods often lead to complex
analytical work the trial-and-error techniques are sometimes found to
be more appropriate to the problem at hand.   An accurate, comprehensive index of performance is a complex expression involving many
variables, including some nonphysical ones.   If the figure of merit is
simplified to the point at which it may be handled analytically, as it is
with ISE and MSE it may not represent true performance.   The ISE
and MSE functions, for example, emphasize large errors more than
they do small errors because $\varepsilon(t)$ appears in the performance function
only as $\varepsilon^2(t)$.   In systems in which small errors are as important
as large errors these functions do not give a true representation of
system accuracy.

It is sometimes objected that the ISE and MSE functions are
unsatisfactory as performance indices because they are insensitive to
changes in the system parameters—that is, the gradients of the function are all very shallow around the minimum point.   Although this is
the case in many systems, it is not generally true.   If, for example,
the magnitude of the performance measure is very small at its minimum point, the performance measure will be reasonably sensitive in
the region around the minimum.   If a designer allows the *model* (see
Fig. 7.28) to have some flexibility in its pole and zero locations he is
sometimes able to reduce the magnitude of the performance index near
its optimum point and thereby increase its sensitivity.

In summary, the optimum design techniques currently in use seem to be more valuable as a secondary design tool than as a primary design tool. They assist in outlining the feasibility of the design and serve as guides which the designer can employ to eliminate some of the guesswork involved in the trial-and-error approach. However, a final design decision remains one which must be made both by the exercise of judgment based upon experience as well as by analysis. A competent systems engineer must have both these commodities available to him.

10.3 LINEAR SYSTEMS WITH DATA SAMPLING

All the analysis and discussion up to this point have been confined to *continuous* or *analog* systems—those systems in which the signals representing physical variables are continuous functions of time. In some systems the signals are not continuous functions of time but exist as a series of pulses or a series of small steps, like a staircase. If the signal exists as a series of pulses, the height of which determines the value of the function, the signal is said to be *sampled*. If the signal appears as a series of small steps it is said to be *quantized*. A continuous signal is sketched in Fig. 10.1a as $x(t)$. The *quantized* version of this signal is shown in Fig. 10.1b as $x_Q(t)$, and the sampled version of $x(t)$ is shown in c. Signals which are quantized or sampled are called *discrete* to distinguish them from *continuous* or *analog* signals. The

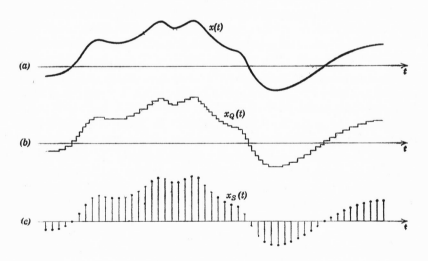

Fig. 10.1.   Continuous, quantized, and sampled signals.

significant difference between the quantized signal and its continuous counterpart is that the continuous signal takes on an infinite number of values as it fluctuates from one level to another, while the quantized or discrete signal takes on only a finite number of values in fluctuating between the same two levels.

A signal may be sampled at a fixed rate or at a rate which changes slowly from time to time. It may also be sampled in a random fashion, the pulses occurring at instants distributed randomly along the time axis. Of course the fixed rate sampling systems are more easily analyzed. The sampling pulse width may likewise change from time to time, and the value of the sampled function along the width of the pulse may be either fixed or fluctuating. Again, the analysis is simplest if the pulse width is narrow enough so that the corresponding continuous function is essentially constant during the pulse. In this case the pulse train may be represented by a series of numbers. Notice that a signal can be both sampled and quantized, so that the series of numbers representing the pulse train takes on only discrete values.

Data sampling and quantizing occur in many modern control systems. The transmitting of signals between components which are separated by long distances invariably introduces noise. To reduce the effects of noise on transmission the signals at the originating point are sometimes quantized so that they may be sent by some form of code with which the noise will not interfere. When the signal is received in quantized form it is often convenient to process the signal (e.g. derive from it control signals to be sent to other parts of the system) with a digital computer. Since the digital computer requires a finite time to perform its arithmetic operations, it must present its output in quantized and sampled form—that is, at the rate of so many solutions per second. Furthermore, in some large systems a single digital computer is shared by several data channels, so that each channel takes its data in sampled form, the computer switching from one channel to the next in sequence.

A system in which only sampled data is available is a radar controlled airplane. The radar (ground based) sweeps the sky at a constant rate, at each sweep detecting the position of the airplane. A directing signal is radioed to the plane to guide it—to a blind landing, for example. Because the radar sweeps the whole sky it can detect the position of the airplane only as a sampled signal and not as a continuous one. A single radar might be shared by several control channels, each guiding an airplane in a different sector of the sky.

The presence of data sampling and quantizing devices in the control loop introduces problems not found in continuous systems. It is obvious, for example, that the stability of a sampled data system is dependent upon the sampling rate. If the sampling rate is too low the controlled element will make large excursions between sampling times, and since the feedback information becomes available only at the sampling instant an unstable oscillation may occur. On the other hand, a digital controller has the capability of generating compensating signals which are not realizable with continuous systems, and this can offset the disadvantages introduced by the sampled data.

A form of analysis which represents the sampling process mathematically is used to assess the disadvantages as well as the potentialities of the sampled data system. This analysis has been developed over a period of years in the field of communication theory. The dynamic equations which represent a sampled data system are difference equations because of the nature of the sampler. Just as the differential equations which represent the behavior of a continuous system are solved by the Laplace transform method, so the difference equations for the sampled data system may be solved conveniently by a transformation method, called the z transformation. This procedure is analogous to the Laplace transformation in that the stability of a feedback system having a sampler in the loop may be determined by using a modified form of Routh's method, by root locus plots, or by real frequency response plots, as in Nyquist's stability method. These operational methods for stability analysis permit the analyst to determine the sampling rate necessary for stability and also to study the effect of changes in other loop parameters, such as loop gain. Several books and articles on sampled data systems are listed as references (5, 6, and 7) and will provide the reader with a complete description of sampled data system analysis.

10.4   NONLINEAR SYSTEMS

A linear system is defined in Chapter 1 as a system whose mathematical model is one or a set of linear equations. A nonlinear system is one whose mathematical model is one or a set of nonlinear equations, usually differential equations. Any physical system is nonlinear, although many may be considered to be approximately linear for most practical purposes if the displacements, velocities, voltages, etc. in the system vary over small ranges only.

A fundamental distinction between linear systems and nonlinear systems is that the principle of superposition holds in linear systems but does not in nonlinear systems. If a linear system having constant parameters is subjected to a step input, for example, the output response shows all the dynamic characteristics of the system. If the input is doubled, the output is doubled but is otherwise exactly of the same form. In a nonlinear system, however, this behavior is not found. Not only the form of the response but also the stability is dependent upon the amplitude of the stimulus. A nonlinear system may be stable for small inputs but may become unstable if the input exceeds a certain level. The nonlinear system may respond in other ways which are peculiar to this type of system. Some of these dynamic phenomena which are peculiar to nonlinear systems are described in the following paragraphs.

Limit Cycle Oscillation. This common form of instability in a nonlinear system is a steady-state oscillation, usually periodic but not necessarily sinusoidal, which results from an initial disturbance or input. The amplitude of the oscillation is the same regardless of the magnitude of the disturbance. It either builds up from a tiny initial transient or decreases from a large amplitude transient to the steady-state oscillation. This cannot occur in a linear system, since there the amplitude of a steady-state oscillation would be proportional to the initial disturbance or input. In some cases the limit cycle oscillation is of such a small amplitude that, although it is a form of instability, its presence does not harm the system performance. In fact, a small oscillation can actually enhance the performance of a servomechanism by effectively reducing the friction level between two mechanical members.

Subharmonic and Superharmonic Oscillations. In a linear system whose input is a sinusoidal forcing function with frequency ω_1 the steady-state output will oscillate only at frequency ω_1, except in the very special case in which the system transfer function has two poles on the $j\omega$ axis at $\pm j\omega_2$. In some nonlinear systems whose input forcing functions are sinusoidal with frequency ω_1, the output will have steady state, nearly sinusoidal, components at ω_1/n or at $\omega_1 m$, where n and m are integers. The lower frequency oscillations are called subharmonics, and the higher frequencies superharmonics, or simply harmonics.

Frequency Entrainment. If a nonlinear system has a natural (or self-excited) limit cycle oscillation of frequency ω_1, and if it is forced by an input at frequency ω_2, it is to be expected that components at both these frequencies (plus harmonics, perhaps) will appear at the output. In some cases, however, if ω_2 is close to ω_1 the output component at ω_1 will vanish, leaving an oscillation at ω_2 only. When ω_2 is not near ω_1, both components are present. The range of values for ω_2 near ω_1 for which this phenomenon occurs is called the *zone of synchronization.*

Asynchronous Quenching.   In some nonlinear systems which, when unforced, have a limit cycle of frequency ω_1 it is possible to quench the limit cycle oscillation by forcing the system at a frequency ω_2. ω_2 need not be related to ω_1 in any special way; consequently, it is called an asynchronous frequency.   Similarly, an oscillation may be induced in some systems at a frequency ω_1 by forcing at an arbitrary frequency ω_2, in which case the phenomenon is called *asynchronous excitation.*

The existence of these and other phenomena not found in linear systems makes the field of nonlinear systems one with almost endless possibilities for study.   The theory of nonlinear differential equations has not been developed to the point where we can tell very much about the solution of the equation from the equation itself, as is possible with linear equations.   Therefore, each new nonlinear equation presents a new problem of solution.

The engineer should bear in mind that a nonlinear system designed to perform a certain engineering task is often simpler, less expensive, and more reliable than a linear system designed to do the same task. Relay operated systems such as thermostatically controlled heaters are an example.   A relay is an effective amplifier and is a much simpler device than the electronic amplifier which produces an output linearly proportional to the input.   The difficult thing about nonlinear systems is their analysis, and this tends to make the controls engineer shy away from using them even though they may do a more effective job in some instances than a linear system.

The analytical techniques used in nonlinear control systems have been developed as a result of work done in nonlinear mechanics and nonlinear circuit analysis.   This work was essentially begun by Liapounoff and Poincaré beginning about 1890 with significant contributions added by Bendixson, Duffing, Van der Pol, Kryloff and Bogoliuboff, Andronow and Chaikin, and many others in recent years. All this work, concerned with finding the solutions (or properties of the solutions, at least) of nonlinear differential equations, has yielded many different methods for solving special equations.   These range from straight analytical methods which give solutions in closed form to approximation methods, linearization methods, numerical integration techniques, topological methods, and analog computer methods. However, at present it appears that no generalized theory of solution can be formulated which will pertain to all nonlinear differential equations.

Only one method of analysis is discussed here.   This *describing function method*, which was first introduced in the United States by Kochenburger in 1950, is an extension of the real frequency response

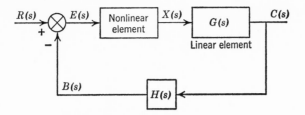

Fig. 10.2.   Nonlinear servomechanism.

approach and is used to predict stability in a restricted class of non-linear servomechanisms.   It is applied to systems such as that shown in Fig. 10.2, in which the loop transfer function can be separated into a nonlinear block followed by purely linear elements.   An ordinary servomechanism with a saturating amplifier is a typical example, where the amplifier characteristics are represented by the nonlinear block, and the remainder of the system is essentially linear.

A *describing function* for the nonlinear element is defined in terms of its response to a sinusoidal input.   If a sinusoidal function is applied to the input of a saturating amplifier the output will be a periodic function, nonsinusoidal, but with a period the same as the input function.   The same is true of many types of nonlinear elements, although it is not generally true.   We are concerned here only with those non-linear elements having this property.   Thus, for the system shown in Fig. 10.2 we have

$$e(t) = A \sin \omega_1 t$$

$$\begin{aligned} x(t) = B_1 \sin (\omega_1 t + \phi_1) &+ B_2 \sin (2\omega_1 t + \phi_2) \\ &+ B_3 \sin (3\omega_1 t + \phi_3) + \cdots \end{aligned} \quad (10.14)$$

Here $x(t)$ is expressed as a Fourier series with ω_1 as the fundamental frequency, which is the same as the input frequency.   If the amplitude of the input A is changed, the size and shape of the output will also change because the element is nonlinear.   Hence we say that the coefficients $B_1, B_2, B_3, \ldots$ and $\phi_1, \phi_2, \phi_3, \ldots$ are functions of A. The describing function of the nonlinear element is defined as a complex number which represents the magnitude and phase relationship of the fundamental term of the output, $B_1 \sin (\omega_1 t + \phi_1)$, to the input.

$$\mathrm{DF} = \frac{B_1}{A} \underline{/\phi_1} \qquad (10.15)$$

The describing function is a sort of "equivalent frequency response function" for the nonlinear element. Since all the higher order terms in $x(t)$ have been neglected, Eq. 10.15 is only an approximation to the actual response characteristics, but it is at least a function which is *amplitude dependent*. This reflects the nonlinear property of the element.

The approximation made by neglecting the higher order terms in $x(t)$ does not introduce a serious error in many systems because of the nature of the linear elements in the loop. In most systems these linear elements act as low pass filters. Most actuators, for example, act as integrators and have a high frequency cut-off rate of 6 db/octave. Other dynamic elements in the loop usually increase the cut-off rate to 12, 18, or 24 db/octave at the high frequencies. Therefore, the high frequency components in $x(t)$ are usually attenuated by the linear elements much more than is the fundamental component, so that the feedback signal $b(t)$ is nearly sinusoidal with an amplitude and phase shift determined by the fundamental component of $x(t)$. Hence, if the describing function is used to represent the nonlinear elements and is treated as an ordinary frequency response function, a Nyquist diagram for the entire loop can be drawn and system stability determined. Now the Nyquist diagram will be amplitude dependent, however, because the describing function is amplitude-dependent.

As an example, consider the saturation nonlinearity shown in Fig. 10.3. Here the element is linear with gain X_s/E_0 for all amplitudes

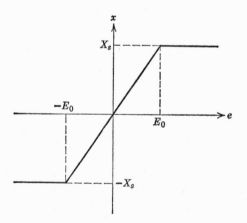

Fig. 10.3. Saturation characteristic.

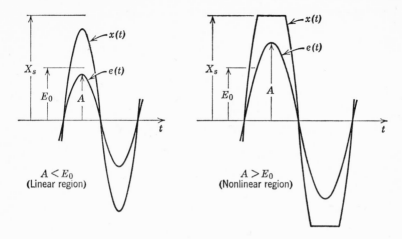

Fig. 10.4. Input-output relationship of saturating element.

of e less than E_0, but nonlinear for amplitudes of the input exceeding E_0. Since there are no energy storage elements in the nonlinear block, the curve in Fig. 10.3 represents the dynamic as well as the static characteristics of the block. Figure 10.4 shows the input-output relationship in this block for two different sinusoidal input signals; the first is below the saturation level, the second above. Figure 10.5 gives a detailed description of $x(t)$ in the saturated case in terms of X_s, E_0, A, and ω_1. Over a period of one cycle $x(t)$ may be expressed

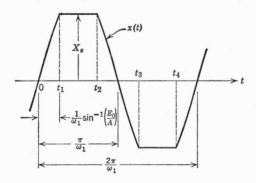

Fig. 10.5. $x(t)$ as a function of A, E_0, and X_s for $A > E$.

as

$$x(t) = \frac{A X_s}{E_0} \sin \omega_1 t \qquad \text{for} \qquad \begin{cases} 0 \leqq t \leqq t_1 \\ t_2 \leqq t \leqq t_3 \\ t_4 \leqq t \leqq \dfrac{2\pi}{\omega_1} \end{cases}$$

$$x(t) = X_s \qquad \text{for} \qquad \begin{cases} t_1 \leqq t \leqq t_2 \\ t_3 \leqq t \leqq t_4 \end{cases} \tag{10.16}$$

where
$$t_1 = \frac{1}{\omega_1} \sin^{-1}\left(\frac{E_0}{A}\right)$$

$$t_2 = \frac{\pi}{\omega_1} - \frac{1}{\omega_1} \sin^{-1}\left(\frac{E_0}{A}\right)$$

$$t_3 = \frac{\pi}{\omega_1} + \frac{1}{\omega_1} \sin^{-1}\left(\frac{E_0}{A}\right)$$

$$t_4 = \frac{2\pi}{\omega_1} - \frac{1}{\omega_1} \sin^{-1}\left(\frac{E_0}{A}\right) \tag{10.17}$$

Using the well-known expression for the first term in the Fourier series we have:

$$B_1 = \frac{\omega_1}{\pi} \int_{-\pi/\omega_1}^{\pi/\omega_1} x(t) \sin \omega_1 t \, dt$$

$$\phi_1 = 0 \tag{10.18}$$

Substituting Eq. 10.16 into 10.18 and evaluating the integral, we have:

$$B_1 = \frac{2}{\pi}\left[A K_L \sin^{-1}\left(\frac{E_0}{A}\right) + X_s \cos \sin^{-1}\left(\frac{E_0}{A}\right) \right] \tag{10.19}$$

where $K_L = X_s/E_0$ and is the gain of the nonlinear element operating in the linear range. The describing function, as defined in Eq. 10.15 is then

$$\frac{B_1}{A} = \frac{2}{\pi}(K_L)\left[\sin^{-1}\left(\frac{E_0}{A}\right) + \frac{E_0}{A} \cos \sin^{-1}\left(\frac{E_0}{A}\right) \right] \tag{10.20}$$

This is plotted against A in Fig. 10.6. Notice that up to the point $A = E_0$ the describing function is simply K_L; it then decreases as A increases.

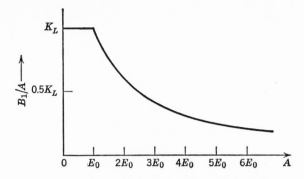

Fig. 10.6.   Describing function for the saturating element.

As an illustration of the way in which the describing function is incorporated into the analysis of a feedback system, consider the system shown in Fig. 10.7.   This system has an unstable inner loop and a saturating element in the outer loop.   Except for the saturating amplifier, this is the same system as that shown in Fig. 7.29.   Figure 10.8 shows a Nyquist plot of $C(j\omega)/E(j\omega)$; this is a "small signal" plot for the amplifier operating so that the error signal is less than E_0.   If $K_L = 10$, the gain margin of the linear system is 2.03.   To determine the effect of the saturating amplifier which appears to be an amplitude-dependent gain, we observe the change in the gain of the loop as the amplitude of the error signal, A, is increased.   A change in gain may be represented simply by moving the -1 point along the negative real axis, since this changes the radial scale of the diagram.   A decrease in loop gain is represented by shifting the -1 point to the left; this is equivalent to shrinking the frequency response locus.   As the ampli-

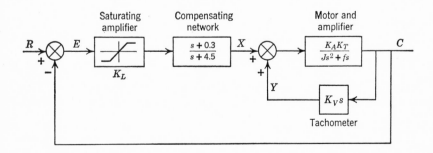

Fig. 10.7.   Servomechanism with unstable inner loop and saturating outer loop.

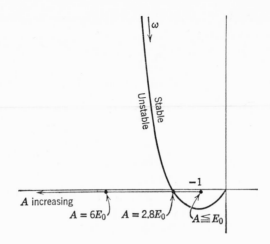

Fig. 10.8. Nyquist plot for outer loop of servomechanism shown in Fig. 10.7, $K_L = 10$.

tude of the error signal increases from E_0, the -1 point moves closer to the unstable point and crosses it at $A \cong 2.8E_0$. The system is unstable for $A > 2.8E_0$. This provides a good estimate of the level to which the error signal must be limited in order to prevent the system from becoming unstable.

A small step input applied to the system produces a linear response. If the size of the step is increased so that the amplifier saturates momentarily, this response will be more oscillatory than will the linear response, since the level of the corrective signal at X will be limited. As the amplitude of the step is increased so that the amplifier is driven farther and farther into saturation, the output oscillations will become larger and larger. Finally, at a critical input level the velocity of the output will reach a point during the oscillation at which the signal at Y will overcome the limited signal at X, the outer loop will become ineffective, and the system will run away in one direction. (In a real system the output would encounter a stop, or the inner loop would saturate, preventing a runaway condition.)

It is not possible to apply the frequency response curve in Fig. 10.8 directly to determine the critical level of the transient input signal, but it can be used to provide an estimate of the critical level. In this system the critical size of the input step would be about $3E_0$.

The describing function can also be used to predict the existence of a limit cycle oscillation and to estimate its amplitude and frequency. Consider, for example, the Nyquist plot shown in Fig. 10.9. If this represents the linear portions of a control system, and if a saturating element is in series with the linear part of the system, the nonlinear element may be represented as an amplitude-dependent shift of the -1 point, as in the previous example. This system has two crossings of the frequency response locus and the describing function locus, a divergent equilibrium point (A_2, ω_2) and a convergent equilibrium point (A_1, ω_1). This terminology is explained in the following paragraph.

If the system is first forced to oscillate so that the magnitude of the error signal is slightly less than A_2 and is then released, the oscillations will die away, since the -1 point is in the stable region. However, if the system is forced to oscillate so that the error signal is slightly larger than A_2 (so that the -1 point is in the unstable region) and is then released, the oscillations will build up until they reach magnitude A_1 and frequency ω_1. Here the oscillations will persist; if they should build up beyond A_1, the -1 point will again be in a stable region and the oscillations will begin to subside, putting the -1 point back to position A_1. In this system, then, we would expect the error signal to exhibit a limit cycle oscillation of amplitude A_1 and frequency ω_1, provided the amplitude of the error signal can be made large enough initially to begin the oscillation. Of course, if the error signal is kept small enough at all times the system will remain stable.

In performing experimental tests on control systems it is therefore wise to investigate the stability of the system at all magnitudes of input which will be encountered in service.

In engineering practice the use of analytical methods for nonlinear systems is somewhat limited because of the difficulty of solving the differential equations involved. Recently digital computers, which have become almost universally available to engineers, have made it possible to obtain numerical solutions and to employ other analytical

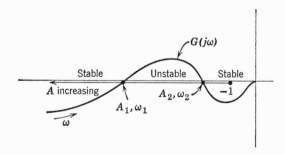

Fig. 10.9. Nyquist plot for conditionally stable control system.

methods.   Another very effective form of analysis from the engineering viewpoint is analog computer simulation.   Here the system under
study is simulated by the electronic components of the computer, and
empirical studies are conducted.   Virtually all forms of commonly
encountered nonlinearities, such as saturation, dead space (or backlash), friction, hysteresis, etc., may be conveniently simulated, and it
is possible, too, to incorporate actual pieces of hardware into the
simulation setup.   This approach leads quickly to practical answers,
even in very complex systems.

10.5   A-C CARRIER SERVOMECHANISMS

An electric servomechanism system is classified as a d-c system or an
a-c system (or a combination of these two) according to the form of the
control signal at various points in the control loop.   Consider the
signal generating potentiometer circuit in Fig. 10.10.   Here the control signal is $\theta(t)$, the mechanical position of the potentiometer wiper;
$e_0(t)$ is the voltage output of this device intended to represent $\theta(t)$.

If $e(t)$, the exciting voltage on the potentiometer, is a source of d-c
voltage—a battery, for example—the output voltage $e_0(t)$ will be
directly proportional to $\theta(t)$.

$$e_0(t) = \frac{E_B}{2} \theta(t) \qquad (10.21)$$

where $e(t) = E_B$, the d-c exciting voltage. $E_B/2$ appears in Eq. 10.21

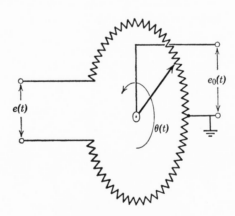

Fig. 10.10.   Control signal generator.

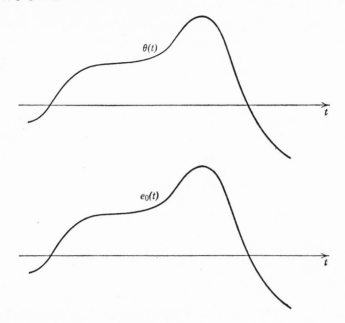

Fig. 10.11. Control signal, $\theta(t)$, and output voltage, $e_0(t)$, for d-c excitation on potentiometer.

since the potentiometer is center-tapped, allowing $e_0(t)$ to become negative as well as positive. Figure 10.11 shows the relationship between $\theta(t)$ and $e_0(t)$ with d-c excitation on the potentiometer. Although $e_0(t)$ is actually a time-varying signal proportional to $\theta(t)$, it is called a *d-c signal* here. In this example it is assumed that no current is drawn through the wiper; consequently, Eq. 10.21 does not reflect any loading errors which will exist if current is drawn from the wiper. Also, the $e_0(t)$ curve in Fig. 10.11 does not show any granularity (tiny steps) which will exist if the potentiometer is wire-wound.

Now, if the excitation voltage on the signal generating potentiometer is an a-c voltage,

$$e(t) = E_M \sin \omega_c t \qquad (10.22)$$

The output voltage is said to be an *a-c signal*. Actually $e_0(t)$ is a modulated a-c signal, where $\theta(t)$ is the modulating function.

$$e_0(t) = \theta(t) \left(\frac{E_M}{2} \sin \omega_c t \right) \qquad (10.23)$$

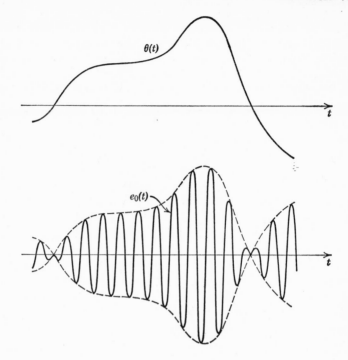

Fig. 10.12. Control signal, $\theta(t)$, and output voltage, $e_0(t)$, for a-c excitation on potentiometer.

Figure 10.12 shows the relationship between $\theta(t)$ and $e_0(t)$. The instantaneous value of $e_0(t)$ is not proportional to $\theta(t)$ as it was in the d-c signal. Rather, $\theta(t)$ determines the *envelope* of $e_0(t)$. Notice that if $\theta(t)$ has very rapid fluctuations the period of $e(t)$ will be too long to provide a clearly defined envelope around $e_0(t)$. For this reason the carrier frequency ω_c should be high enough to provide a clear definition of the envelope of $e_0(t)$. If $\theta(t)$ is described in terms of its frequency spectrum in which ω_θ is the highest significant frequency (e.g. the highest break frequency), and if $\omega_c = 10\omega_\theta$, the envelope of $e_0(t)$ will be defined well enough for most practical purposes.

Small two-phase induction motors are used as the actuating element in many electrical servomechanisms. One phase is fed with a fixed a-c voltage while the other, the control phase, is an a-c signal of the type shown in Fig. 10.12, arranged so that the carrier voltage is 90° out of phase with the voltage on the fixed phase. The motor serves as a demodulator, delivering to the load shaft a torque which is essentially proportional to the envelope of the control phase voltage. In these systems it is convenient to use a-c excitation on the position sensors (potentiometers, synchros, or differential transformers) and a simple amplifier built to have the proper gain properties in the region of the carrier frequency. Shaft velocity sensors operating on a-c for tachometer feedback may also be easily constructed and built into the system.

The a-c servomechanism would be nearly ideal from the standpoint of simplicity of design if simple networks could be employed effectively to provide lead and lag compensation in the loop. Unfortunately, the electric networks studied in Chapter 3 will operate successfully only on d-c signals; the poles and zeros of the network transfer function define the dynamic relationship between the input and output voltages. In an a-c servomechanism, however, the poles and zeros of the network transfer function must define the dynamic relationship between the *envelope* of the input voltage and the *envelope* of the output voltage rather than the relationship between the input and output voltages themselves. The difficulties involved in the design of networks for compensating a-c systems are best illustrated by a consideration of the real frequency response of the network, the envelope of the a-c signal being a sinusoidal function of time.

When $\theta(t)$ is a sinusoidal function, Eq. 10.23 becomes

$$e_0(t) = \theta_M \sin \omega_s t \left(\frac{E_M}{2} \sin \omega_c t \right) \tag{10.24}$$

where θ_M is the maximum displacement of the wiper arm from its center position and ω_s is the frequency of the mechanical oscillation, the signal frequency. Equation 10.24 may be written as

$$e_0(t) = E_0[\cos (\omega_c - \omega_s)t - \cos (\omega_c + \omega_s)t] \tag{10.25}$$

where $E_0 = (E_M \theta_M)/4$.

Equation 10.25 shows that the modulation process has produced a voltage composed of two equal components, each of which is a sinusoidal voltage fluctuating at a *sideband* frequency to the carrier frequency. Notice that $e_0(t)$ does not contain a component at the carrier frequency ω_c. For this reason a-c signals which are modulated by sinusoidal functions are sometimes called *suppressed carrier signals*.

The carrier frequency in an a-c servomechanism should be much higher than the highest signal frequency of interest. Signal frequencies at which compensation is required are usually only a few cycles per second at the highest. 60 and 400 cps are the most commonly used carrier frequencies in the United States. It is apparent from Eq. 10.25 that if a network having $e_0(t)$ as the input is designed to attenuate the amplitude and to shift the phase of the envelope of $e_0(t)$ by prescribed amounts without introducing a distortion in the output of the network, it must attenuate each of the sideband components in $e_0(t)$ by the same amount. This means that the attenuation characteristics of the network must be similar to those shown in Fig. 10.13. The significant changes in the curve take place in a very narrow band of frequencies (because ω_s is small), and the curve is symmetrical around the carrier frequency ω_c. Similar requirements are made of the phase shift characteristics of the network. *Twin-T* and *bridged-T* type networks have the requisite frequency response properties for suppressed carrier compensating networks; however, these networks are symmetrical in that they require two component values to be precisely equal. Consequently, when the networks are constructed, the components must be selected and matched.

A more serious problem which arises in the use of suppressed carrier networks is that in most systems the frequency of the a-c power supply is subject to drift. When such a drift occurs, the frequency response characteristics of the network are no longer symmetrical about the carrier frequency, and distortion appears at the output of the network, rendering it ineffective in the job it was designed to do. If the important range of signal frequencies is zero to 3 cps, for example, a drift in the carrier frequency of just 1 cps will introduce very serious distortion. For this reason suppressed carrier networks are not frequently used.

The scheme in Fig. 10.14 indicates the way in which ordinary d-c networks bring about lag and lead compensation in a-c carrier servomechanisms. First the a-c signal is demodulated, producing the envelope as a d-c signal. This is then operated upon by the d-c compensating network, the output of which is the desired envelope of the a-c signal. A modulator is used to generate the compensated suppressed carrier signal from the compensated d-c signal. Recent

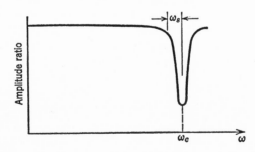

Fig. 10.13.   Attenuation characteristics of network designed to operate on a suppressed carrier signal.

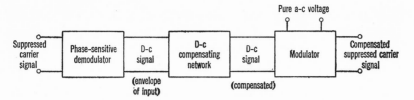

Fig. 10.14.   Scheme used to compensate a-c signal with a d-c network.

advances in solid state electronic circuitry have made possible demodu-
lators and modulators of small size and weight and high reliability,
so that the scheme illustrated in Fig. 10.14 is found in many modern
servomechanism systems.

10.6   CONCLUSION

It is appropriate here to review the value to the practicing engineer
of the elementary forms of analysis which have been presented in this
book.

Control system engineers usually find themselves working either on
practical problems, such as component design or application problems,
or on theoretical problems, such as research in optimal control methods.
However, to do effective components work the practical man must
have some capability in system analysis and, similarly, the theoretician
must have an appreciation of the practical limitations of hardware
devices.

The material in this book can be considered as an introduction to
control system engineering for both the practical engineer and the
engineer who will become a theoretician or research worker.   Both of
these engineers will want to supplement this material with further
study of the physical characteristics of control system hardware,
especially electric and fluid power actuators, transducers, amplifiers,
electric networks, analog and digital computers, inertial instruments,
and other specialized subjects.   The practical engineer will want to
make a very thorough study of these subjects and in addition
will want to gain experience in design, through on-the-job study,
as soon as possible.   The material in this book will provide an
adequate background in systems analysis for the practical engineer.

Further study in mathematics is required for the engineer headed
for theoretical work.   A rigorous study of ordinary differential equations, transformation methods including Fourier and Laplace trans-

forms and complex variable theory, matrix theory, and probability theory are considered prerequisite to the study of advanced control system theory. Advanced control system theory consists of studies in optimum design techniques, sampled data systems, nonlinear systems, and the mathematics which is required for those studies including the calculus of variations and advanced methods for solving nonlinear differential equations. All of these studies form a basis for the understanding of the general control system problem, which is described in the following paragraphs.

Figure 10.15 is a simplified version of the general control system configuration. A more general diagram would show the plant having several inputs and several outputs; however, this simpler diagram will suffice to illustrate the complexities of the general control system problem. Here the dynamic characteristics of the plant are described by one or more differential equations, represented as

$$f(x,C,D) = 0 \qquad (10.26)$$

Similarly, the controller characteristics are represented by one or more differential equations:

$$g(C,R,N,x) = 0 \qquad (10.27)$$

The analysis problem may be summarized as follows: Given the set of differential equations g and f and the functions $R(t)$, $N(t)$, and $D(t)$, find $C(t)$ and $x(t)$. Linear servomechanism theory (root locus method or Nyquist, Bode and Nichols charts) may be utilized to solve the analysis problem if all the differential equations are ordinary, linear and have constant coefficients, and if $R(t)$, $N(t)$, and $D(t)$ are deterministic functions. In fact, as we have seen, linear servomechanism theory is essentially a collection of techniques developed specifically for this purpose. However, the plant and controller of many real systems cannot be adequately described by such simple equations. In the

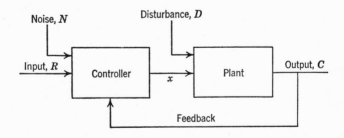

Fig. 10.15. General control system configuration (simplified).

most general system the equations will be nonlinear, have time-varying coefficients, and $R(t)$, $N(t)$, and $D(t)$ will be random functions of time. Linear servomechanism theory may be extended to handle a restricted class of such equations, but for the analysis of the general system recourse must be made to the general theory of differential equations or to automatic computing methods for solving the equations.

The synthesis problem, as applied to the general configuration in Fig. 10.15, is considerably more difficult than the analysis problem. Consider first a purely linear system in which the synthesis job has been completed to the point of choosing a configuration for the controller; the only remaining job is simply to select the values of the controller parameters (amplifier gain, pole and zero values, etc.). If only one parameter is to be found, the root locus or Nichols chart offer a convenient approach to the problem, since the whole solution is displayed graphically as a function of the single variable. Even if mild nonlinearities exist in the plant these techniques are useful, if not exact, when extended by the describing function. If two parameter values must be selected, the root locus and frequency response methods become much more cumbersome but are still useful. However, if three or more parameters are variable, the conventional servomechanism techniques are usually of little use in selecting the optimum combination of parameter values. This is especially true if the system is of high order and has several minor control loops.

Now consider the more general synthesis problem of finding the best configuration for the controller as well as the controller parameter values, given the plant characteristics. Here the problem is that of finding the g functions in Eq. 10.27 which satisfy the system performance specifications. These specifications are usually given (or translated into) constraints placed upon $C(t)$, $x(t)$, and $R(t)$. Analytical methods of optimization involving the calculus of variations or numerical methods of analysis utilizing automatic computers must be employed in this problem.

Finally, consider the most general synthesis problem in which the characteristics of the plant are unknown or may change in unpredictable ways while the system is in operation. Also, the statistical characteristics of the input signal, noise, or disturbance may change during operation and even the performance criterion may change. The problem of designing a controller under these difficult circumstances is called the *adaptive control problem*. The adaptive control problem has received extensive attention in research circles during recent years. Many interesting and useful ideas for the design of specific types of systems have resulted. However, at the present time no single general approach to the adaptive control problem exists nor does it seem likely that such an approach can be developed, utilizing present day mathematics.

REFERENCES

1. Seifert and Steeg, *Control Systems Engineering*, McGraw-Hill, 1960.
2. Newton, Gould, and Kaiser, *Analytical Design of Linear Feedback Controls*, Wiley, 1957.
3. Tsien, *Engineering Cybernetics*, McGraw-Hill, 1954.
4. Bellman, *Adaptive Control Processes: A Guided Tour*, Princeton University Press, 1961.
5. Ragazzini and Franklin, *Sampled-Data Control Systems*, McGraw-Hill, 1958.
6. Jury, *Sampled-Data Control Systems*, Wiley, 1958.
7. Tou, *Digital and Sampled Data Control Systems*, McGraw-Hill, 1959.
8. Higgins, "A Resume of the Development and Literature of Nonlinear Control System Theory," *Trans. of ASME*, Vol. 79, No. 3, April 1957.
9. Ku, *Analysis and Control of Nonlinear Systems*, Ronald Press, 1958.
10. Kazda, "Workshop Session in Lyapunov's Second Method," University of Michigan, Industry Program of the College of Engineering, September 1960.
11. Grief, "Describing Function Method of Servomechanism Analysis Applied to Most Commonly Encountered Nonlinearities," *Trans. of AIEE*, p. 243, 1953.
12. Schultz and Rideout, "Control System Performance Measures: Past, Present, and Future," *IRE Trans. on Automatic Control*, Vol. AC-6, No. 1, February 1961.
13. Letov, *Stability in Nonlinear Control Systems*, Princeton University Press, 1961.
14. Chang, *Synthesis of Optimum Control Systems*, McGraw-Hill, 1961.
15. Graham and McRuer, *Analysis of Nonlinear Control Systems*, Wiley, 1961.
16. Peterson, *Statistical Analysis and Optimization of Systems*, Wiley, 1961.

appendix 1 Table of Laplace Transformations

In this book we are concerned with "transient" time functions—that is, time functions which are zero up to a specified instant of time (usually $t = 0$) and equal to the given function for time after that instant. Therefore, $f(t) = A \cos \omega t$ really means $f(t) = u(t)A \cos \omega t$ where $u(t)$ is the unit step function, as shown in Fig. A.1. In the following table of Laplace transform pairs $f(t)$ is written without the unit step; nevertheless it should be understood to exist.

The Laplace transformation integral

$$\mathcal{L}\{f(t)\} = \int_0^\infty f(t)^- \epsilon^{st} \, dt = F(s)$$

will exist only for special $f(t)$ functions. $f(t)$ must be sectionally continuous (only a finite number of discontinuities allowed in any finite interval) and of exponential order for its Laplace transform to exist. A function of exponential order is one which remains smaller than $\epsilon^{\alpha t}$ as $t \to \infty$ for any α. Thus ϵ^t is of exponential order while ϵ^{t^2} is not. In this book only $f(t)$ functions which are transformable are employed.

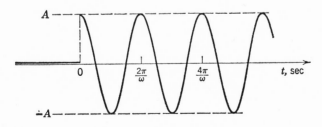

Fig. A.1. $f(t) = U(t) A \cos \omega t$.

421

Table of Laplace Transformations

Pair Number	$F(s)$	$f(t)$	
1	s	$u_2(t)$	Unit doublet at $t = 0$
2	1	$u_1(t)$	Unit impulse at $t = 0$
3	$\dfrac{1}{s}$	$u(t)$	Unit step at $t = 0$
4	$\dfrac{1}{s^2}$	t	Unit "Ramp" starting at $t = 0$
5	$\dfrac{n!}{s^{n+1}}$	t^n	$(n = 1,2,3, \ldots)$
6	$\dfrac{1}{s+b}$	ϵ^{-bt}	
7	$\dfrac{1}{(s+b)^2}$	$t\epsilon^{-bt}$	
8	$\dfrac{n!}{(s+b)^{n+1}}$	$t^n \epsilon^{-bt}$	$(n = 1,2,3, \ldots)$
9	$\dfrac{\omega}{s^2 + \omega^2}$	$\sin \omega t$	
10	$\dfrac{s}{s^2 + \omega^2}$	$\cos \omega t$	
11	$\dfrac{\omega}{(s+b)^2 + \omega^2}$	$\epsilon^{-bt} \sin \omega t$	

12	$\dfrac{s+b}{(s+b)^2 + \omega^2}$	$\epsilon^{-bt} \cos \omega t$
13	$\dfrac{\omega^2}{s(s^2+\omega^2)}$	$1 - \cos \omega t$
14	$\dfrac{s+a}{s^2+\omega^2}$	$\dfrac{1}{\omega}(a^2 + \omega^2)^{\frac{1}{2}} \sin(\omega t + \psi)$ $\psi = \tan^{-1}\dfrac{\omega}{a}$
15	$\dfrac{s+a}{s(s^2+\omega^2)}$	$\dfrac{a}{\omega^2} - \dfrac{(a^2+\omega^2)^{\frac{1}{2}}}{\omega^2} \cos(\omega t + \psi)$ $\psi = \tan^{-1}\dfrac{\omega}{a}$
16	$\dfrac{s+a}{(s+b)^2+\omega_0^2}$	$\dfrac{1}{\omega_0}[(a-b)^2 + \omega_0^2]^{\frac{1}{2}} \epsilon^{-bt} \sin(\omega_0 t + \psi)$ $\psi = \tan^{-1}\dfrac{\omega_0}{a-b}$
17	$\dfrac{K}{s+b+j\omega_0} + \dfrac{\bar{K}}{s+b-j\omega_0}$ where $K = |K| @ \underline{/K}$ $= n + jm$ $|K| = \sqrt{n^2 + m^2}$ $\underline{/K} = \tan^{-1}\dfrac{m}{n}$ $\bar{K} = n - jm$	$2|K|\epsilon^{-bt}\sin(\omega_0 t + \phi)$ where $\phi = \tan^{-1}\left(\dfrac{n}{m}\right) = 90° - \underline{/K}$

Table of Laplace Transformations (Continued)

Pair Number	$F(s)$	$f(t)$
18	$\dfrac{\omega_n{}^2}{s[(s+b)^2+\omega_0{}^2]}$	$1 + \dfrac{\omega_n}{\omega_0}\epsilon^{-bt}\sin(\omega_0 t - \psi)$ $\quad \omega_n{}^2 = b^2 + \omega_0{}^2$ $\psi = \tan^{-1}\left(\dfrac{\omega_0}{-b}\right)$
19	$\dfrac{\omega_n{}^2}{s(s^2+2\zeta\omega_n s+\omega_n{}^2)}$	$1 + \dfrac{1}{\sqrt{1-\zeta^2}}\epsilon^{-\zeta\omega_n t}\sin\left(\omega_n\sqrt{1-\zeta^2}\,t-\psi\right)$ $\psi = \tan^{-1}\dfrac{\sqrt{1-\zeta^2}}{-\zeta}\qquad(\zeta<1)$
		Notice that Pairs 18 and 19 are different forms of the same function where $\omega_0 = \omega_n\sqrt{1-\zeta^2}$ and $b=\zeta\omega_n$.
20	$\dfrac{s+a}{s[(s+b)^2+\omega_0{}^2]}$	$\dfrac{a}{\omega_n{}^2} + \dfrac{1}{\omega_0\omega_n}[(a-b)^2+\omega_0{}^2]^{\frac{1}{2}}\epsilon^{-bt}\sin(\omega_0 t+\psi)$ $\psi = \tan^{-1}\dfrac{\omega_0}{a-b} - \tan^{-1}\dfrac{\omega_0}{-b}$ $\omega_n{}^2 = b^2 + \omega_0{}^2$
21	$\dfrac{1}{s(s+b)}$	$\dfrac{1}{b}(1-\epsilon^{-bt})$
22	$\dfrac{s+a}{s(s+b)}$	$\dfrac{a}{b}+\left(1-\dfrac{a}{b}\right)\epsilon^{-bt}$
23	$\dfrac{1}{s(s+b)^2}$	$\dfrac{1}{b^2}[1-(1+bt)\epsilon^{-bt}]$

24	$\dfrac{s+a}{s(s+b)^2}$	$\dfrac{a}{b^2} + \left(\dfrac{b-a}{b}\,t - \dfrac{a}{b^2}\right)\epsilon^{-bt}$
25	$\dfrac{1}{s(s+b)(s+c)}$	$\dfrac{1}{bc} + \dfrac{c\epsilon^{-bt} - b\epsilon^{-ct}}{bc(b-c)}$
26	$\dfrac{s+a}{s(s+b)(s+c)}$	$\dfrac{a}{bc} + \dfrac{a-b}{b(b-c)}\epsilon^{-bt} + \dfrac{a-c}{c(c-b)}\epsilon^{-ct}$
27	$\dfrac{1}{s(s+c)[(s+b)^2+\omega_0^2]}$	$\dfrac{1}{c\omega_n^2} - \dfrac{1}{c[(b-c)^2+\omega_0^2]}\epsilon^{-ct} + \dfrac{1}{\omega_0\omega_n[(c-b)^2+\omega_0^2]^{1/2}}\epsilon^{-bt}\sin(\omega_0 t - \psi)$
		$\psi = \tan^{-1}\left(\dfrac{\omega_0}{-b}\right) + \tan^{-1}\left(\dfrac{\omega_0}{c-b}\right)$
		$\omega_n{}^2 = b^2 + \omega_0{}^2$
28	$\dfrac{s+a}{s(s+c)[(s+b)^2+\omega_0^2]}$	$\dfrac{a}{c\omega_n^2} + \dfrac{c-a}{c[(b-c)^2+\omega_0^2]}\epsilon^{-ct} + \dfrac{1}{\omega_0\omega_n}\left[\dfrac{(a-b)^2+\omega_0^2}{(c-b)^2+\omega_0^2}\right]^{1/2}\epsilon^{-bt}\sin(\omega_0 t + \psi)$
		$\psi = \tan^{-1}\left(\dfrac{\omega_0}{a-b}\right) - \tan^{-1}\left(\dfrac{\omega_0}{-b}\right) - \tan^{-1}\left(\dfrac{\omega_0}{c-b}\right)$
		$\omega_n{}^2 = b^2 + \omega_0{}^2$
29	$\dfrac{1}{(s+\beta)(s^2+\omega^2)}$	$\dfrac{\epsilon^{-\beta t}}{\beta^2+\omega^2} + \dfrac{\sin(\omega t - \psi)}{\omega[\beta^2+\omega^2]^{1/2}}$
		$\psi = \tan^{-1}\dfrac{\omega}{\beta}$

The following pairs define important properties and operations used in transformation analysis.

30 Linearity	$C_1F_1(s) + C_2F_2(s) + \cdots$	$C_1f_1(t) + C_2f_2(t) + \cdots$

Table of Laplace Transformations (*Continued*)

Pair Number	$F(s)$	$f(t)$
31 Differentiation	$sF(s) - f(0^+)$	$\dfrac{df(t)}{dt} = f'(t)$
32 Multiple Differentiation	$s^n F(s) - s^{n-1}f(0^+)$ $\quad - s^{n-2}f'(0^+)$ $\quad - \ldots - f^{(n-1)}(0^+)$	$\dfrac{d^n f(t)}{dt^n} = f^n(t)$
33 Indefinite Integral	$\dfrac{1}{s}[F(s) + f^{(-1)}(0^+)]$	$\displaystyle\int f(t)\, dt = f^{(-1)}(t)$
34 Definite Intergal	$\dfrac{F(s)}{s}$	$\displaystyle\int_0^t f(t)\, dt = \int_{-\infty}^t f(t)\, dt - f^{(-1)}(0^+)$
35 Delayed Function	$\epsilon^{-\tau s}F(s)$	$f(t - \tau) \qquad t \geq \tau$
36 Exponential Multiplier	$F(s - b)$	$\epsilon^{bt}f(t)$
37 Time Scale Change	$\alpha F(\alpha s)$	$f\left(\dfrac{t}{\alpha}\right)$
38 Initial Value Theorem	$\displaystyle\lim_{t \to 0^+} f(t) = \lim_{s \to \infty} sF(s)$	provided $\lim\limits_{s \to \infty} sF(s)$ exists.
39 Final Value Theorem	$\displaystyle\lim_{t \to \infty} f(t) = \lim_{s \to 0} sF(s)$	provided $\lim\limits_{t \to \infty} f(t)$ exists, that is, provided $f(t)$ is a "stable" function.

426

appendix 2 Physical Constants, Units, and Conversion Factors

Control system engineers must work with data which come from many sources and are expressed in various systems of units. It is usually desirable to express all the data pertinent to a given problem in a consistent set of units. Some physical constants and conversion factors which are useful in converting data from one set of units to another are presented in this section.

We assume here that mass, length, time, and electric charge are the physical concepts to be called "basic" to our system of units. Force is defined in terms of mass and acceleration.

NEWTON'S LAW OF GRAVITATION

Newton discovered, and many experimenters have verified, that a mutual force of attraction, called a gravitational force, exists between two bodies by virtue of their masses. The magnitude of the force is

$$F = K \frac{M_1 M_2}{r^2} \qquad (A2.1)$$

where M_1 and M_2 are the masses of the bodies, r is the distance between their centers of mass, and F is the gravitational force acting on each body. K is the "gravitational constant" and is equal to 6.670×10^{-8} if the masses are in grams, the distance in centimeters, and the force in dynes. It has been found that the gravitational attraction between the earth (M_1) and a mass of one gram (M_2) located at sea level at 45° latitude is 980.665 dynes (this number varies somewhat with longitude). In a different set of units the force of attraction between the earth (M_1) and a mass of one slug (M_2), at the same location, would be 32.174 lb.

CONSISTENT SETS OF UNITS

Three sets of units in engineering use today are:

1. Foot-pound-second (ft-lbs-sec) set wherein the slug is the unit of mass, the foot is the unit of length, and the pound is the unit of force.
2. Centimeter-gram-second (cgs) set wherein the gram is the unit of mass, the centimeter is the unit of length, and the dyne is the unit of force.
3. Meter-kilogram-second (mks) set wherein the kilogram is the unit of mass, the meter is the unit of length, and the newton is the unit of force.

Time is measured in mean solar seconds in each of these sets of units. The reason these sets of units are called consistent is that in the numerical expression of Newton's second law relating force, mass, and acceleration (in constant mass systems) one force unit is equal to one mass unit multiplied by one acceleration unit. Thus we have:

$$F = M \times a$$
$$(1 \text{ lb}) = (1 \text{ slug}) \times (1 \text{ ft}/(\text{sec})^2)$$
$$(1 \text{ dyne}) = (1 \text{ g}) \times (1 \text{ cm}/(\text{sec})^2)$$
$$(1 \text{ newton}) = (1 \text{ kg}) \times (1 \text{ meter}/(\text{sec})^2) \qquad (A2.2)$$

Therefore, a one gram mass released from rest at sea level will accelerate toward the center of the earth at 980.665 cm/sec^2 because the earth, as mentioned above, exerts a force of 980.665 dynes on the one-gram mass. A two-gram mass at sea level will feel a force of 1961.33 dynes due to the earth's gravitational attraction, hence it too will accelerate from rest at 980.665 centimeters/sec^2. Similarly, any mass released from rest at sea level will accelerate downward at this same rate, so the constant 980.665 is sometimes called "the acceleration due to gravity."

IMPROPER UNITS AND HYBRID SETS OF UNITS

Occasionally laboratory instruments for measuring force will be calibrated in mass units (a "gram gauge" is one example) and instruments for measuring mass will be calibrated in force units (the household scale calibrated in pounds is one example). Consequently engineering data on equipment is sometimes given in improper units. For example, manufacturers of large electrical machines often give the moment of inertia of the rotor in pound (feet)^2.

To convert the quantity expressed in improper units to its correct numerical value in a consistent set of units we simply interpret the correct meaning of the improper unit and reexpress it in its correct unit. For example, an object which "weighs" 75 pounds has a mass of 2.331 slugs. Thus a moment of inertia of 192 lb (ft)^2 is, in a consistent set of units 5.967 slug (ft)^2 or 8.091 kg (meter)^2.

Sometimes mass will be expressed as the ratio of force to acceleration. For example, a mass of 3 slugs may be called 3 lb/ft/(sec)^2. Frequently a hybrid set of force and acceleration units will be used. An example is: $M_1 = 28.3$ oz/in./(sec)^2. When expressed in a consistent set of units $M_1 = 21.225$ slugs.

Force Conversion Factors

1 lb = 444,822 dynes
1 lb = 16.0 oz
1 oz = 27,801.4 dynes
1 lb = 4.44822 newtons
1 newton = 10^5 dynes

Mass Conversion Factors

1 slug = 14.59388 kg

Length Conversion Factors

1 in. = 2.54001 cm
1 ft = 0.304801 m

Power Conversion Factors

1 newton-meter/sec = 1 watt
1 w = 1 joule/sec
550 lb-ft/sec = 1 hp
1 hp = 745.7014 watts
1 v-amp = 1 watt

Energy Conversion Factors

1 dyne-centimeter = 1 erg
1 joule = 10^7 erg
1 newton-meter = 1 joule
1 newton-meter = 0.737561 ft-lb
1 newton-meter = 10^7 dyne-cm
1 in.-oz = 70,615.7 dyne-cm

Mathematical Constants

$$\pi = 3.141593$$
$$\epsilon = 2.7182818$$
$$\log_{10} 2 = 0.30103$$
$$1 \text{ radian} = 57.29578°$$

Moments of Inertia

Body of Mass M	Axis	Moment of Inertia
Solid right circular cylinder of radius R	Longitudinal axis	$M\dfrac{R^2}{2}$
Solid right circular cylinder of radius R, length L	Transverse diameter	$M\left[\dfrac{R^2}{4} + \dfrac{L^2}{12}\right]$
Solid right cone, radius of base R	Axis of revolution	$M(\tfrac{3}{10})R^2$
Sphere, radius R	Any diameter	$M(\tfrac{2}{5})R^2$

$$1 \text{ slug } (\text{ft})^2 = 1.35582 \text{ kg } (\text{m})^2$$
$$1 \text{ slug } (\text{ft})^2 = 13,558,200 \text{ g } (\text{cm})^2$$

Miscellaneous

A mass of 453.5924 g will be attracted to the earth with a force of 1 lb at sea level.

Problems

Chapter 2

2.1 $f(t) = 3 + 5t - 2 \sin \omega_0 t$
Find $F(s) = \mathcal{L}\{f(t)\}$.

2.2 Given the differential equation: $\dddot{x} - 2\ddot{x} + 5\dot{x} = 0$ and the initial conditions: $\ddot{x}(0^+) = 1$, $\dot{x}(0^+) = x(0^+) = 0$ find the solution, $x(t)$. Is $x(t)$ a "stable" function?

2.3 Given the differential equation: $\ddot{x} + 2\dot{x} + 6x = 3\epsilon^{-3t}$ and the initial conditions $\dot{x}(0^+) = 0$, $x(0^+) = 1$, find the solution, $x(t)$. Is $x(t)$ a "stable" function?

2.4 Given the integral equation: $f(t) = \int_0^t f(t)\, dt + \epsilon^{-4t}$
Find $f(t)$.

2.5 If $H(s) = \dfrac{9}{(s+3)^2}$ find $h(t) = \mathcal{L}^{-1}\{H(s)\}$.

2.6 If $B(s) = \dfrac{(3s+6)(s-1)}{s(s+1)(s^2+4s+4)}$ find $b(t) = \mathcal{L}^{-1}\{B(s)\}$.

2.7 Given $D(s) = \dfrac{K(s+2)}{s(s+3)^2(s+4)}$ find the initial value of $d(t)$. Determine the value K should have if the final value of $d(t)$ is to be unity.

2.8 Given $F(s) = \dfrac{2(s+1)}{(s+2)}$ find $f(t) = \mathcal{L}^{-1}\{F(s)\}$.

2.9 In the circuit shown in Fig. P2.9, the switch is closed at time $t = 0$, the initial charge on the capacitor is Q_0 coulombs, and the applied voltage is

$e(t) = E\epsilon^{-\alpha t}$. Find the current $i(t)$ if $\alpha \neq \dfrac{1}{RC}$. Find $i(t)$ if $\alpha = \dfrac{1}{RC}$.

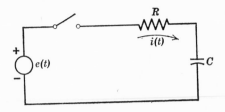

Fig. P2.9.

Chapter 3

3.1   Find the transfer function relating $e_0(t)$ to $e_1(t)$ for the R-L circuit shown in Fig. P3.1.

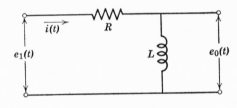

Fig. P3.1.

3.2   If $i(t)$ is considered to be the input quantity in the R-L circuit and $e_0(t)$ is the output, find the transfer function for the circuit.

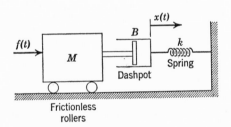

Fig. P3.3.

3.3   A force $f(t)$ is applied to the mass-dashpot-spring system shown in Fig. P3.3. Derive a transfer function relating the displacement of the dash-pot case, $x(t)$, to the applied force.

3.4 A linear system has a transfer function $G(s)$ relating the input $x_1(t)$ to the output $x_0(t)$. Show that $g(t) = \mathcal{L}^{-1}\{G(s)\}$ is the response of the system to a unit impulse input. Also show that the response of the system to a unit ramp input is equal to the time integral of its reponse to a unit step input.

3.5 How is the response of a linear system to a unit ramp input $(x_1(t) = t)$ related to its response to a unit parabolic input $(x_1(t) = t^2)$?

3.6 A 10-volt step input is applied at $t = 0$ to the R-L circuit shown in Fig. P3.6, and the resultant output is one of the two curves shown. Find the value of R_2 and determine the time t_1 if $R_1 = 500$ ohms and $L = 2$ henries.

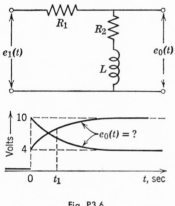

Fig. P3.6.

3.7 A thin disk of uniform material weighs 25 lb and is 50 cm in diameter. How much torque (measured in newton-meters) is required to accelerate the disk 10 deg/sec/min about its polar axis?

3.8 A flywheel, viscous damper, and rotary spring are coupled through gears to a massive steering wheel as shown in Fig. P3.8. A torque, T_1, is applied

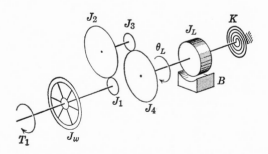

Fig. P3.8.

to the steering wheel. Gear 1 has r_1 teeth, gear 2 has r_2 teeth, etc. Neglect the friction and backlash of the gears. All gears are 3 mm thick, made of steel whose specific gravity is 6.7, and have the same size teeth. Gear 4 is 4 cm in diameter; $r_1 = 30$, $r_2 = 100$, $r_3 = 25$, $r_4 = 140$. If $J_w = 100$ gram $(\mathrm{cm})^2$, $J_L = 1700$ gram $(\mathrm{cm})^2$, $K = 9.35$ Newton-meters per radian, and T_1 is a step of 1 newton-meter applied at $t = 0$ find the value B must have if the motion of θ_L is to be critically damped, and find the instant at which $\theta_L(t)$ reaches 90 percent of its final value.

3.9 An armature controlled, separately excited, d-c servomotor such as that shown in Fig. 3.21 has a rated armature voltage of 250 volts, and the following parameter values are also known:

$$R_a = 25 \text{ ohms}$$

$$L_a = 0$$

$$\text{Stall torque at rated voltage} = 3.7 \text{ ft-lb}$$

$$\text{No load speed at rated voltage} = 2000 \text{ rpm}$$

The motor is at rest when a battery whose terminal voltage is 100 volts is switched on to the armature terminals. A record of the transient response shows that the shaft velocity reached one-half its final value 34.6 msec after the closure of the switch.

Find the moment-of-inertia of the armature shaft and B, the viscous friction coefficient of the shaft.

3.10 Specify the torque-squared-to-inertia ratio for the motor in Problem 3.9.

3.11 An operational amplifier has a gain of -1000 and the input and feedback elements shown in Fig. P3.11. Find the transfer function $\dfrac{E_0(s)}{E_i(s)}$. Assume that the grid current is zero.

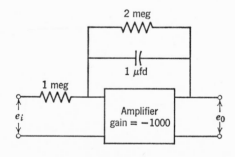

Fig. P3.11.

3.12 A small two-phase a-c servomotor whose moment of inertia is 5.7 gram-$(\mathrm{cm})^2$ and having the speed-torque characteristics shown in Fig. P3.12a

is connected, through a gear set, to a spring load as shown in Fig. P3.12b.   The moment of inertia of the pinion gear is 0.5 gram (cm)^2, the driven gear is of the same material and has the same thickness as the pinion, but has six times the diameter.   The spring constant of the load is 2000 dyne-cm per degree.

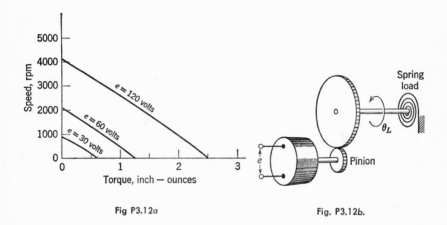

Fig P3.12a Fig. P3.12b.

Derive a transfer function (which will be valid for low speeds of the motor shaft) relating the position of the load shaft, θ_L, to the voltage applied to the control winding of the motor, e.

3.13   In Fig. P3.13, x_2 is the displacement of mass M_2 from its rest position and F is a force applied to mass M_1.   The weightless cable moves the pulley without slipping.   Derive a transfer function relating x_2 to F.

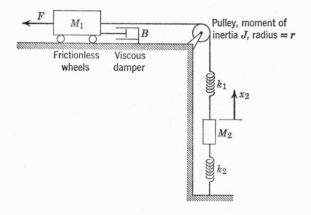

Fig. P3.13.

3.14   Expand the following functions into partial fractions:

(a) $\dfrac{6(s^2 + 3.666s + 3)}{s^3 + 6s^2 + 11s + 6}$.

(b) $\dfrac{16(s + 1)}{s^4 + 4s^3 + 8s^2 + 8s}$.

(c) $\dfrac{3(s^2 - 0.333s + 0.666)}{s^3 + 2s^2 + 2s + 1}$.

(d) $\dfrac{2s + 30}{s^2 + 10s + 50}$.

Chapter 4

4.1   Figure P4.1 is a pole-zero plot of $Q(s)$, drawn to exact scale.
(a) Express $Q(s)$ in analytical form.
(b) Find $q(0^+)$, $\dot{q}(0^+)$, $\ddot{q}(0^+)$, and $q(\infty)$ using the initial value and final value theorems.

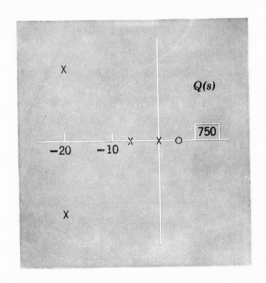

Fig. P4.1.

4.2   Consider the general form of the function $Y(s)$:

$$Y(s) = \frac{K(s^m + a_1 s^{m-1} + \cdots + a_m)}{(s^n + b_1 s^{n-1} + \cdots + b_n)} = \frac{K(s + Z_1) \cdots (s + Z_m)}{(s + P_1) \cdots (s + P_n)}.$$

(a) Show that $Z_1 + Z_2 + \cdots + Z_m = a_1$ and that $P_1 P_2 \cdots P_n = b_n$.

(b) Using the final value theorem determine how the terms in $Y(s)$ must be related to one another in order that $y(\infty) = A$.

(c) Determine the relationships which must exist in order that $y(\infty) = 0$.

(d) Which relationships must exist in order that the rth derivative of $y(t)$, and all lower ordered derivatives, have initial values equal to zero?

4.3 $y_0(t)$, sketched to scale in Fig. P4.3, is the output response of a system whose input is a unit step. Find the transfer function of the system.

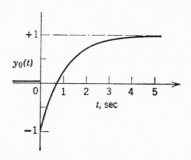

Fig. P4.3.

4.4 Construct a pole-zero map of $F(s) = \dfrac{(220)(s + 3)}{(s^2 + 14s + 24)(s^2 + 14.1s + 49.7)}$.

Notice that the residues at the two poles in the vicinity of $s = -7$ are both very much larger than the residues at the other two poles. Does this mean that the transient terms in $f(t)$ corresponding to the other two poles may be neglected? Explain.

4.5 In Problem 3.3 let $v(t)$ be the velocity of the car. If $M = 1$ kg, $k = 144$ newtons/meter, $B = 12$ newton-sec/meter, and $f(t)$ is a step of 8 newtons applied at $t = 0$, find, by using Figs. 4.39 through 4.44:

(a) The final velocity of the car, $v(\infty)$.

(b) The peak velocity of the car.

(c) The instant at which the car first reaches its final velocity.

(d) The instant at which the peak velocity is reached.

4.6 Refer to the rate gyroscope diagram in Fig. 4.46. The wheel is made of steel whose specific gravity is 7.0, the diameter is 4 cm, the thickness is 2 cm, and the wheel speed is 20,000 rpm. The moment of inertia of the gimbal assembly (including wheel) about the z axis is 2000 gram (cm)^2. The dashpot provides a damping torque, about the z axis, of 160,000 dyne-cm/rad/sec. The output potentiometer has an active winding of 15 deg, is excited by 1 volt, end to end, and has a center tap which is grounded.

Let θ_y be the angular position of the base (about the y axis) with respect to an inertial reference frame. Assume that the base is rotated such that

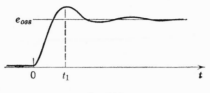

Fig. P4.6.

$\theta_y(t) = t$. Figure P4.6 is an accurate sketch of the output voltage that results from this motion of the base.

(a) Find e_{oss}.

(b) Specify t_1, the instant of peak overshoot.

4.7 In Problem 4.6 assume that the steady-state gimbal deflection for an input rate (about the y axis) of 10 rad/sec is to be no more than 5 deg.

(a) How should the spring constant be altered to satisfy this specification?

(b) Would this alteration affect the dynamic performance of the rate gyro? How?

4.8 $Q(s) = \dfrac{K}{s(s + P)(s^2 + 2\zeta\omega_n s + \omega_n{}^2)}$

(a) What value must K have in order that $q(\infty) = 1$?

(b) Prove that $q(t)$ will not overshoot its final value if $P < \zeta\omega_n$.

4.9 Refer to the hydraulic valve and ram system diagrams in Figs. 4.48, and 4.49   A one-volt step input is applied to the input of the amplifier at $t = 0$,

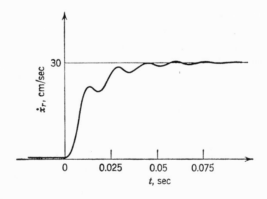

Fig. P4.9.

and the resultant ram velocity is recorded in Fig. P4.9.   The following system parameters are known, find A, L, k, and B.

$$M = 5.0 \text{ grams}. \qquad \mu = 13.6$$
$$R_L = 180 \text{ ohms}. \qquad K_M = 10^6 \text{ dynes/amp}.$$
$$r_p = 500 \text{ ohms} \qquad K_v = 3000 \text{ (cm)}^3/\text{sec/cm}.$$

Make use of the curves in Figs. 4.55 through 4.60.

4.10   An accurate sketch of $f(t)$ is given in Fig. P4.10.   Find the poles, zeros, and constant multiplier of $F(s)$ by decomposing $f(t)$ in the manner described in Section 4.4.

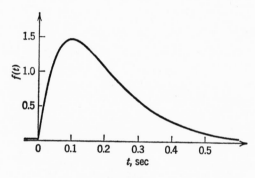

Fig. P4.10.

4.11   An accurate sketch of $h(t)$ is given in Fig. P4.11.   Find $H(s)$ in the same way $F(s)$ was determined in Problem 4.10.

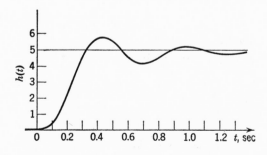

Fig. P4.11.

4.12 An accurate sketch of $g(t)$ is given in Fig. P4.12.   Find $G(s)$.

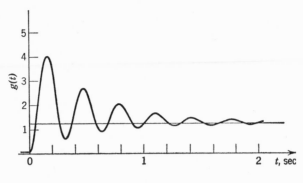

Fig. P4.12.

4.13 An accurate sketch of $m(t)$ appears in Fig. P4.13.   Find $M(s)$.

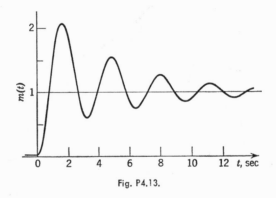

Fig. P4.13.

4.14 An accurate sketch of $p(t)$ appears in Fig. P4.14.   Find $P(s)$.

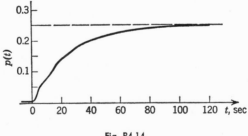

Fig. P4.14.

4.15 An accurate sketch of $r(t)$ appears in Fig. P4.15. Find $R(s)$.

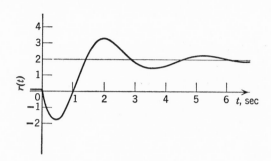

Fig. P4.15.

4.16 A sixth order system has the following transfer function:

$$G(s) = \frac{561 \ (s^2 + 3.05s + 2.1)}{(s + 12)(s^2 + 4s + 25)(s^3 + 5.4s^2 + 8.4s + 4)}$$

Find a third order transfer function which is a reasonable approximation to $G(s)$.

4.17 Given the transfer function of a second order system:

$$\frac{Y(s)}{X(s)} = \frac{K(s + Z)}{(s^2 + 2\zeta\omega_n s + \omega_n{}^2)}$$

where K and Z are adjustable parameters. If the input is a ramp: $x(t) = At$ determine what values K and Z must have if $y(t)$ is to approach $x(t)$ for large t (i.e. $[x(t) - y(t)] \to 0$ as $t \to \infty$).

4.18 With K and Z adjusted to satisfy the condition stated in Problem 4.17, show that if $x(t)$ is a step input $y(t)$ must overshoot its final value.

Chapter 5

5.1 Refer to the block diagram in Fig. P5.1. Derive the following transfer functions:

(a) $\dfrac{\varepsilon(s)}{R(s)}.$ (b) $\dfrac{C(s)}{R(s)}.$ (c) $\dfrac{X(s)}{R(s)}.$

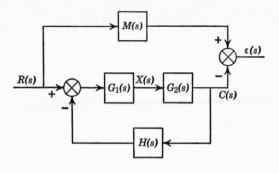

Fig. P5.1.

5.2 Refer to Fig. P5.2. Derive the following transfer functions:

$(a)\ \dfrac{C(s)}{R(s)}.$ $(b)\ \dfrac{\varepsilon(s)}{R(s)}.$ $(c)\ \dfrac{C(s)}{D(s)}.$ $(d)\ \dfrac{\varepsilon(s)}{D(s)}.$

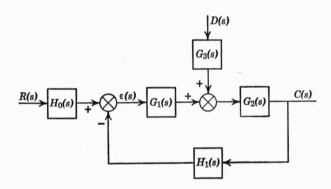

Fig. P5.2.

5.3 Why do $G_1(s)$, $G_2(s)$, and $H_1(s)$ appear in the denominators of each of the transfer functions in Problem 5.2 while $H_0(s)$ and $G_3(s)$ do not?

5.4 Refer to Fig. P5.4. Find $\dfrac{C(s)}{R(s)}$.

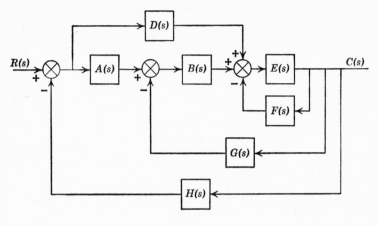

Fig. P5.4.

5.5 Refer to Fig. P5.5, if $K = 136$. (a) Find $\dfrac{C(s)}{R(s)}$. (b) Find the steady-state gain of the system.

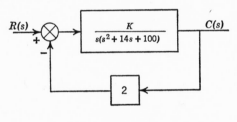

Fig. P5.5.

Chapter 6

6.1 Use Routh's method to determine how many roots of each of the following equations lie inside the left-half s plane.

(a) $s^4 + 8s^3 + 32s^2 + 80s + 100 = 0$.

(b) $s^5 + 10s^4 + 30s^3 + 80s^2 + 344s + 480 = 0$.

(c) $s^4 + 2s^3 + 7s^2 - 2s + 8 = 0$.

(d) $s^3 + s^2 + 20s + 78 = 0$.

(e) $s^4 + 6s^2 + 25 = 0$.

6.2 (a) Using Routh's array, determine the relationships which must exist among the coefficients of the following fifth order equation if all its roots are to lie in the left-half s plane:

$$a_5s^5 + a_4s^4 + a_3s^3 + a_2s^2 + a_1s + a_o = 0.$$

(b) In Problem 6.1 (a) replace the coefficient 32 with a parameter k and determine the range over which k can be varied and still keep all four roots in the left-half s plane.

6.3 $G(s) = \dfrac{K(s + 1)}{s(s + 2)(s + 4)(s^2 + 2s + 9)}$ is the forward path transfer function of a unity feedback control system. Make a root-locus diagram for this system and determine the range over which K can be varied and the system remain stable. Determine the points at which the root locus crosses the $j\omega$ axis.

6.4 $G(s) = \dfrac{K}{s(s + 1)(s + P)}$ is the forward path transfer function of a unity feedback control system. It is found that the system is stable only for $0 < K < 2.0$. Find P from a root-locus diagram, and check your answer using Routh's rule.

6.5 The input to a unity feedback system is a step, $r(t) = 5u(t)$, and the output $c(t)$ is shown in Fig. P6.5. Find $G(s)$, the forward path transfer function.

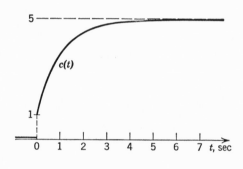

Fig. P6.5.

6.6 Show that the root loci for a system whose open-loop transfer function is

$$G(s) = \frac{K}{s(s + \alpha)(s + \beta)}$$ cross the $j\omega$ axis at the points $s = \pm j\sqrt{\alpha\beta}$.

6.7 A nonunity feedback positional servomechanism is shown in Fig. P6.7. Neglect the inertia of the gears and the loading effect of the feedback filter on the output potentiometer. The active winding on both potentiometers is 360 deg. E_1 is 6.28 volts and E_o is 12.56 volts. The speed-torque data for the bare motor is:

$J_M = 0.01$ slug $(\text{ft})^2$.
Stall torque (with $e_M = 100$ volts) $= 1$ ft-lb.
No load speed (with $e_M = 100$ volts) $= 2.5$ rad/sec.
The gear ratio is $5:1$ and J_L is 0.75 slug $(\text{ft})^2$.

The system is at rest, $\theta_i = \theta_o = 0$, when the input potentiometer shaft is suddenly rotated 5 deg (step) at $t = 0$.

In response to this input the output is:

$\theta_o(t) = A_o + A_1 \sin(10t + \phi) +$ (decaying transient).

Find A_0, A_1, ϕ, K_A, and C.

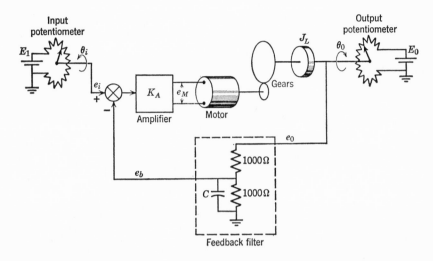

Input potentiometer

Output potentiometer

Gears

K_A

e_M

Amplifier

Motor

$1000\,\Omega$

C

$1000\,\Omega$

Feedback filter

Fig. P6.7.

6.8 In the electrohydraulic servomechanism described in Figs. 6.26, 6.27, 6.28, 6.29, and 6.30 assume that the spring constant k is altered so that as K_A is increased from its normal operating point the system breaks into oscillation at a frequency of 130 cps. All other system parameters remain the same. Find the new value for k and the critical setting (stability limit) for K_A.

6.9 $G(s) = \dfrac{K}{s(s+P)(s^2+4s+16)}$ is the transfer function of the forward path of a unity feedback control system. Draw root-locus diagrams for $P = 5$, $P = 4$, and $P = 3$ superimposed upon one another and note the significant trend in these diagrams as P is varied around the point $P = 4$.

6.10 In a nonunity feedback system (Fig. 6.36)

$$G(s) = \frac{K_1(s+1)}{s(s+3)(s+5)^2}.$$

$$H(s) = \frac{K_2(s+3)}{(s+1)}.$$

(a) Find K_1 and K_2 if the steady-state gain of the system is to be unity.

(b) Find $W(s)$ for $K_1 = 600$ and $K_2 = \frac{1}{3}$ by means of the root-locus plot.

6.11 In a nonunity, *positive* feedback system

$$G(s) = \frac{K(s+1)}{s^2 + 4s + 9}.$$

$$H(s) = \frac{3}{s+3}.$$

Make a root-locus plot for this system and find the number of poles of $W(s)$ which occur in the right-half s plane for:

(a) $K = 6$.

(b) $K = 7$.

(c) $K = 10$.

6.12 A block diagram for an electro-hydraulic servomechanism is shown in Fig. P6.12. Find the gain of the preamplifier if the response $x_r(t)$ to a step input, $e_i(t) = u(t)$, is to be as fast as possible but without any overshoot.

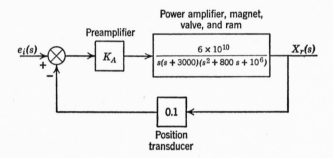

Fig. P6.12.

Chapter 7

7.1 In the second order system shown in Fig. P7.1 adjust the feedback gain k so that the output $c(t)$ will show an overshoot between 5 and 10 percent in response to a step input, and at the same time the steady-state gain of the system will be at least 0.25.

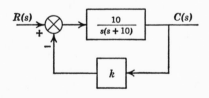

Fig. P7.1.

7.2   The block diagram in Fig. P7.2 is representative of a continuous process control system where the three controller gains K_D, K_P, and K_I are adjustable to provide an acceptable dynamic performance for the system.   Find a combination of these three gains which will satisfy the following performance specifications:

(a) For $r(t) = At$ the steady-state error must be zero.

(b) For $r(t) = u(t)$, a unit step, $\varepsilon(t)$ must be less than 0.05 for $t > 4.0$ sec

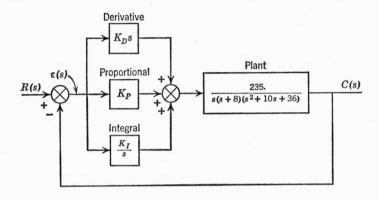

Fig. P7.2.

7.3   If, in the network shown in Fig. 7.13, C_1 is 1.0 μf and the transfer function is:

$$\frac{E_0(s)}{E_i(s)} = \frac{(s + 100)(s + b)}{s^2 + 115s + 500}$$

find R_1, R_2, C_2, and b.

7.4   An electromechanical servomechanism such as that described by Fig. 6.17 and Fig. 6.18 has the following parameter values:

$E_0 = E_1 = 12.57$ v.   Bare motor data
$\gamma_0 = \gamma_1 = 360°$. $J_M = 35.0$ gram(cm)^2
Gear ratio = 30.   For $E_R = 100$ v.
$J_0 = 31,500$ gram (cm)^2. $T_M = 733,000$ dyne-cm.

$$\frac{E_m(s)}{e(s)} = \frac{K_A}{0.01s + 1}.$$ $\omega_M = 1,000$ rpm.

The damping coefficient on the output shaft, B_0, can be adjusted by using damping fluids of various viscosities. K_A is also adjustable.   Find the numerical values of B_0 and K_A that will satisfy the following performance specifications on this system. B_0 should be as small as possible.

(a) A static error of 0.1° must produce at least 45 in.-oz of torque on the output shaft.

(b) In response to a step input $c(t)$ should be as fast as possible, but with less than 5 percent overshoot.

Determine the static error which will cause the motor to saturate, assuming a rated voltage of 120 v.

7.5 In the system shown in Fig. P7.5 the error is defined as $\varepsilon(t) = r(t) - c(t)$. Find an $H(s)$ that will make the steady-state error zero when $r(t)$ is a ramp function.

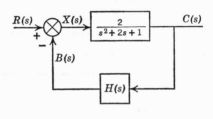

Fig. P7.5.

7.6 Refer to the general control system diagram in Fig. 7.1. Assume that $M(s) = \dfrac{10}{s + 10}$ and that $W(s)$ is a unity feedback system in which $G(s) = \dfrac{20}{s(s + 20)}$. Find the simplest compensator, $G_c(s)$, to be placed in series with $G(s)$ so that the steady-state error is zero when $r(t)$ is a ramp function.

7.7 In the system shown in Fig. P7.7 K_1 must be at least 100. Find an $H_c(s)$ such that the response to a step input will satisfy the following two conditions:

(a) $\varepsilon(t)$ will first reach zero in less than 1 sec.

(b) $c(t)$ will overshoot no more than 5 percent.

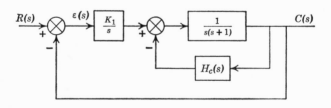

Fig. P7.7.

7.8 A feedback system has a plant whose transfer function is $\dfrac{100}{s(s^2+100)}$.
Design some compensation (series, feedback, or a combination of these) which will give the system a steady-state gain of unity, and a step response that is as rapid as possible but with less than 10 percent overshoot.

7.9 Refer to Fig. P5.2. Let $H_0(s) = 1$ and $G_3(s) = 0.2$. Assume that the plant is $G_2(s) = \dfrac{K_2}{s^2(s+3)}$. Devise compensating functions $G_1(s)$ and $H_1(s)$ and specify gain K_2 to satisfy these two performance requirements:

(a) For $r(t) = At$ (with $d(t) = 0$) the steady-state value of $\varepsilon(t)$ must be zero.

(b) For $d(t) = A \sin 4t$ (with $r(t) = 0$) the peak value of the steady-state oscillation of $\varepsilon(t)$ must be less than $0.006A$.

Chapter 8

8.1 The transfer function for a certain system is $\dfrac{Y_o(s)}{Y_i(s)} = \dfrac{5(s+10)}{(s+1)^2(s+50)}$.
If $y_i(t) = 3 \sin 6t$ find $y_o(t)$ and express the amplitude ratio $M(6)$ in decibels.

8.2 Two operational amplifiers, each with a gain of -10^7, are connected in series with the input and feedback networks shown in Fig. P8.2. Find:

(a) The frequency at which the system phase shift is $-90°$.

(b) The resonant frequency and the M_P of the system.

(c) The d-c gain of the system, that is $M(0)$.

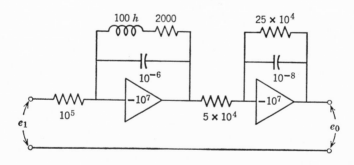

Fig. P8.2.

8.3 $G(s) = \dfrac{100(s^2+6s+16)}{s^5+13s^4+99s^3+342s^2+710s+195}$ is the transfer function of a linear system.

(a) Find the d-c gain of this system.

(b) Find the phase shift for $\omega = 0$.

(c) Find $\phi(\omega)$ for $\omega \to \infty$.
(d) Is this system stable?
(e) Find the frequency at which $\phi(\omega) = -180°$.

8.4 The table in Fig. P8.4 lists the phase shift, at several different frequencies, of a system whose transfer function is $W(s)$. The d-c amplitude ratio of the system is known to be 20 db. Find $W(s)$.

ω rad/sec	$\phi(\omega)$ degrees
1	-7
5	-26
10	-47
20	-67
30	-76
50	-87
80	-108
100	-148
150	-253
200	-259
400	-267
900	-269

Fig. P8.4.

8.5 The frequency response curve (amplitude only) for a minimum phase system is drawn in Fig. P8.5. A unit step input is applied to this system at $t = 0$. Write the expression for the output response to the step input.

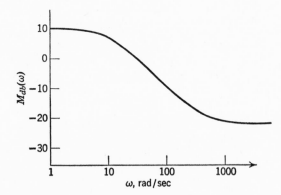

Fig. P8.5.

8.6   The frequency response curve (amplitude only) for a minimum phase system is drawn in Fig. P8.6.   Find the transfer function for this system.

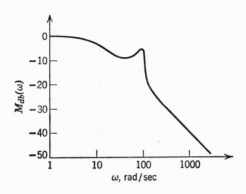

Fig. P8.6.

8.7   The frequency response curve (phase shift only) for a system whose transfer function has no poles or zeros in the right-half s plane is drawn in Fig. P8.7.   The amplitude ratio is known to be -12 db at $\omega = 1$ rad/sec. A unit step input is applied to this system at $t = 0$.   Write the expression for the output response.

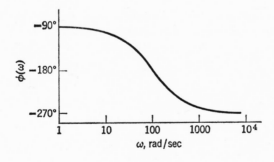

Fig. P8.7.

Chapter 9

9.1   The forward path transfer function of a unity feedback system (see Fig. 9.1) is $G(s) = \dfrac{K}{s(s + 10)}$.   If $r(t) = A \sin 10t$ and the steady-state error is

$\varepsilon(t) = \sqrt{2}\,A\sin(10t + 45°)$ find K and the steady-state component of $c(t)$.

9.2 The forward path transfer function of a unity feedback system is $G(s) = \dfrac{K}{s(s+20)(s+40)}$. Using the s plane contour shown in Fig. P9.2 plot $G(j\omega)$ and determine the N, Z, and P terms of the Nyquist equation for:
- (a) $K = 40{,}000$.
- (b) $K = 50{,}000$.
- (c) $K = -40{,}000$.

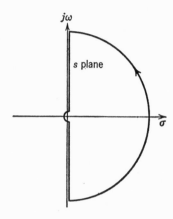

Fig. P9.2.

9.3 Repeat Problem 9.2 if $G(s) = \dfrac{K(s^2 + 4s + 9)}{s(s+8)(s^2 - 2s + 9)}$ for:
- (a) $K = 40$.
- (b) $K = 100$.
- (c) $K = -4$.
- (d) $K = -40$.

9.4 In a unity feedback system $G(s) = \dfrac{K}{s(s^2 + 6s + 100)}$ and K is set so that the system M_P is 1.5. Find the numerical value of K, the system resonant frequency, the gain margin, and the phase margin.

9.5 In a unity feedback system $G(s) = \dfrac{500(s+1)}{s(s-3)(s^2 + 16s + 100)}$. Find the gain margin and the phase margin of the system.

9.6 In a unity feedback system $G(s) = \dfrac{K}{s(s+40)^2}$. Using the Nichols chart find the maximum K that will satisfy the following three requirements simultaneously:

(a) $M_P \leq 1.42$.

(b) Phase Margin $\geq 45°$.

(c) Gain Margin ≥ 4.0.

What is the system resonant frequency at this setting for K?
If a step input is applied to this system at $t = 0$ find the instant at which the peak overshoot occurs, and the percentage overshoot.

9.7 Show that the M circles for a unity feedback system, when plotted on the $\dfrac{1}{G(j\omega)}$ plane, are concentric circles about the -1 point on that plane, and that the N "circles" are radial lines through that point.

9.8 For a nonunity feedback system $W(s) = \dfrac{G(s)}{1 + G(s)H(s)}$. Show that the M_P and resonant frequency of the system can be read directly from a polar chart on which $H(j\omega)$ is added to $\dfrac{1}{G(j\omega)}$. Compare this technique of inverse polar plotting for determining M_P and ω_r with the lengthier process of Nichols chart plotting plus Bode chart plotting that is described in Section 9.3.

9.9 $G(s) = \dfrac{250}{s(s+4)(s+6)}$ is the transfer function of an actuator which is to be controlled by a unity feedback loop in the usual fashion. Devise a series compensator which will satisfy the following performance specifications:

(a) System $M_P < 3$ db.

(b) System phase shift at $\omega = 4.5$ to be less than $40°$.

(c) Open-loop gain at $\omega = 0.5$ to be greater than 18 db.

State the gain margin, phase margin, and resonant frequency obtained with your compensator.

9.10 The block diagram for an electro-hydraulic servomechanism is shown in Fig. P9.10. An undesirable a-c voltage at 30 cps is induced into the feedback

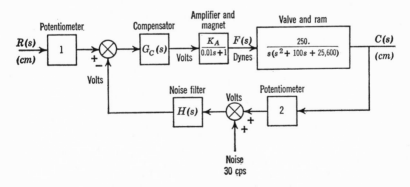

Fig. P9.10.

potentiometer circuit by vibration of the output member. A noise filter is used to attenuate this undesirable a-c signal. A series compensator is also used to provide the desired system performance. Find an $H(s)$ and a $G_c(s)$ which will satisfy the following performance specifications:

(a) Static gain of system, $C(0)/R(0)$, to be unity.

(b) Noise attenuation of the filter to be at least 40 db at 30 cps.

(c) Static gain of the series compensator to be at least unity.

(d) $K_A \geqq 6000$.

(e) System M_P to be between 1 db and 4 db.

(f) System resonant frequency to be at least 40 rad/sec.

Answers to Problems

Chapter 2

2.1 $F(s) = \dfrac{3}{s} + \dfrac{5}{s^2} - \dfrac{2\omega_0}{s^2 + \omega_0{}^2}$.

2.2 $x(t) = \dfrac{1}{5} + \dfrac{\epsilon^t}{2\sqrt{5}} \sin{(2t - 63.5°)}$, unstable.

2.3 $x(t) = \tfrac{1}{3}\epsilon^{-3t} + \epsilon^{-t} \sin{(\sqrt{5}\,t + 41.8°)}$, stable.

2.4 $f(t) = 0.2\epsilon^t + 0.8\epsilon^{-4t}$.

2.5 $h(t) = 9t\epsilon^{-3t}$.

2.6 $b(t) = 6\epsilon^{-t} - 1.5 - 4.5\epsilon^{-2t}$.

2.7 $d(0^+) = 0$, $K = 18.0$.

2.8 $f(t) = 2u_1(t) - 2\epsilon^{-2t}$
($u_1(t)$ = unit impulse).

2.9 For $\alpha \neq \dfrac{1}{RC}$, $\quad i(t) = \dfrac{\alpha EC\epsilon^{-\alpha t}}{RC\alpha - 1} + \left[\dfrac{Q_0\alpha - \dfrac{Q_0}{RC} + \dfrac{E}{R}}{1 - RC\alpha} \right] \epsilon^{-\frac{t}{RC}}$.

For $\alpha = \dfrac{1}{RC}$, $\quad i(t) = [\alpha(EC - Q_0) - EC\alpha^2 t]\epsilon^{-\alpha t}$.

Chapter 3

3.1 $\dfrac{E_0(s)}{E_1(s)} = \dfrac{s}{s + R/L}$.

3.2 $\dfrac{E_0(s)}{I(s)} = Ls$.

3.3 $\dfrac{X(s)}{F(s)} = \dfrac{1/M}{s^2 + \dfrac{k}{B}\,s + \dfrac{k}{M}}$.

3.5 $x_0(t) = \dfrac{1}{2} \dfrac{d}{dt} (x_0(t))$.
Ramp   Par

3.6 $R_2 = 333$ ohms, $t_1 = 2.4$ msec.

3.7 0.001033 newton-meters.

3.8 $B_{\text{crit}} = 0.372$ newton-meter/rad/sec
$t_{90} = 0.0775$ sec.

3.9 $J = 11.98 \times 10^{-4}$ kg (meter)^2
$B = 0.0139$ newton-meter-sec.

3.10 $\dfrac{T^2}{J} = 21{,}010. \quad \dfrac{\text{newton-meter}}{(\text{sec})^2}$.

3.11 $\dfrac{E_0(s)}{E_i(s)} = -\dfrac{0.999}{s + 0.501}$.

3.12 $\dfrac{\theta_L(s)}{E(s)} = \dfrac{10.1}{s^2 + 14.5s + 131} \dfrac{\text{rad}}{\text{volt}}$.

3.13 $\dfrac{X_2(s)}{F(s)} = \dfrac{k_1}{as^4 + bs^3 + cs^2 + ds + k_1 k_2}$

where $a = M_1 M_2 + \dfrac{M_2 J}{r^2}$

$b = M_2 B$

$c = k_1 \left(M_1 + M_2 + \dfrac{J}{r^2} \right) + k_2 \left(M_1 + \dfrac{J}{r^2} \right)$

$d = B(k_1 + k_2)$.

3.14 (a) $\dfrac{1}{s + 1} + \dfrac{2}{s + 2} + \dfrac{3}{s + 3}$.

(b) $\dfrac{2}{s} + \dfrac{2}{s + 2} - \dfrac{2}{s + 1 + j\sqrt{3}} - \dfrac{2}{s + 1 - j\sqrt{3}}$.

(c) $\dfrac{6}{s + 1} - \dfrac{3s + 4}{s^2 + s + 1}$.

(d) $\dfrac{1 + j2}{s + 5 + j5} + \dfrac{1 - j2}{s + 5 - j5}$.

Chapter 4

4.1 (a) $Q(s) = \dfrac{750(s - 4)}{s(s + 6)(s^2 + 40s + 625)}$.

(b) $q(0^+) = \dot{q}(0^+) = 0$, $\ddot{q}(0^+) = 750$, $q(\infty) = -0.8$.

4.2 (b) All the poles except one must lie in the left-half s plane, one pole must lie
at the origin (this requires $b_n = 0$), and $Ab_{n-1} = Ka_m$.
(c) All the poles must lie in left half plane.
(d) $n > m + r + 1$.

4.3 $G(s) = \dfrac{-(s-1)}{(s+1)}.$

4.4 No. The two terms in $f(t)$ corresponding to poles at $s = -7$ and $s = -7.1$ are both very large but they have opposite signs and therefore, taken together, do not contribute a predominant amount to $f(t)$.

4.5 (a) 0.667 meter/sec.
(b) 0.86 meter/sec.
(c) $t = 0.102$ sec.
(d) $t = 0.2$ sec.

4.6 (a) 0.141 volt.
(b) 0.035 sec.

4.7 (a) k increased from 20×10^6 to 84.5×10^6 dyne-cm/rad.
(b) Response time reduced by better than 2 to 1 but sensitivity reduced by more than 4 to 1. Damping ratio less by about a factor of 2.

4.8 $K = P\omega_n{}^2.$

4.9 $A = 5.$ (cm)^2.
$L = 8.5$ hy.
$k = 8 \times 10^5$ dynes/cm.
$B = 400$ dynes-sec/cm.

4.10 $F(s) = \dfrac{40}{(s+10)^2}.$

4.11 $H(s) = \dfrac{4000(s+2.5)}{s(s+2)(s+10)(s^2+4s+100)}.$

4.12 $G(s) = \dfrac{1000(s+1)}{s(s+2)(s^2+4s+400)}.$

4.13 $M(s) = \dfrac{4.28(s+0.2)(s+1.4)}{s(s+0.3)(s+1)(s^2+0.4s+4)}.$

4.14 $P(s) = \dfrac{0.01}{s(s+0.04)(s^2+0.2s+1)}.$

4.15 $R(s) = \dfrac{-8(s-1)}{s(s^2+1.2s+4)}.$

4.16 $G(s) \cong \dfrac{49}{(s+2)(s^2+4s+25)}.$

4.17 Two conditions: (i) $K = 2\zeta\omega_n.$

(ii) $Z = \dfrac{\omega_n}{2\zeta}.$

4.18 Consider ramp input: $\dot{y}(0) = 0$, $\dot{y}(\infty) = A$, and $y(t) \to At$ as $t \to \infty$. Therefore, for some $t = t_1$ $\dot{y}(t_1) > A$. Also, $y_{\text{step}}(t) = \ddot{y}_{\text{Ramp}}(t)$, therefore at $\text{input} \qquad \text{input}$
t_1, $y_{\text{step}}(t_1) > y_{\text{step}}(\infty)$.

Chapter 5

5.1 (a) $\dfrac{M(s) + M(s)G_1(s)G_2(s)H(s) - G_1(s)G_2(s)}{1 + G_1(s)G_2(s)H(s)} = \dfrac{\varepsilon(s)}{R(s)}.$

(b) $\dfrac{C(s)}{R(s)} = \dfrac{G_1(s)G_2(s)}{1 + G_1(s)G_2(s)H(s)}.$

(c) $\dfrac{X(s)}{R(s)} = \dfrac{G_1(s)}{1 + G_1(s)G_2(s)H(s)}.$

5.2 (a) $\dfrac{C(s)}{R(s)} = \dfrac{H_0(s)G_1(s)G_2(s)}{1 + G_1(s)G_2(s)H_1(s)}.$

(b) $\dfrac{\varepsilon(s)}{R(s)} = \dfrac{H_0(s)}{1 + G_1(s)G_2(s)H_1(s)}.$

(c) $\dfrac{C(s)}{D(s)} = \dfrac{G_2(s)G_3(s)}{1 + G_1(s)G_2(s)H_1(s)}.$

(d) $\dfrac{\varepsilon(s)}{D(s)} = \dfrac{-H_1(s)G_2(s)G_3(s)}{1 + G_1(s)G_2(s)H_1(s)}.$

5.4 $\dfrac{C(s)}{R(s)} = \dfrac{E(s)[D(s) + B(s)A(s)]}{1 + E(s)[D(s)H(s) + B(s)H(s)A(s) + B(s)G(s) + F(s)]}.$

5.5 (a) $\dfrac{C(s)}{R(s)} = \dfrac{136}{(s + 4.91)(s^2 + 9.09s + 55.35)}$

(b) $\dfrac{C(0)}{R(0)} = 0.5.$

Chapter 6

6.1 (a) 4.   (d) 1.
    (b) 3.   (e) 2.
    (c) 2.

6.2 (a) (i) All the a's must have the same algebraic sign, and be nonzero.
      (ii) Assuming all the a's are positive, these two conditions must hold:
        1. $a_3a_4 > a_2a_5$.
        2. $a_1a_4(a_2a_3 + a_0a_5) + a_0a_5(a_1a_4 + a_2a_3) >$
          $a_4(a_0a_3{}^2 + a_1{}^2a_4) + a_5(a_1a_2{}^2 + a_0{}^2a_5).$
    (b) $k > 20.$

6.3 $0 < K < 86$
    $s = \pm j2.7.$

6.4 $P = 1.$

6.5 $G(s) = \dfrac{(1/4)(s + 5)}{s}.$

6.7 $A_0 = 5$ deg.
    $A_1 = 6.32$ deg.
    $\phi = -71.5°$
    $K_A = 4000$ volts/volt.
    $C = 200$ μfd.

6.8 $k = 46.04 \times 10^6$ dynes/cm.

$K_{A \text{ crit.}} = 4,566$ ma/volt.

6.10 (a) $K_2 = \frac{1}{3}$

$K_1 < 750.$

(b) $W(s) = \dfrac{600(s + 1)}{(s + 3)(s + 9.57)(s^2 + 0.43s + 20.89)}$.

6.11 (a) Zero.

(b) Two.

(c) One.

6.12 $K_A \cong 112.$

Chapter 7

7.1 Impossible; for overshoot requirement: $5.22 < k < 7.35$ for steady-state gain requirement: $0 < k < 4$.

7.2 $K_P = 2.55$, $K_D = 0.3$, $K_I = 1.2$ is one combination which satisfies the design requirements.

7.3 $R_1 = 200,000$ ohms, $R_2 = 100,000$ ohms, $C_2 = 0.1$ μfd, and $b = 5.0$.

7.4 $B_0 = 33.3 \times 10^6$ dyne-cm-sec

$K_A = 4140.$ volts/volt.

Linear range: $-0.83° < \varepsilon < +0.83°$.

7.5 The simplest solution is $H(s) = \dfrac{0.25}{s + 0.5}$.

7.6 $G_c(s) = \dfrac{10P}{s + P}$ where P is chosen to give an acceptable system response.

7.7 $H_c(s) = 10(s + 5)$

$K_1 = 109.$

Chapter 8

8.1 $y_0(t) = 0.094 \sin (6t - 137.5°) +$ transients

$M(6) = -30$ db.

8.2 (a) 10.48 rad/sec.

(b) 9.9 rad/sec, and -5 db.

(c) -20 db.

8.3 (a) 8.2 or 18.2 db.

(b) 0°.

(c) $-270°$.

(d) Yes.

(e) 6.14 rad/sec.

8.4 $W(s) = \dfrac{10^6}{(s + 10)(s^2 + 20s + 10^4)}$.

8.5 $3.16 - 3.08\epsilon^{-10t}$.

8.6 $\dfrac{10(s+100)^2}{(s+10)(s^2+40s+10^4)}$.

8.7 $0.25t - 0.005 + 0.25t\epsilon^{-100t} + 0.005\epsilon^{-100t}$.

Chapter 9

9.1 $K = 100$.
$c(t) = A \sin (10t - 90°)$.

9.2 (a) $N = -1$, $P = 1$, $Z = 0$ stable.
(b) $N = 1$, $P = 1$, $Z = 2$ unstable.
(c) $N = 0$, $P = 1$, $Z = 1$ unstable.

9.3 (a) $N = -1$, $P = 3$, $Z = 2$ unstable.
(b) $N = -3$, $P = 3$, $Z = 0$ stable.
(c) $N = 0$, $P = 3$, $Z = 3$ unstable.
(d) $N = -2$, $P = 3$, $Z = 1$ unstable.

9.4 $K = 313$.
$\omega_r = 9.3$ rad/sec.
Gain Margin = 1.9.
Phase Margin = 77°.

9.5 Conditionally stable,
Gain margin = 1.34 and 0.875.
Phase margin = 1.8°.

9.6 $K = 32,000$.
$\omega_r = 19$ rad/sec.
$t_p = 0.17$ sec.
Overshoot = 24.8%.

9.9 $G_c(s) = \dfrac{5.71(s+1.5)}{(s+21)}$ will satisfy the design requirements.
$\omega_r = 7.5$ rad/sec.
Gain margin = 11.4 db.
Phase margin = 44°.

9.10 Hint: try $H(s) = \dfrac{s^2 + 35,400}{(s+60)(s+1180)}$,
$G(s) = \dfrac{9(s+60)}{(s+500)}$ as a first trial.

Index

461